Happy B[irthday]

With all my
love to my
sweetie. March, 1980

Love
Marge

The BLACK MARCH

The BLACK MARCH
The Personal Story of an SS Man

By PETER NEUMANN

Translated from the French by
CONSTANTINE FITZGIBBON

WILLIAM SLOANE ASSOCIATES, New York, 1959

CONTENTS

Part I—DAWN

Part II—AT THE ZENITH

Part III—TWILIGHT

Part IV—NIGHT

Part I

DAWN

1. I Am Sworn In

It has been a wonderful day: a day I shall never forget.

The six hundred boys of the 27th Troop of the Wittenberge Hitler Youth are assembled in the forest of Havel, drawn up in square formation.

The Klauss Ranke and Georg Betewski sections have been formed up on either side of the clearing. The local Ludwig Somster group, which is to take the oath, is at the far end, where the forest road begins.

All around us the waiting crowd murmurs its impatience. People have come from all over Brandenburg. Even, it seems, from Berlin, although that is more than seventy miles from Wittenberge.

In front, a hundred yards away, stands a tall rostrum, bristling with microphones and with the regional flags of the Hitler Youth. An enormous flag with a black swastika in a white circle on a red background hangs majestically down to the ground, covering the entire front of the platform.

Since early afternoon we have been waiting for Shir.[1] He is coming specially from Berlin to address us. There is no doubt in anyone's mind that a direct connection existed between the appearance at Havel of the Führer's delegate and the march on Vienna which all the Prussian and Brandenburg newspapers are forecasting as imminent.

Kurt von Schuschnigg, the Austrian Chancellor, had decided long

[1] Nickname of Baldur von Schirach, Reichsminister and leader of the Hitler Youth.

3

ago upon a plebiscite intended to ascertain the pro- or anti-German sentiments of the Austrian people. But the day before yesterday, on March 11, 1938, the Vienna government received an ultimatum demanding that this farce be canceled immediately.

Nobody yet knows what Schuschnigg's reply has been.

Suddenly a tremendous roar arises from the crowd.

Preceded by six motorcyclists in black crash helmets, the Opel Kapitän bearing Schir's gray and gold flag has appeared at the end of the clearing. Standing up in the back of the car, which has a retractable top, the Reichsminister smiles and waves. With his other hand he supports himself against the frame of the glass partition. He looks astonishingly young, a radiant figure.

The shimmering sunlight that streams down through the branches of the tall pine trees plays for a moment on the polished surface of the car as it slows down and stops beside the rostrum.

Von Schirach steps briskly out of the Opel, walks the few yards and quickly climbs the wooden steps, adjusts one of the mikes and turns to face us.

"*Heil Hitler!* Comrades, I have great news for you. Henceforth the Third Reich will embrace seven more provinces."

A storm of applause rises toward Schir, which he quells with a gesture of his hand.

"Since yesterday, March 12, the Vorarlberg, Tirol, Salzburg, and the eastern territories have been returned to the bosom of the great German Confederation! Seyss-Inquart, Minister of the Reich, has taken the place of the former Austrian Chancellor."

A prolonged ovation again breaks from the serried crowd.

"Comrades," Schir continues, again holding out both arms to check the applause, "let us not forget that this victory represents the breaking of the first link in the chain—the chain forged by the *Diktat* of Versailles, and intended to enslave us!"

A thunderous cheering greets these words.

This infectious enthusiam is frightfully exciting. I can feel the blood pumping heavily through my veins. My eyes grow misty as Schir continues his speech. Mechanically my fingers close about the new dagger which has just been issued to me. Fervently my fingers trace the Gothic lettering engraved on the hilt, *Treue bis auf dem Tod* ("Faithful unto Death"). The blade is razor-sharp, but at this moment I feel I could willingly plunge it into the plam of my hand. Then the first blood to stain the virgin steel would be my own.

Baldur von Schirach goes on speaking. He addresses us at length on the subject of the human race, and the Germanic peoples in particular.

"All of you," he says, "represent, for a Germany on the march, the symbol of our future world, the concrete base upon which will rest the destiny of the Third Reich of Greater Germany. Deep-rooted and powerful motives lie behind the total reorganization of the nation. Remember that the earth is in a state of perpetual evolution. Biological and physiological metamorphoses are taking place in man before our very eyes. These will directly influence generations yet unborn."

Schir stops for a moment. When he begins again, he hammers out each word:

"We Germans are not prepared to undergo these mutations like the lower animals, like unthinking cattle. Quite the contrary, we must control and encourage these changes. We must help them. Before other races, which are decadent or even completely degenerate, we must reach that state of the perfect and complete human animal —the Superman!"

The Reichsminister slowly enunciates each phrase, while a more profound silence descends upon the forest.

"To achieve this end," he concludes, "to obtain the victory, the total victory that will reward us for our sacrifice, it is imperative that no one and nothing be allowed to stand in our way. One of our first objectives is to obtain, by every means in our power, a German race that is mentally and physically pure. You young people are the future élite of our race. It is essential that you safeguard your bodies, your blood, your muscles and your minds most carefully against all degrading contacts! So that one day you may offer them, pure and unsullied, to the Fatherland. The task of your educators is to make you the governors of the Europe of tomorrow. You must be faithful in heart to the mission with which our Führer has entrusted you—by blind acceptance of the discipline imposed upon you, and obedience to the orders given you, no matter what they may be. *Heil Hitler!"*

A roar of passionate enthusiam, deafening and unending, thunders upward.

Schir smiles, waves, then turns to the group of officials standing behind him. As though on impulse, he suddenly runs down the steps of the rostrum.

Although this was not part of the program, he walks toward us and begins to inspect us. Passing between the ranks, he has a kind word for everyone, questioning a Gefolgschaftführer[2] on his athletic achievements or giving a friendly pat on the cheek to some boy who blushes scarlet with embarrassment. We are transfigured with pride and happiness.

An hour later the ceremony of swearing in the new Hitler Youth members begins.

At a sharp blast on a whistle, six Scharführer of the local Somster group step forward and form up in a semicircle at the foot of the rostrum.

Six standard-bearers then detach themselves from the flanking sections and march toward the boys of the Somster group. When they are face to face, a sharp word of command brings them to attention.

Berlme, the leader of the band, gives the signal.

Impressive, sonorous and vibrant, the notes of the *Horst Wessel Lied* accompany the slow dipping of the flags.

Schir, very serious now, his eyes gazing straight in front of him, pronounces the formal words of the oath.

And all the Scharführer, the index and middle fingers of their right hands resting on the handles of the banners, repeat after him:

"Do you swear, like your forefathers, the knights of the Holy Ger-

[2] For this and other designations in the Nazi Youth Organization and for SS ranks, see Appendix.

manic Empires, always to help those other Germans who are your brothers? Fearlessly to defend women and children? To be ready to help others in misfortune? To dedicate yourselves completely to the ideal of the German cause?"

"We swear!"

The storm of voices reverberates through the clearing, then rises among the dark pines, drowning the songs of the birds and the buzzing of the insects. This oath, to keep the faith for four years, echoes from tree to tree, from valley to valley, to fade out gently on the banks of the distant Havel.

"Do you swear, in all circumstances and unto death, to be faithful to the oath you have sworn to your leaders, to your country and to our Führer—Chancellor Adolf Hitler?"

"We swear!"

Berlme turns again toward his bandsmen.

Brass, saxophones, drums and fifes ring out. They give a stirring rendition of *Deutsch mein Bruder,* followed by the staccato, booming notes of *Deutschland über alles.*

A long blast on the whistle and it is over . . .

Schir salutes once again, his right arm raised. He comes quickly down the steps of the rostrum and steps into the Opel Kapitän, which moves off almost at once.

The crowd is already dispersing. It is strangely silent.

For a little while we remain, unable to speak, trying to preserve, like a photographic print in our mind's eye, the memory of all that has happened.

It is only when Ranke begins to shout like a madman that we break ranks.

And at that moment it seems to me that Ranke has committed sacrilege, that he has destroyed a magnificent and eternal dream, a dream which has carried us on a blare of trumpets and a clangor of brass to the supreme heights of those glorious deeds performed by our fathers and grandfathers on the Marne and at Sedan: a dream in which we saw before our eyes the heroic charge of the "Uhlans of Death," lances leveled as they hurled themselves upon the foe.

With my teeth clenched, my hand clutching my dagger, I repeat the oath:

"Treue bis auf dem Tod!"

It is this, the first significant event of my adult life, which gives me the idea of keeping a diary.

At first I planned to inscribe on the flyleaf in beautiful Gothic lettering, "Journal of a Young German and of his Age." On reflection, I decide this verged on the pretentious. So, no title.

Most of the pupils at the Schiller School kept a detailed record of all their actions and thoughts. Hitherto I had regarded this as a ridiculous occupation, or at best a complete waste of time.

I have changed my mind.

On returning home from the Havel forest that Sunday evening I told my father what I planned to do. He laughed; he obviously regarded me as a young fool. He has never understood anything about anything. He is not likely to start showing signs of intelligence at his age. . . .

He has always been a thoroughly discontented man, peevish and embittered. Perhaps it is because he realizes now, as he grows old, that basically he has not made much of a success of life.

My grandfather was a postman, and since there were four children in the family, my father was not allowed to complete his education. His was a sad childhood, with little or no education and a series of dreary, ill-paid jobs. A humble career, a humdrum life, a wretched existence.

There is only one thought ever in his mind: who will be on duty tomorrow as ticket collectors on the Kiel-Berlin line? A ticket collector and in the second class at that! That is my father. It is astonishing how hard parents find it to understand that the mediocrity of their station in life exercises a profound influence on the behavior and outlook of their children.

Thus my father's dreary way of life has certainly produced many complexes in me. To have friends whose social background is superior to one's own—what a terrible humiliation!

Karl von Reckner, Michael Stinsmann, Mitzi Brüdle, and the rest . . .

"But aren't you coming, Peter Neumann? On Sunday at our house. There'll be the X's and the Y's, and we'll have a wonderful time!"

They can go to hell for all I care! Why should I accept their damned invitations, just so they can show off their social superiority and the luxury of their homes?

And when one is invited out, one has to return the hospitality. But how can I ask Karl, Michael or Mitzi to 37 Heiligengasse?

My mother, with her arms always damp and red from washing and scrubbing, receiving the son of Colonel Count von Reckner, wiping her hands on her apron before inviting him into her dreary kitchen . . .

I can see it all.

"Come in then, dear! Just let me take these clothes and things off the wicker chair and you can sit down. . . ."

There is only Lena, my sister; she might perhaps interest the great Reckner.

A funny girl, Lena!

Eighteen years old, which is a year more than me, with blond hair, a pretty little triangular face, a body which has the right vital statistics, and in addition to these marvels the most charmingly bitchy nature that I have ever come across.

For her part, she might perhaps be not indifferent to Karl's languorous and impertinent stares and to that ridiculous pose of permanent and beautiful melancholy which he fancies.

Klauss, my brother, cannot look at him without immediately pulling faces and making would-be jokes about his affected manners.

Klauss is only ten, but according to Wittenberge gossip he is a real young terror, the worst from Brandenburg to Holstein.

He has been a Pimpfe[3] for less than a year, but he has already reached the rank of Jungschaftführer.

[3] The name given to young boys of ten to fourteen years who belonged to the Deutsches Jungvolk (German Young People).

I don't know if this is solely on account of his exceptional talent for destruction and disorganization, which is truly phenomenal, or whether he has real qualities of leadership; but the fact remains that it is most surprising.

My father explained to me the other day that it is simply because his officers discovered in him one faculty unusual in a child of his age. He can spot, with disconcerting ease, any Jew who is not wearing his yellow star.

He orders them to report to the local Hitler Youth section, which takes the necessary action.

My father was not at all pleased when he learned about this.

2.   Our Education

At the central school in Wittenberge, Julius Streicher is very much admired. He is the perfect German, and a devoted follower of the Führer.

Unfortunately he has taken it into his head to alter the German university system from top to bottom, perhaps because he was once a teacher himself.

Since the decree of last January there has been no delay in carrying this out.

Fifty-four hours of lectures per week instead of forty as in the past. And eight hours of political instruction on top of that, of which two are devoted to racial theory.

In addition, the college is now supervised by a great oaf of a Pomeranian, sent by the Party, and who in fact now controls the Schiller School. It seems that since the decree was put into effect, all the day schools, training colleges and boarding schools have been effectively put under the direction of an official of the Nazi Party.

Woe to the conquered!

This morning Plätschner, the professor of political instruction, was in terrific form. If one of those redoubtable bogies, an enemy of the Party, of Germany, and of Europe, whom we have heard so much about, had fallen into his hands today, I believe—to use his favorite expression—he would have crushed him beneath his iron heel, making the impure blood spurt out for the general good of all humanity.

There is nothing half-hearted about old Papa Plätschner. I sometimes wonder if he suffers from a persecution mania.

Unless these violent outbursts of hatred are only an outlet for conjugal troubles. And God knows he has enough of those, poor devil. God, and a large number of Wittenberge lads. Sixteen to twenty-two . . . That is the tender age that appeals to our dear Frau Plätschner!

Quite apart from eccentric injections of theoretical sadism, his lectures are in general first-rate.

Yesterday his subject was the story behind the Party's battle against Thälmann's Red Front. This must be at least the twentieth lecture we have had on the subject, but Plätschner revives our interest every time.

We began by examining the results of Germany's economic troubles which dated from the death of Stresemann on October 3, 1929. At that time the German economy, under pressure from international capitalism and cheated by the so-called Victorious Powers, who had imposed the *Diktat* of Versailles, was slowly dying. Ten million Germans voted Communist.

The Red Front shared power with Düsterberg's German Nationalists and the venerable but senile Marshal von Hindenburg.

The poverty was appalling.

The governments which succeeded one another were all incapable of producing a remedy for the cancer which was gnawing at the vitals of the Reich, or of curing the hemorrhage which was bleeding it white.

Six million unemployed queued up at the soup kitchens. The engineer dressed like a tramp humbly awaited his turn between the ruined industrialist and the unemployed metal worker. It was a time when important connections and an impressive bank account were needed in order to get a ton of coal.

Thälmann himself was satisfied with a series of conferences on wage claims, sowing discord and fomenting strikes, thus reducing millions more workers to despair.

It was at this time that the star of the man who was to become

Führer of the Third Reich began to shine, casting a single ray of hope upon the spectacle of desolation presented by a disunited Germany in a state of total chaos.

From 1918 to 1930 the number of followers of National Socialism rose from 111 to more than eight million.

Adolf Hitler, conscious of his mission, knew himself to be the only man able to pump into an exhausted Germany that regenerating serum which alone would give her the strength to surmount present disaster, avoid bankruptcy and escape from falling into the abyss where the formidable tentacles of international plutocracy were waiting to strangle her.

Supported by the millionaire patriots Klaess, Thyssen, Mortcher, Kirdorf and Krupp, and backed by the entire population, the Führer rose to power.

He never forgot that the NSDAP was, above all, the party of the German workers. With a final gesture of generosity, he invited the Communists to re-enter the national front, the only movement which would enable the Reich to survive.

But the orders from Moscow were uncompromising: The advance of the Party of Liberation was to be stopped at all costs.

And so the struggle began against a cruel, vindictive and bitter foe, who could not tolerate the victorious birth of the Third Greater German Reich.

The Party itself could not forgive this act of rebellion by traitors to our country, men in the pay of foreign powers and Russian extremists.

It never did forgive them; but the fact remains that it was the cruelty of the Reds, allied to the Jewish reactionaries, which was first responsible for the pitiless repression and inhuman violence of the struggle.

Horst Wessel, a martyr to our cause, said before he fell on the rebel barricades at Wedding,[1] on February 23, 1930:

"Nazis! If a Red puts your eye out, blind him. If he breaks one of your teeth, tear his throat out. If he wounds you, kill him."

[1] Working-class district in northeast Berlin.

As we were leaving the lecture, Franz Hättenschwiller took me by the arm.

"Do you think old Plätschner's trying to drive us out of our wits with all this stuff of his? I don't know if he's been told to lay it on thick, but he seems completely balmy to me."

He walked beside me in silence. I felt he wanted to ask me something, and that all this about Plätschner was just to open the conversation.

Franz is my best friend. By pure coincidence, his father, who also works for the railways, was transferred to Wittenberge at the same time as mine. Before that we both lived in Hamburg, and after the great Hanseatic capital, Wittenberge struck us as tame and dull. We were happy together, though, and felt less like exiles when we both entered the Schiller School.

After a while, he decided to come out with whatever it was he wanted to say. It obviously stuck in his throat.

"Peter," he said, "do you think the Führer wants war?"

I looked at him in surprise. "Nobody can want war, Franz! But you know as well as I do that war is sometimes necessary."

He stopped, and looked at me gravely. "So you think it's inevitable? That's what I think, too. Adi[2] actually only wants one thing—to provoke France and England so that he can have a valid reason for going to war. But another thing is equally certain, and that is that the people themselves long for peace and—"

"What's all this about?" I interrupted, glancing down at him.

Franz is an inch or two shorter than I. Five foot eight or nine to my five foot eleven. His eyes seemed to avoid mine.

I shrugged my shoulders. "Anyone would think you were scared, Franz! A little bit . . . well . . . surprising, considering you're a Gefol in the Hitler Youth."

We walked on again.

"In my opinion," I continued, "the Führer knows exactly what he's doing. Besides, the people . . ."

[2] Hitler.

I waved my hand vaguely.

"What are the people? It's 'them,' 'him,' 'it'; but it isn't 'us' any more, Franz! We aren't part of the people any longer. So what does their opinion matter to us? Or their fears? Or their lies?"

I saw something like astonishment and incredulity in his eyes. He did his best to smile. It was a funny smile, though.

"You're a strange chap, Peter. Maybe you're right, fundamentally. I'm always trying to analyze everything, to understand."

He thought for a moment before adding, "Perhaps, too, the reality is a thousand times more violent, more exciting than the expectation. Or the waiting."

I seized hold of his arm. "Listen to me, Franz. Even if life is filled with battle and pain and an endless struggle to create an ideal, that, in my opinion, is infinitely preferable to a dull, humdrum existence involving no danger."

We had reached the corner of the Brennerstrasse and the Ferndplatz. The lights were green and we stopped again.

"At least that's what I think, Franz," I went on. "Nietzsche was the first to teach us that man sublimates himself by fighting with all his strength, unto death if need be, for his chosen ideal."

The lights switched to red and we crossed over.

"I used to be like most people," I went on. "I thought all that sort of thing was just a lot of hot air. I've changed my mind since then."

He smiled wryly. "You'd make a great lawyer, Peter!"

After a brief silence, he went on. "But I'm just talking. I think it's simply that I've got less faith and less confidence in the future than you have." He gave me his hand. "It's a good thing you're here to keep me up to scratch."

I slapped him on the back and said, "Snap out of it, idiot. I hope all this hasn't spoiled your appetite."

He gave me a friendly wave and set off toward the Perlebergstrasse.

I, too, went home.

I had no lectures that afternoon. When Klauss got back from school at five o'clock he bullied me into helping him with his homework.

Glancing through his schoolbooks, I noticed again how different they are from those I had only a few years ago. The change has been particularly marked since Streicher became head of his Institute of Political Instruction at Berlin University.

Here is a math problem, picked out at random:

> A Stuka on take-off carries twelve dozen bombs, each weighing ten kilos. The aircraft makes for Warsaw, the center of international Jewry. It bombs the town. On take-off with all bombs on board and a fuel tank containing 1,500 kilos of fuel, the aircraft weighs about eight tons. When it returns from the crusade, there are still 230 kilos of fuel left. What is the weight of the aircraft when empty?

Here is another one I had to solve for Klauss:

> The iniquitous Treaty of Versailles, imposed by the French and the English, enabled international plutocracy to steal Germany's colonies. France herself acquired part of Togoland. If German Togoland, temporarily under the administration of the French imperialists, covers fifty-six million square kilometers and contains a population of eight hundred thousand people, estimate the average living space per inhabitant.

I also glanced at some of the chapters in his history of Europe.[3] This scholarly work maintains:

> The French Revolution had as its principal aim the extermination of the French aristocrats of Aryan blood. It was fomented by the Judaeo-Mediterranean elements who wished to seize power in order to enslave the people. After the Vendée revolts, the French of Nordic origin, hunted down because of their pure blood, fled to Germany. . . .
> The extremist, left-wing elements then assumed power and carried

[3] *Geschichte als national politische Erziehung* ("History as National Political Education") by Prof. Dietrich. A book written for young people and distributed to the schools in 1937.

out a reign of terror lasting for several years. Anyone who did not support their cause was ruthlessly guillotined. . . .

Later, the imperialistic militarism of the French produced as dictator an officer of Italian origin, Napoleone Bonaparte, who adopted a French name and became Napoléon Ier.

Napoleon was a barbarous dictator who had only one objective: the enslavement of Europe, and above all the annihilation of Prussia."

One passage, devoted to the 1914-18 War, is particularly interesting:

In 1914 Germany, which had become an industrial power of the first magnitude, represented a mortal danger to international Jewish capitalism. The factories of the Ruhr were producing to capacity. The economy was prosperous. The Germans, the freest people in the world, had reached a higher social level than any other country in Europe. The country was self-supporting and did not need either foreign goods or raw materials.

All this must obviously give rise to jealousy among the rapacious plutocrats of England, France and America. Since each of these powers was too weak to attack us openly and honorably, they decided to join together in order to conquer us. The Reich, which lacked at that time an Adolf Hitler, could not prevent the infiltration of certain disloyal elements into our government. Germany was betrayed.

Erzberger, a Jew, signed a shameful armistice which bound us hand and foot.

Two years later, in the Black Forest, he paid for this foul betrayal with his life. He was executed by patriots.

Later, the French tried to starve out the population of the Ruhr, and in defiance of treaties which they had signed, reoccupied the right bank of our German Rhine. But the heroic miners of Dortmund, Essen and Duisburg showed the French that they would willingly face death if only Germany might live.

Our Führer, who at that moment was beginning his crusade for a liberated Reich, happy, democratic and free from Jews, swore to be revenged upon the French and to reoccupy one day the territory of Alsace-Lorraine, which they had seized.

The geography books are also very different from what they were even a few years ago.

I found the book by Fritz Brennecke and Paul Gierlich most fascinating.

Germanic civilization, [I read] the only pure one, was created two thousand years ago in the northern territories now called Sweden and Norway. It spread slowly, like oil upon water, across Jutland, Fionia and the islands of Seeland and Laaland.

In due course these Aryan peoples became separated from one another.

Some established themselves in what is now our country. Others moved overseas to the islands of Britain and Ireland. Still others went to the plains of eastern and western Gaul, which was then a backward country and which they civilized.

In the Middle Ages, more Aryan races, of Nordic origin, installed themselves in central and southern Europe. Later still, other Germanic people moved into what had been Slav- or Carpathian-held lands, driving out the descendants of those barbarous tribes which had come from the East.

Among all these people of Nordic origin, some preserved the full purity of their blood, but others crossbred; such was the case with the descendants of the ancient Vikings, established in the French territory called Normandy.

All these territories, occupied today by minorities of Germanic origin, must necessarily reunite eventually to form again the great German confederation first founded by the Emperor Karl the Great.[4]

Similarly, such countries as Switzerland, Luxemburg, Flanders, Wallonia, Poland, the Sudetenland, Rumania, Hungary, Slovakia, the Baltic states, and above all Alsace-Lorraine, must in the years to come be integrated into Germany. No German is entitled to rest in peace until this mission to liberate the oppressed brother peoples is accomplished. The day will come when our Führer shall give the signal for battle. Woe betide any who then crosses our path.

There is also a chapter devoted to the Russians.

[4] Charlemagne.

Russia, governed today by the most ruthless police terrorism ever known, would constitute a great danger to Germany were not our Führer, Adolf Hitler, in power. The Russian is still only half civilized. The Asiatic hordes which form nearly three-quarters of the Soviet population have not reached the standard of life achieved by our ancestors two hundred years ago.

The Russians live in constant fear of imprisonment and deportation.

If the Soviet Republics were powerful enough eventually to do so, they would one day attack Germany and attempt to destroy your Fatherland.

That is why it is vital for the Reich to be always on its guard, for our future power is the surest guarantee of our freedom. The German people must never for a single moment lose sight of the fact that Bolshevism means pillage, murder and annihilation.

Klauss had finished the essay he had to write.

I put his schoolbooks back in his leather satchel and turned toward him.

"Look here, Peter," he said, waving a menacing finger at me, "I won't have you meddling in my affairs any longer!"

He was trying to look important.

"I should think a Jungschaftführer," he went on, "has the right to keep secrets, even from his own brother! I don't go looking through *your* books and papers, do I?"

A slap on the face put an end to the matter.

Klauss looked furious for a moment, then started to laugh, rubbing his cheek. "Gosh! You seem to be well up to date with the new von Metzsch education methods."

I leaned toward him, rather interested. "What do you mean? Who's been talking to you about von Metzsch?"

He had adopted that superior manner again, which I loathe; it makes him look like a peacock spreading its tail as it watches some mangy, molting duck go waddling by.

"The *Führerprinzip* [leadership principle]," he informed me, with a dictatorial air. "It's the new educational system organized by Streicher, our leader, so that we schoolchildren can become good

Germans and know everything about our country and the dangers that threaten it."

He glanced up at me.

"The two most important are Communism and the Jews. In the future, teachers and professors won't be decadent old graybeards, way behind the times; they'll be young masters sent from the SS, or Party members at least."

He gave me another sidelong glance to see if I was impressed by his new role of budding political-education expert.

"All our teachers will have ranks, as in the Army. Every now and then they'll make reports to their superiors about the progress we've made and the racial results we've achieved."

"What do you mean—'racial results'?" I asked.

"Racial results, racial results! Well, it's the number of Jews we've nabbed at school, or in the streets. My goodness, haven't they taught you anything?"

I let him go on since I was curious to hear more.

"Where was I? Oh, yes, the business with our teachers . . . The new principal called us all together last Monday and explained to us why the Führer had decided to sack all the doubtful ones. A lot of them were ex-Communists or had Jewish blood, and there was a danger they might corrupt us by a bad educational system."

He sounded suddenly bored.

"Some we like. With the ones we don't, or who aren't Party members, we're always on guard. The Jungbannführer have advised us to watch them and to make notes of anything that seems strange in their behavior. We've got to report everything they do or say and watch them wherever they go."

He puckered his lips and gave a grunt of irritation. Then he sighed.

"It's quite a job! All this stuff has to be handed in to the Jungzug, who gives it on to the Fähnlein, who passes it to the Stamm, who in turn hands it to the Gebiet and then the Obergebiet. As for what the Obergebiet does with it, we couldn't care less! But the annoying part is that it often leads to trouble. And it's always the boy who made the first report who catches it. So actually, when the teacher does something fishy, we don't usually bother to report it any more."

I was somewhat taken aback.

All the same, I wanted to know what he had been told about von Metzsch, the recently appointed principal of the university.

"Who exactly is this von Metzsch?"

Klauss said disdainfully, "You don't seem to know anything! Lieutenant General Horst von Metzsch has been appointed by Julius Streicher to the supreme command of the German Education Corps. Our educational system is to follow the hierarchical military system of the SS. Also, and we don't care for this quite so much, there's to be corporal punishment as well. Gosh! Just do the slightest thing wrong and they give you the works!"

He paused for a moment. But not wishing, probably, to miss such a golden opportunity of showing me how perfectly he had been instructed as a Jungerschaftführer, he went on.

"There's another thing that has changed since General Metzsch was appointed. We now have two hours' extra instruction in racial theory per week. And since last month it has been made compulsory to stick up the new issue of the *Stürmer* on the school walls each Monday."

I know what the *Stürmer* is. It is a weekly paper, started by Streicher, which deals only with the racial question, and especially with the Jews.

Thumbing through its pages one sees caricatures ridiculing the Jews, grotesquely drawn. The written text is aimed at opening the eyes of the public to the "Israelite peril." It gives inside information on the Jewish hold on industry and commerce, lists of secret societies recently uncovered and a host of other such matters.

There are also news items, all on the same subjects. A regular classic is the story of the German girl, raped by a Jew, who produced a horribly deformed child.

I, too, know all about the Jews. Nevertheless I find this sort of thing pretty silly.

I also know that the Führer loves to read the *Stürmer* and that he waits impatiently for each new issue to be brought to him hot from the presses.

Klauss, seeing me sunk in thought, went back to his homework. I leaned over his shoulder. He was writing:

> The Reich, with our Führer supreme at its head,
> Pursues its relentless crusade without rest.
> Come, follow us, lad, you are German and proud,
> The drums are beating, the banners unfurled.
>
> Behind us we leave a path swept clean and pure,
> Where Jewry has perished, the skies here are blue.
> But on the horizon are still leaden clouds,
> Jewry raises its head again, let us strike it down.
>
> Youth of Germany, show us the strength of your arm,
> The dagger that kills must strike without fear.
> Youth of Germany, show us the strength of your arm,
> The dagger that kills must strike without fear.
> Hurrah for the struggle, the gallant crusade,
> To our soldiers all glory, the chains are untied.[5]

[5] *Juden Lebenschreibung* ("Jewish Biography") by Gustav Neidel.

3. Recollections of Bavaria

Summer 1938. For two days we have been at the Sonnenwend-lager[1] at Urfeld, on the shores of Lake Walchen, in the Garmisch Alps.

We are going to spend the greater part of our vacation in these wild and magnificent surroundings. Wittenberge now seems very far away. Face to face with these mountains, their summits eternally covered with snow, one feels that one is in a completely new world, a new atmosphere. The countryside seems to breathe freedom and purity. Everything is simple and easy. Life is very different here from the harassing, troubled and depressing existence in Branden-burg.

Or can this be simply my own distorted view of the world? For I have unpleasant memories of my last days at Wittenberge.

I was rather tired after all the cramming I had to do to get my *Abitur*—for I am now a Bachelor of Arts. And then what happened at home depressed me completely in the end.

Several months ago Lena got to know a young Untersturmführer of the SS (Schutzstaffel). Since then she has never stopped talking about his physical, esthetic and moral qualities, "like a Greek God" and so on and so forth.

Briefly, she went completely crazy about him.

One day, about two months ago, she suddenly decided to in-troduce this paragon to my father. So she brings him along, all

---

[1] Summer camps for the Hitler Youth on vacation.

23

dressed up in his fanciest uniform, and we have to do the honors at 37 Heiligengasse for the benefit of this lady-killer.

Heinrich Griessling, SS, of the Leibstandarte AH [2] seemed very much at home. Smiling and sure of himself, he swaggered in, bowed to Mutti, gave his hand to my father and deigned to honor Klauss and myself with a nod. He was tall, blond, with a hard, square face, mean little gestures and a dry voice; there seemed to be nothing of the Don Juan about him.

After a few moments of stilted conversation, or rather of a clipped monologue punctuated by long moments of embarrassing silence, he came, if one may so put it, to the point. Without beating about the bush, he explained to my father that during the last three months he had had the opportunity of summing up Lena's good and bad qualities, that on the whole he found that the former outnumbered the latter, and that he had the honor, therefore, to ask for her hand in marriage.

To have a man arrive at four thirty and ask for his daughter's hand at four fifty hardly gave my father time to formulate such vague ideas as he might have had on the subject.

He tried to explain this.

But Griessling did not give him time to do so. He announced peremptorily that Lena and he loved each other, that they were both young, free and healthy, and that there was no reason to delay the marriage. It seemed odd that he had even bothered to come to the house and had not simply taken Lena away with him at once.

He also added that this union would be a very auspicious one, since it would conform to the marriage ethics of National Socialism. What had National Socialism to do with it?

To conclude this strange interview, he announced that he would return in three days' time to learn my father's decision. But he remarked that Lena and he could dispense with his approval, if need be.

[2] The Leibstandarte AH (Adolf Hitler Regiment) was the Führer's personal bodyguard. It contained the élite of the Nazi storm troops, men of the SS who had won their spurs in the SA (Sturmabteilung) or in the course of repressive operations.

As soon as this astonishing young man had stalked out, we all stared at each other and at Lena.

She, with a nasty expression and in a bantering tone, said, "Actually, if all men were like him," and she turned toward us as she said it, "life would be very much simpler. The Führer wouldn't find it such hard work building the new Germany. Heinrich knows what he wants. Me, too! I love him; that's fair enough. There's no need for a long discussion or an interminable engagement!"

"But do you know him at all well?" ventured Mutti. "Do you know what sort of a man he is and if he's capable of making you happy? This job of his, for instance—what does he do exactly?"

"His job?" said Lena icily. "His job is to protect the Führer and the great Nazi Reich! Isn't that enough?"

My father muttered something about her being an idiotic child, or else a fallen woman. To put an end to the discussion, he said that before going any further he would make some discreet inquiries about Griessling.

Unfortunately these inquiries did not produce very favorable results for the Untersturmführer.

Father learned that in fact he was a drunkard and a woman-chaser, with neither morals nor religion—I am only repeating his words—but there was also something far more serious.

Griessling was made an officer as a result of circumstances which are worth relating.

Two years ago, in 1936, he was only an Oberscharführer, stationed at Allenstein, in East Prussia.

Allenstein contained at that time a very large population of Polish Jews. After the riots of June 1936 in Prussia and Silesia—riots pro-voked by the Jewish minority which blamed the NSDAP Unions for their dismissal from the factories—very severe disciplinary measures were taken.

The pogrom started on the night of July 28-29. All Jewish shop-keepers were driven from their shops, which were then pillaged and burned. The SS, their fingers on the triggers of their sub-machine guns, fired on all those who tried to run away. They went upstairs in the houses of the orthodox Jews and forced everybody to come down, clubbing them with their rifle butts.

Heinrich Griessling's enthusiasm for this work earned the particular commendation of his superiors that night.

His specialty was children.

He did not miss them. On the pretext—rightly or wrongly, he should know best—that they were trying to escape, he shot them down with prolonged bursts of fire, spraying the Jews' houses with his submachine gun.

When the operation was over, a large part of the Talmud brigade found itself in paradise. Those who remained alive were shipped off to the concentration camp at Schneidemühl.

Next day Griessling was promoted to Hauptscharführer and, a month later, to Untersturmführer.

On reflection, I don't know what to think of this type of disciplinary operation.

Alfred Rosenberg proved in the *Myth of the 20th Century* that the Jews have done great harm to Germany and to the whole of Europe.

The Führer was the first man in the world really to react, with force, against the Jewish menace.

I am convinced that it is essential for our future to eliminate the Jews from certain professions and to prevent them from obtaining control in matters vital to our country.

But I have never understood the use or value of such disciplinary operations and executions.

However, the Führer, who has already demonstrated again and again that he is rarely deceived, doubtless has valid reasons for giving such orders.

I read somewhere that it is necessary for the strength and power of a régime that its goal should not be represented by a purely abstract ideal, but should be made concrete by some especially vulnerable element which may be attacked and easily destroyed.

This spurs on the partisans of the régime and neatly canalizes their hatred.

If this is so, this role would suit the Jews admirably.

All this, however, is of little interest to me.

To return to Heinrich Griessling and my father, I think it would be superfluous to state that Papa Neumann was not overflowing with enthusiasm when he learned that his future—and how!—son-in-law was not the innocent, pure young man that he had hoped for.

It was a noncommissioned officer at the Ludendorff Barracks who told him all this about Heinrich. This worthy soldier added that in his opinion Untersturmführer Griessling was a real hero, with a brilliant future ahead of him. . . .

But you should have heard Papa when he returned that evening! As soon as he saw Lena he went for her, bellowing like a madman, "Never, do you hear! I'll never give my daughter to a murderer!"

Lena went white and drew herself up quickly, rocking the chair on which she had been seated.

"Heinrich, a murderer?"

"He's a foul criminal, that's what he is! A disgusting killer! He has a terrible reputation for cruelty, after that Jewish business at Allenstein. . . . Kirnste told me all about it! And you want me to let you marry this—this sadist who enjoys nothing better than massacring children! You'd like an orange-blossom wedding, I expect. . . . And why not get the brothers and sisters of the kids he murdered to carry your train? And then you can lie beside him in bed all night, and he can give you the gory details! Telling you who he's been murdering all day?"

"Shut up, Father, or I'll *make* you keep quiet," snapped Lena.

Father gazed at her incredulously, uncomprehending. Painfully he gasped out the words, "My own daughter's no better than filth! My daughter. My children . . . They're rotten! They're not human beings any longer!"

I remember that I got up, clenching my teeth. There are some things one will not put up with, even from one's own father.

But before I had time to do anything, he had slapped Lena's face, hard.

My sister did not react. She said nothing. She picked up her coat, went out and slammed the door behind her.

I told Father he had done wrong. He stared at me wildly, as though he did not understand, and then suddenly fell against the corner of the table, sobbing.

I believe that I should have despised him less if he had not given way to this stupid outburst of bourgeois sentimentality.

An hour later Lena returned. She was accompanied by Heinrich.

The Untersturmführer did not greet anyone as he came in. He was furious, and there was a strange expression on his face. His jaw was thrust forward as though he longed to kill somebody.

Without a word he crossed the living room, took a chair and sat down upon it astride. He looked around the room; then his gaze rested on Father. He said, "This is a very tedious business, Herr Neumann. Your daughter has just revealed to me that you are a bad German. You have gravely insulted me and our Führer. That is both unwise and dangerous. Especially coming from a man like yourself."

His eyes rested for a moment on Lena before he went on.

"Your daughter, most fortunately, is a good citizen and was at pains to inform me of something which my superiors in the Pots-dammerstrasse will be most interested to learn."

He began to smile slightly.

"There was certainly a slight omission on your part when you filled in your paper this year. Actually you were involved in ex-tremist activities in 1932. You were a member of the Red Front, I believe?"

Father turned toward Lena and stared at her as though he were seeing her for the first time. Then his face hardened.

"Let's get to the point," he muttered. "What do you want?"

"Nothing, Herr Neumann. Nothing at all," replied Griessling. "Only I am rather uncertain as to what the consequences of an inquiry by the State Police might be, unless, of course—"

Father interrupted. "Never, do you hear? You'll never get Lena as long as I'm alive. Even if it means my death."

Heinrich got up at once. His expression was now very unpleasant. "It'll mean your death all right, Herr Neumann; you'll die. Yes, you can take my word for that."

He marched off without another word, taking Lena with him.

Father said nothing; he went up to his room, his shoulders hunched.

Mutti murmured in tones of horror, "Betrayed by his own daughter! Oh, my God, it can't be true!"

She also went upstairs a few minutes later.

Personally, I was very surprised. I was quite unaware that my father had ever been involved in extremist activities. Lena must have learned all this in confidence from Mutti.

But how strange it all is. I cannot imagine him fighting on the barricades! With his mean little life as a railway official, it must have been a sort of revolt, a strange reflex action against a pointless and sterile existence. The Reds certainly crossed his path at the right time and pinned him, like so many others, like a ridiculous butterfly on the great chart of their anarchistic struggles to destroy Germany.

But what had they hoped to achieve, the fools!

The Reich at that time had been in a state of complete chaos and total disorganization. The Brown Shirts, or SA, represented the only element of stability upon which we, the German people, were able to lean. As for the Reds, they had had their day.

Disorder, injustice, misery, the breakup of individual lives and of the nation, lies and corruption. . . . That is what they had brought us.

In 1923 the Germans were quite ready to trust a régime which would bring them, now that the war was over, not happiness—that would be asking too much—but a simple assurance of peace and security for the future.

Instead, those people, who talked of nothing but equality, who literally choked themselves with the violence of their insane shouting, bellowing slogans about fraternity and socialism, thought of nothing save how best to fill their own pockets at the expense of the community—as they did in Bavaria the moment they had power.

The mass of the people were even more wretched, debased and despised than they had been under the Hohenzollerns.

Every sensible German knows that the Jews and the Communists can only bring us ruin and decay, and the inevitable death of our German inheritance.

Only decadent peoples, brutalized by idiotic propaganda, could possibly observe our devotion to our Führer open-mouthed, as though it were something horribly abnormal. The Führer has given us back our faith in a Greater Germany and a better future. Only degenerates can be surprised by our love and trust, by our determination to follow him and to help him turn the pages of our history more quickly so that we may see the results in our own lifetime. . . .

No, I certainly cannot believe that my father was right.

He was mistaken, perhaps. But in some very important matters one is not allowed to make mistakes. He must accept the just punishment for his stupidity and errors. It is sometimes hard to have to reason like this about the persons who brought you into the world, but I do consider of all human contingencies the only one which counts is the triumph of National Socialism. It is only logical that everything must bow before its laws.

Father was arrested three days later by the Gestapo.[3]

Heinrich and Lena were married a month after that.

In accordance with the normal procedure, we have received a copy of the official report of his arrest, which gives a brief account of the main charges against him:

> The Chief of Police, and Chief of the Wittenberge Security Service. April 24, 1938, Potsdammerstrasse 29.
>
> To the Judiciary and Disciplinary Administration Branch.
>
> A charge being brought by SS Untersturmführer Heinrich Griessling, on the evidence of Fräulein Lena Neumann, a detailed

---

[3] Contraction of Geheime Staatspolizei. (Secret State Police).

inquiry was carried out into the anti-Nationalist activities and falsification of official declaration forms on the part of one Friedrich Neumann, ticket collector employed in the second-class section of the Mecklenburg-Holstein Railway Company.

The inquiry has shown beyond doubt that Friedrich Neumann, between 1930 and 1932, was engaged in ceaseless Communist and extremist activities.

Furthermore, it has been proved that at this time the accused was in contact with unidentified correspondents residing in Polish territory.

Preliminary proceedings are being taken.

A charge of high treason, betrayal of his country and assisting the enemy was laid before the Attorney General of the Reich, at the Berlin People's Court, on April 20, 1938.

The accused has been placed under close arrest.

Signed: Otto Eugen Marsch, SS Sturmbannführer.

Secret State Police—Wittenberge Division.

I have only been at Urfeld for six days, but I think my morale is already picking up. The unpleasant events at Wittenberge are, I am glad to say, beginning to fade into the distance.

The mass PT and the games and maneuvers leave me very little time for black moods and useless brooding.

Yesterday, in the course of a short ceremony which took place in a clearing in the forest of Oberau, I was promoted to Gefolgschaftführer.

Of course I had to stand everybody drinks. Karl, Michael and I put away so much Pilsen that we were not very pretty sights by evening. However, we managed to get back to camp without incident, and without being spotted.

I am beginning to like Reckner much better. He seems to be more simple and natural here than he was in Wittenberge. He has left his snobbery behind him in Brandenburg. As I get to know him better, he seems more human.

Michael is more reserved. One never knows quite what is going on in his head or exactly what he is thinking. He is shy and retiring, but he has sudden and alarming fits of temper. He lost his mother. He told me some months ago that she was Jewish and that she committed suicide at the time of the great pogroms of 1933. He made me swear never to reveal what he had told me about his origins. I felt at the time that he was overcome by the burden of his parentage, and that a subconscious urge had forced him to share his secret with somebody else.

My best friend is still Franz. Good old Franz, with his hesitant manner, his air of being permanently astonished by what he sees and hears, his endless questions asked apparently at random, his faithful dog's eyes that gaze so fervently at those whom he trusts.

He is a being without will power, but an incomparable friend. I feel that he would muster every ounce of courage he possesses to protect me and to keep me from danger, and that he would even risk his life for me if the need arose.

The camp is situated right on the edge of Lake Walchen.

It consists of twenty-six blocks of huts, laid out in the shape of a star. In the center, on a raised platform decorated with enormous banks of flowers and shrubs, a vast swastika flag floats from a ship's mast at least sixty feet high.

There are fifty boys per hut. Each block is composed of three huts, and this makes up a Gefolgschaft.

The twenty Gefolgschäfte make up a Bann, and here at Urfeld we are commanded by Bannführer Phillip Gasser, an athletic SS man of about thirty, who has distinguished himself, it seems, as a Dornier pilot in the Spanish Civil War.

In addition to the blocks where the boys are housed, there are the huts of the divisional command post, the regimental CP, the hospital, the kitchens, the common rooms or lecture rooms, and the storeroom.

We are organized like an infantry division on maneuvers. That is the theme for this year's camp. We lead the lives of real foot-sloggers, and it isn't always so funny.

That brute Gasser makes us get up at five o'clock every morning.

A wash in the lake, coffee and black bread, salute to the flag and then on parade.

This is followed by two hours of combat training in the woods, with firing practice, and sport until noon.

Then, just for a change, from one till three we have racial and political instruction.

This is where Gasser's powers of oratory come into their own. Amplified by loudspeakers, his voice rises to a crescendo as he works himself up against the Jews. Starting off in a persuasive murmur, he passes through stages of sneering mockery and contemptuous raillery, then suddenly bursts out into protracted yells of anger and prophetic bellowings which delight our hearts. Because we know perfectly well that any moment the wretched man will start stammering. The roars like a wild beast at death's door soon give way to incomprehensible stutterings and vague mumblings, while his face becomes a dull brick-red, bathed in sweat. It is at this moment that he always gives up, finishing his speech with a concluding remark which usually has no connection whatever with the subject of his lecture. He then steps down with great dignity from the platform, to the frenzied applause of his delirious audience. Our enthusiasm springs principally from the knowledge that we'll hear no more of him until tomorrow morning.

Franz and I decided to go to Munich this afternoon.

A large, lanky fellow, ash-blond, with the square head of a Pomeranian set awkwardly on his sloping shoulders, stopped me on the way out.

"Hey, you, Gefol, come here a minute!"

He was wearing the green armband of camp superintendent, which is the only reason I did not give him a sharp answer, because I don't much like being addressed in that tone of voice.

"What's up? Don't want to pass through Control?" he sneered.

He came closer, an unpleasant expression on his face.

"Your permits—and quick!"

We did as we were told, but he can't have liked the look of us, for he added nastily, "Handkerchiefs, pockets, comb, wallet?"

We were compelled to let him check that our handkerchiefs were clean and properly ironed, that our pockets held only what is strictly necessary, that our combs weren't full of hair and dandruff, that our wallets contained nothing except our essential papers and identity cards.

Only after all this had been gone through did he let us pass, but his little piglike eyes seemed filled with regret that he couldn't penalize us.

A fellow we shan't forget in a hurry. . . .

We take the four-thirty bus and at five o'clock we arrive at the sunny Kirchallee, ablaze with the colored summer dresses of the jolly Bavarian girls.

We had decided to go and see a film about the life of Frederick the Great at a theatre in the Kaufingerstrasse.

We enter the Kursaal, filled with smoke and humid as a Turkish bath. The film has already started.

Half an hour of it is enough for me. It is a gloomy and boring historical melodrama, enlivened from time to time by a Voltairian witticism which is greeted with noisy laughter by the solemn, bearded figures of the period, assembled for no apparent reason in one of the rooms of the Sans Souci palace.

I start to wriggle and fidget in my seat and am feeling thoroughly uncomfortable. Suddenly the pencil of light from a flashlight held by an usherette showing somebody to their seat reveals a girl whom I had not even noticed in the seat next to mine.

The little that I see of her shows that she is in every way worthy of closer attention: red, full lips, the down-covered cheeks of a girl entering womanhood, suggestive curves outlined by the light from the projector, chestnut hair tied back behind her head.

I notice at once that this sweet creature is glancing slyly at me out of the corner of her eye, while I pretend to be following this obscure story which an even more obscure film producer is attempting to unfold for us on the screen.

Franz, who has noticed my new interest, keeps giving me violent nudges with his knee, presumably with the intention of egging me on to be bold.

Actually, I don't normally go in for this sort of thing. In spite of my cocky manner, I feel stupidly frightened.

The film ends at last to a fanfare of fifes and drums and a shot of the Prussian flag floating victoriously above a nation once again at peace. The lights go up.

My neighbor is even more attractive than I had suspected.

I assume my most sophisticated manner as I light a cigarette, after offering one to Franz. Then I lean toward her and ask in a friendly voice, "I trust the smoke doesn't bother you, Fräulein?"

She smiles, as though to say, Ah ha, I wondered just how you were going to start, and replies, "Not at all! I sometimes smoke myself."

I hasten into the breach which my ingenious apology has opened for me and offer her a cigarette.

Soon we are chatting away like old acquaintances. I learn that she is only sixteen and is in Munich for the summer holidays. She comes from Stuttgart, where her parents are in business. She is studying at the Technical College there.

As soon as the performance is over, we all three go out into the street.

The Kaufingerstrasse is not quite so lively as before. The last orange rays of the setting sun light up the faces of passers-by and are reflected in the windows of the numerous clothing shops to be found in this district.

I suggest to Franz that he might care to return to Urfeld alone, but he doesn't seem to understand that his presence is not wanted any more.

Finally the poor old chap goes off, looking down in the mouth and probably sighing over the inconstancy of my friendship.

But it is not every day that one meets a Brigitta!

As soon as we are on our own, we find it has become much harder to think of anything to say.

I take her arm.

"Would you like something to drink? The cafés aren't too noisy at this hour. We can have a quiet chat."

She accepts, with a smile and a nod. We enter a small beer hall.

When we have sat down, I ask her, "Beer, fruit juice or vermouth?"

It is obvious at once that she has not had many opportunities to visit a café with a young man. She seems suddenly embarrassed, but ventures timidly, "Lemonade, if you don't mind."

My courage has deserted me again, too, and I have lost the dominating manner I had earlier. I don't know exactly why.

She starts chattering very quickly, maybe to hide her awkwardness. Her full and terribly tempting lips form silly little unimportant phrases to which I listen with as much rapt attention as if she were giving me a detailed analysis of a work by Dietrich or Rosenberg.

I notice how astonishingly white her teeth are, and I see the tiny tip of her red tongue, visible for a moment as she pronounces certain letters. Freckles, a dimple, greenish-blue eyes, a tiny mole on the side of her nose . . .

"You're not even listening!" she complains suddenly.

I am taken aback and smile at her.

"One meets two sorts of people in life," she explains to me. "There are those you distrust and dislike on sight and those you trust and feel at home with, and I think that you . . ."

She lifts her eyes to mine, then blushes.

I take her hand, which is lying discreetly on her knee. "That I?"

She draws back her hand, picks up her bag from behind her, and gets to her feet.

"Shall we go?"

I leave a mark on the table, and we go out under the indifferent gaze of the customers and the obsequious smile of the waiter.

Without a word said, we set off toward the Isar. It is now quite dark, and the linden trees down by the quay give out an almost intoxicating scent. Around the street lamps ephemeral clouds of greenish wings are whirling.

We stroll along the bank, and every few yards we pass courting couples locked in each other's arms.

Finally we find an empty bench and sit down. The river flows by and the dark water reflects the bluish light from the lamps on Prater Island and on the Maximilian Bridge.

I put my arm around her and draw her to me.

"I'm still waiting. You never finished your sentence . . ."

In the darkness I can feel that she is looking at me, and she murmurs softly, "I think perhaps you're one of the ones I could like."

Without really knowing how it happened, my mouth is pressed against those lips which have filled me with such desire.

We arranged to meet next day at the corner of the Goetheplatz and the Häberlstrasse.

She turns up, smiling, her figure well set off by a pale suit which becomes her, outlining her slender waist and her graceful thighs. Her hair isn't tied back today and falls loosely on her shoulders. She is very slightly made up. I am not particularly surprised because I know that she is not a member of the BDM.[4]

"Hello, Mr. Peter," she says, with a smile.

"Yesterday 'Peter' was enough . . ." I reply.

Without a word she takes my arm.

The bus for Starnberg is about to leave and we get on just as the conductor is closing the door.

Half an hour later we are beside the lake. Although it is almost the end of August and of the holiday season, there is quite a crowd on the shores of Lake Starnberg. Boys and girls in bathing suits are seated on the stone wall, talking and laughing noisily. Others are playing ball on the sand.

I turn to Brigitta. "Shall we bathe? What do you think?"

She blushes slightly and replies, "If you like, Peter. . . . Yes, I'd love to!"

[4] The Bund Deutscher Mädel, Nazi organization for young German girls, was very strict in questions of morals—make-up prohibited.

We walk down to the beach and make our way toward a hut papered with brightly colored posters. I know that bathing suits can be hired there.

They tell us all the cabins are occupied. While we wait I suggest to Brigitta that we go across to the bar. There are half-naked young men and girls all around us, and paradoxically it is we who feel almost embarrassed at being fully dressed.

A few moments later a beach attendant comes to tell us that there is a cabin available.

We follow him and stop outside a little door while he takes a key from his pocket. Before we realize what he is up to he pushes us inside and shuts the door behind us.

I am slightly annoyed. Not for myself, of course, but for Brigitta. My first reaction is to go out again, but the fear of being laughed at by the attendant, who must be waiting for us to come out and give him his tip, makes me stop and think again.

Brigitta says nothing. She simply smiles.

"We'll have to make the best of it," she says after a moment. "But I hope you'll be good," she adds teasingly.

She starts to undress. I turn my back and follow her example.

The cabin is very narrow and for a brief moment I feel the coolness of her thigh against my leg.

Foolishly, I now feel myself blushing.

Very soon we're out on the beach.

Brigitta really looks wonderful in her black bathing suit: her blue eyes, her chestnut hair, her bronzed skin against the back—a perfect ensemble.

There are too many people to make swimming a pleasure. After a quick dip we lie down on the sand. I slide my arm beneath her head and we lie there in silence, letting the sun caress and warm our naked bodies.

But it is growing late, and I have to be back at Urfeld by eight o'clock.

Once again we go back to our cabin.

This time it is she who suddenly presses her body to mine. I take her gently in my arms, delicately, as one would a fragile, precious Bayreuth china doll.

Almost roughly, her lips are crushed against mine.

My hands caress her golden shoulders, still warm from the sun. Suddenly I feel her yielding.

"No, Peter! No . . . I'm scared! No, no . . . This is the first time. . . . Peter, my darling!"

My first conquest as a man. . . .

September 2. Sedan Day. For two days now a regular army of Pimpfen has invaded Urfeld. They are to participate this afternoon and evening in the commemoration ceremonies to celebrate the French surrender of Sedan in 1870.

In the meantime they have sown the seeds of disorder and anarchy everywhere, for they cannot stop playing at war.

This morning, probably to get themselves in trim, they have been on "maneuvers" in the Oberau forest. They organized a splendid game which consists of a mock frontier battle.

The French, allied to the English plutocrats, have tried by treachery to attack German soil. The valiant soldiers of the Reich have flung them back across the Rhine.

So two armies are formed. From where I am writing I can hear the shouts and bellows of the boys who are pretending to be the Franco-English. Actually they know that it isn't going to be at all funny for them, and that blows with sticks and stones will rain down on them thicker than a summer hailstorm.

At noon the vanquished army returns, cross, disheartened and covered with bruises.

The others are singing:

> Six score cartridges slung across my chest,
> And a grenade in my hand,
> Come, Bolshevik, I'm ready. . . .

In the afternoon, the mass ceremony was held on the shores of Lake Walchen.

The Hitler Jugend and the Deutsches Jungvolk were paraded; they goose-stepped past, one hand on their daggers, the other beating time to the hymns that glorify the Third Reich.

At one hundred yards from the official platform we sang *Deutsch mein Bruder.*[5]

Look straight ahead, look always in front.
Conquer your fear and find the true path
To happiness. Death you must always defy,
There must be no trembling, no hesitation.
Ask for nothing, do not complain. . . .
Cowardice is nought but disgrace and defilement,
Dying for the country which once gave you birth
Is for the soldier perfect honor and glory.

Soon there will come a sweet purifying springtime
When all those our brothers shall once more be free
From the terrible yoke of their foreign oppressors.
Your courage is needed, and even your life,
Our honor must no more lie crushed on the ground.
We must break the great chains, learn to die for our land.

Fight on, fight on! Our forefathers urge us.
Fight on, fight on! The flag silently tells us.
Fight on, fight on! We have taken our oath.
Fight on, fight on! We have sworn it till eternity.

To celebrate in a fitting manner the first Sedan Day since the liberation of Austria, now free and independent and a part of the Reich, it was decided at the last moment that we should this evening salute our brothers beyond the Karwendel Alps.

We set off in the direction of the old frontier. When I say *we,* I mean an Unterbann, that is, about six hundred boys.

[5] "My German Brother" by Rudolf Steigen.

By way of Bad Tölz, Gmund and Lake Tegern we arrived at Wildbad Kreuih, the last stretch of country before we reach the mountains. We had to finish our journey on foot.

Torches were handed out. This was a wise precaution, for the countryside was as dark as a railway tunnel and there was thick mist.

"Fall in! Quick! Come along, get moving!"

The Bannführer suddenly started to shout, "Parade march! Forward, march!"

And so we all set off behind Gasser. God knew where. . . .

After some five hundred yards we stopped, to our considerable astonishment, in front of the village graveyard.

An order rang out.

"Torches alight!"

The only trouble was that we had not been prepared for this!

We could only muster one box of matches among every five or six boys. Finally, after some fumbling and angry shouts from those who burned their fingers, each boy was carrying a lighted torch at arm's length. At arm's length, certainly, for we quickly discovered that the chemical flare is an idiotic gadget which belches forth fountains of sparks and scatters flames everywhere, particularly in one's hair.

We marched through the cemetery gate.

It was a fantastic scene, this sinister cohort of spooks, lit by ghostly flares, marching through the graves, their faces livid. The torches threw furtive, flickering shadows among the tombstones and the crosses that stood out in strange relief beside the paths through the graveyard.

Gasser ordered us to form up in a semicircle around him, and addressed us:

"Comrades! We are gathered here this evening to celebrate, with the whole of our nation, the glorious anniversary of the destruction of French imperialism. Our fathers, in 1870, built the road to freedom for us. Faced with a pitiless enemy whose only aim was the annihilation of our eternal Prussia, cradle of our present-day Germany, they fought with every ounce of their strength, and with their blood—and they conquered!"

The Bannführer paused for a moment. In the suddenly silent night, the hissing of the torches and the sighing of the wind through the treetops were loud and deeply impressive.

"Look around you at these iron crosses beneath which your fore-fathers lie," he went on. "They suffered so that you could see before you a clear horizon, free of danger and purged of the dark miasmas created in the swamps of international plutocracy."

Gasser went on for quite a long time, but I stopped listening for I was utterly enthralled and fascinated by the extraordinary and sinister scene. Rising up mistily from the darkness, with set, enamel smiles, were soldiers wearing the Bismarckian *Pickelhauben* and grenadiers in the steel helmets of the Argonne; they seemed to thank us for having come to visit them, for not having forgotten their sacrifice.

Gasser wound up his harangue with the words:

"Comrades! We too must take our oath to follow the path which the glorious dead of our country's history have marked out for us. The day will come when we must embark upon a new battle for liberation, united behind the red and black banner of our Führer. From this very moment, we must hold ourselves in readiness! *Heil Hitler!*"

We left the cemetery and, singing as we went, took the road up toward the pass.

It was a rough climb, the stones on the path rolled beneath our feet, but we shouted into the night the words of *Demutigen Befreiung:*[6]

> What is this shadow so vast
> Which raises its menacing hand
> To torture our sore oppressed brethren?
> 'Tis the enemy of our proud German land.

[6] "Liberation of the Humble" by Theodor Kaeppler.

We soon noticed hundreds of lights advancing toward us.

We arrived at the top of the Achen Pass at the same moment as the newly formed troops of the Austrian Hitler Youth.

With our flares raised high, we saluted them.

4. The Napola

Autumn 1938. I have been back in Wittenberge for several days.
Father has not yet been set free. He was transferred a month ago
to the detention prison at Neubrandenburg. He was living in that
town at the time that the acts of which he is accused took place.

I have applied to the director of the National Political Training
Schools (the Napolas), asking to be enrolled when term starts.
About twenty of us from the central school have done the same.

I wouldn't at all mind becoming a Party official. It is an interesting job, and with a little luck, one might hope to become an
Ortsgruppenleiter or perhaps even a Kreisleiter.

I succeeded in making up Karl's and Franz's minds for them, and
their applications were sent to Berlin at the same time as mine.

Michael, however, wanted more time to think it over.

These National Political Training Schools have only operated
since January 1934. Their purpose is the molding and instructing of
the men destined to occupy high positions in the Party, or preparing
them for training in the paramilitary units of the SA or SS.

Our home has really become worse than depressing since Father
was taken away. I feel I want to get the hell out of it as soon as
I possibly can.

Mutti weeps all day long. The apartment is permanently invaded
by neighbors trying to be consoling and sympathetic. They get very
much under my feet, I find.

As for Klauss, he is becoming more and more intolerable. I can't take him anywhere without him making himself conspicuous by eccentric behavior or by his way of looking down his nose at people to see if they may have any Jewish characteristics.

He calls it giving them the racial once-over.

They get a complete course on the subject at his school. The shape of face, eyes, teeth, hair, pigmentation of the skin, style of dress, way of walking and talking and so forth.

In the case of women, they are recommended to look out for the way they hold themselves and for signs of early obesity about the hips.

At the moment he doesn't hesitate to insult anybody who finds his behavior in any way odd.

Yesterday, in a bakery on the Marktplatz, he stared for a long time at a fat lady guzzling cream cakes, until at last she said crossly, "Perhaps you can tell me, young man, whether your inspection is likely to continue much longer?"

Stunned by such audacity, he stared at her from his full height of four feet six and said sharply, "Madam, I'm carrying out the mission I've been entrusted with, which is to detect everywhere the enemies of our people, whenever and wherever they may be found."

What can you say to that?

I mumbled vague excuses about lack of discipline, badly brought-up children, etc. After a box on the ear I dragged away our brave little sleuth-cum-knight-errant, and we went home.

That greedy woman eating her cream cakes, an enemy of the people!

Really, Klauss is beginning to overdo it.

I hear in a letter from Berlin that by virtue of my diplomas and references, I have been admitted to the Holstein Napola.

Karl and Franz have also been accepted. So we shall probably go there together.

We are to be at Plön, in Schleswig-Holstein, not later than October 6.

We have only three days to get ready. But the excitement of leaving, and above all the prospect of entering the Party training college, lends us wings.

Our luggage is soon ready.

Last formalities, final instructions, and the train moves off.

We wave to old Wittenberge, and leaning out of the windows we start to sing Brown Shirt songs, like so many beer-hall heroes.

November 2. The Napola at Plön is an old barracks for non-commissioned officers, converted to its present purpose. It is gloomy, icy and horrid.

The college is like the countryside, cold and melancholy.

Over the swamps and canals of this landscape winds of gale force coming from far away howl endlessly. The peasants here are cross-grained and suspicious, and when we meet them they avoid us as though we were vermin.

Strange people. Strange country. . . .

We have been issued the college uniform: a fawn shirt, field-gray trousers and a swastika armband.

I don't know exactly what purpose it is supposed to serve, but we have to carry a bayonet which hangs most elegantly at our side and swings rhythmically as we walk.

Yesterday we underwent a very thorough medical examination, followed shortly afterward by an intelligence test.

Then we had to run a hundred meters and show our skill at the high jump, the long jump and putting the weight. According to our prowess in these activities, we shall be directed into one of the numerous athletic groups which seem to play an important part at Plön.

Racial instruction is given by an old man with a gray beard whose only god is Houston Chamberlain.[1]

[1] Houston Stewart Chamberlain, an English writer who emigrated to Germany at the beginning of the century, was one of the pioneers of National Socialism. Hitler

He entered with his beard waving in the wind, a grim expression on his face and looking extremely important. He hurried straight across to his desk, climbed onto the little platform and finally turned to face us.

"Good morning, gentlemen! I have not come here to give you a lecture or to make a welcoming speech, no doubt others have already attended to that."

He scrutinized our faces keenly.

"Today, so that we can get to know each other, we shall start off with an outline of the basic causes of the racial struggle in our country, particularly the anti-Jewish struggle." Before going on, he assumed a menacing stance.

"There are people who imagine that our hatred of the Jews is founded on no valid grounds and is merely the product of unreasonable spite or of a decayed militarism."

The graybeard (he is called Julius Mackner, and I shall have to remember that) gave a loud laugh and roared, "Immeasurable idiocy! A sinister myth invented by the propaganda of the decadent or capitalist nations for the benefit of their brutalized populations. Those nations, which accuse us of an abnormal and inhuman racialism, forget just one fact: it wasn't we who began the struggle against the Israelites. Throughout the ages orthodox Jewry has been persecuted. The Jew was the enemy of the Roman Empire. He was the enemy of ancient Greece, of Pharaonic Egypt, of Babylon."

Mackner suddenly came down from the platform and began to walk between the benches.

"They imagine, perhaps, that we Germans are the first people anxious to safeguard the purity of our race. Who was it who said that the ancestral blood should in no circumstances be vitiated, if the degeneration of the race was to be avoided? Was it us? No, it was the Jews themselves."

---

admired him greatly and never concealed the fact that Chamberlain was, with Rosenberg, one of the principal inspirers of *Mein Kampf*. Chamberlain wrote a violently anti-Semitic work famous in Germany in the Nazi period, *The Foundations of the 19th Century*.

He strode up and down, stooping slightly, his hands clenched behind his back.

"Read the *Protocols of the Elders of Zion*. They say that it's a forgery! What difference does it make? The idea behind it is not forged. That constant dissimulation, that gift of ubiquity which they seem to possess, that permanent hold over public figures, those prolific reproductive powers which are so characteristic—all these are the weapons, and the poisons, of the Jew."

Mackner went back to his place and sat down.

"You have heard about the difficult economic conditions which arose in the postwar period. You have heard of this great influx of Jews from the East or Middle East, flinging themselves upon the body of Germany like jackals upon a wounded animal. You've been told about the great industrial power of the Jews, their control of the banks, their combinations to crush German trade. Propagandist fiction? On the contrary! Literal and undeniable truth."

Suddenly he raised an enormous fist and brought it down with a crash on his desk.

"In *Mein Kampf* the Führer has said that the mixing of races was unacceptable. The nation must keep its strength and its blood intact if it is to conquer. The reason for the degeneration and extinction of certain peoples is frequently their inability to safeguard their integrity and to keep their blood free from pollution by foreign blood, which first corrupts, then submerges, and finally destroys them. . . ."

He stood up.

"Gentlemen, that is all for today. On Tuesday we shall analyze these problems a little more closely."

"If you drive a car up too steep a grade, and the engine cannot develop enough power, you will inevitably get stuck sooner or later. If you are flying a plane and haven't enough power, you won't get stuck. But you'll break your neck!"

The gliding instructor is explaining the finer points of his delicate science, which consists of juggling with winds and altitudes.

We have already made several flights with a copilot, and today we're to go up alone.

Karl has already passed his flying test with the mark "quite good." So he looks down on us from the heights of his experience.

Filled with self-importance, he remarks to me, "To stay in the air, you have only to work on the principle that the vertical thermal currents on which your glider rests derive from the fact that some parts of the earth's surface are warmer than others."

Oh, Lord, I'm getting quite a lecture!

Undaunted, Karl goes on. "General principles. Over towns, villages, rocks, hills or low mountain ranges you are borne upward. Over lakes, the seas or forests, no upward currents and you must expect a loss of speed."

I am soon ready to put these fine theories into practice.

I am given a Hessenland glider. I check the instructions for the last time and run through the actions to myself. To climb, pull the joy stick back; to come down, joy stick forward. Rudder bar and joy stick to the left, the machine moves to the right. Rudder bar and joy stick to the right, rudder and machine both move left.

If I don't break my neck with all this, it will be because I have a good memory.

Off we go! The launching gear goes into violent action and I am shot upward like an arrow. I try to remember the instructor's advice. Keep the joy stick forward, get on the proper line of flight as soon as possible. . . .

I am now at an altitude of six or seven hundred feet, a marvelous feeling. There is no sound except for the gentle rustle of the wind against wings and fuselage.

Below me I can see Lake Plön. My altimeter tells me I am climbing. I can see the whole of the Kiel Bay coast now, with the islands of Fehmarn and Lolland ahead. But I must watch out that I am not carried out to sea. I bank slowly to the left. The Hessenland, streamlined as a needle, responds splendidly. I shall make a little tour over the outskirts of Kiel. I can see steamers on the canal.

But before I realize it, I find I have been flying for nearly a quarter of an hour. I must think about coming down.

The landing takes place without a hitch, and I am greeted by the shouts and congratulations of Franz, Karl and the instructor. I am a little giddy from this first solo flight, and my ears are buzzing slightly.

But what will one not do to gain the admiration of one's friends?

I received a letter from Brigitta this morning. The poor girl complains that I don't think of her enough. She cried, evidently, while writing it. She has plucked at my heartstrings with her letter; it seems so full of the deep tragedy of discarded mistresses, the damp stains left by tears, and so on. Enough to fill you with remorse, so that you don't want to write a letter ever again.

I think I shall hang on to Brigitta, all the same. But she certainly cannot realize that with all we have to do in the day, it is very difficult to find a free moment for writing letters.

Sunday—a day I shall always remember. Franz, Karl and I went to Hamburg.

The Hanseatic capital is noisy, dirty, smoky and full of activity. In the evening Karl wanted to go to a joint he knew in San Pauli.

This nightclub, located near the Landing Bridge, was, in fact a brothel; everything about it was horrible. We had no sooner set foot in the place than we were picked up by three hostesses. "Hostesses" was the right word for them, as their one object was to offer us the hospitality of their beds.

Obviously it was difficult to refuse them the drinks which they had so kindly offered to have on us.

After a few moments, one of these gracious ladies of easy virtue tried to put her arms around my neck. I repulsed her advances quite gently. I don't care for that sort of familiarity.

Franz and Karl, on the other hand, seemed to be letting them-

selves go with a quite disgusting lack of discrimination. I wanted
to put a stop to these goings on; I don't like that kind of sordid fun.

I got up and said, "Coming, men? I could do with a breath of
fresh air."

Franz got up at once, but Karl, who was already rather tight,
stared blankly at me. "But it's fine here!" he said.

He turned to his *femme fatale* and added, "And Gretel is charming! You're sweet, aren't you, Gretel? You have pretty hair, a
pretty little mouth, nice little breasts, a dear little . . ."

He was pretty far gone, and the time had come to act. I gestured
to Franz, and we tried to lift Karl up, each taking one of his arms.
But the girls weren't standing for that. One of them jumped up
and started screeching, "Leave him alone, you silly boys! Just because
you're not proper men—and at your age you damned well ought
to be—why should you stop him having a bit of fun if he wants to?"

All at once the whole room was staring at us. Our discretion and
dignity as students of a state college had been greatly damaged.

I turned pale and restrained myself with difficulty. But I managed
to reply quite calmly, "You can see my friend isn't well. Anyhow,
we've got to get back to barracks."

"Listen to him! Not very well, if you please. And his nanny's
come to take him home, bless his little heart! More likely you're
just a bunch of scared kids that don't know what to do when you
find yourselves with a woman."

She started to laugh, a vulgar, coarse laugh which showed her
bad teeth.

"And they want to build a new Germany with the likes of you!
If your Führer could see you now, shaking in your shoes, he'd give
you the Iron Cross, Second Class, for sure!"

Now it was my turn to play her game.

"The Führer," I replied, "absolutely forbids any member of the
Hitler Youth to contaminate himself by copulating with whores of
your sort!"

She didn't answer, but her face went waxy and she turned her
head away, seeking the support of her companions.

But they, perhaps not wanting to see a brawl start and the police arrive, preferred to keep their mouths shut.

We got hold of Karl again, who was obviously in a doze, and managed with difficulty to lead him out.

Once there he was sick, and after that felt slightly better.

A taxi took us to the station and somehow or other we got back to Plön.

The year 1938 is drawing to a close.

The day before yesterday we celebrated Christmas in the big armory. The whole school was there, and each student was entitled to a slice of goose, half a bottle of wine, any number of cakes and sweets, a speech by SS Standartenführer Kurt von Berschtold, director of the Napola, and a photograph of Schir and Goebbels shaking hands.

A tree had been decorated with hundreds of little multicolored electric candles and at midnight they were all switched on.

I think many of us must have remembered our chilhood as we sang the Christmas carol:

> Stille Nacht,
> Heilige Nacht . . .

Rather foolishly, Karl and Franz and I embraced.

In a corner of the hall we clasped hands and swore, that night, to preserve our friendship faithfully no matter what might happen.

March 16, 1939. Winter has gradually come to an end. As month succeeded month and day followed day, it pursued its steady course: the fields re-emerged from their covering of snow, the ice on the rivers melted, the buttercups lifted their heads again; it was spring. . . .

I am just nineteen.

This is not particularly interesting to anyone else, but to me it is extremely important, for the coming year will certainly decide my future.

Actually last month SS Standartenführer von Berschtold called us all together on the parade ground to give us some important news.

Thirty students have been chosen, on the basis of marks gained, to attend a course at Ordensburg.[2]

We three are on the list.

The chosen students are given two days to accept or refuse, for only volunteers go to Ordensburg.

We looked at each other. One minute, and our decision was taken. We accepted.

[2] In full, Blutordensburg (Citadel of the Order of Blood)—educational HQ of the Nazi régime, where the future élite of Germany were trained.

5. Vogelsang

Vogelsang Castle, April 1939. This Ordensburg is in an old medieval castle on the edge of a little mountain lake, in the middle of the Eifel.

The countryside is most picturesque. Little valleys, pine woods and plains stretch gently away to Aachen.

Behind the castle is dense forest. From my room I can hear the roar of the rushing streams, pouring down from the Talps-Urft.

Here at Vogelsang we are in the Junkers' paradise.

This sort of paradise, however, does not seem to confer immortality. An impressive cemetery with thousands of flower-covered mounds is located immediately behind the outbuildings. The black crosses and the memorials are more numerous than on a battlefield.

They evidently do a lot of dying in the Ordensburg.

We should have spent three months doing preliminary training at Krössinsee (Krossino), in Pomerania. But six of us, owing to the excellence of our reports from the Hitler Youth, were sent straight to Vogelsang.

We shall do the preliminary three months' course here. That is to say, we shall not be considered as students during this period, but as "observers undergoing instruction."

Actually you have to be at least twenty-five and have proved yourself in the ranks of the Party before being admitted as a Junker.

On arrival we underwent a very thorough medical and racial examination. Probably this will not be repeated at the two other castles where we shall also have to spend some time.

Two Medical Corps majors, the castle commandant and about a dozen men in white coveralls were present at this impressive ceremony.

We were not so impressive.

Stark naked, we were examined in turn by these various inquisitors, who interrogated us closely.

All these gentlemen had to learn the thrilling facts that I am called Peter Neumann, that I was born on March 16, 1920, at Hamburg, that my height is five feet eleven and that I have a fair complexion and blond hair.

At one point I had to stand in front of a gentleman in civilian clothes who suddenly peered at my nose and jerked out, "Are you of Jewish origin, or Jewish yourself? Was your father Jewish? Did your parents ever work for Jews?"

This seemed odd, for these same questions had been put to me times without number during the past few years.

I adopted my most casual manner and replied in the negative.

"Have you ever been convicted of a serious offense?"

"No."

"Have you ever been involved in any political activity other than that laid down by the Party?"

"No."

Satisfied by my answers, he sent me on to the next interrogator.

"What illnesses have you had?"

What does one say? I reeled off, at random, measles, scarlet fever, and other childhood ailments.

Then came yet another eyesight test. Teeth—the slightest trace of decay was noted—weight, chest measurements, X rays.

At the end of it all they were unable to find the slightest cogenital defect in me, or the smallest signs of potential disorder.

Franz and I were very pleased to have been judged worthy to attend the formidable course of the Order of Blood. I say "Franz and I," because poor Karl was sent off to Krössinsee. He hadn't quite made the grade and was not allowed to come straight to the Eifel.

We had a lecture this morning on the origins of the swastika and the reasons for its adoption as the symbol of National Socialism

With a piece of chalk in his hand, a young professor in SS uniform explained to us; "The figure seven, among the ancients, as in Germanic mythology, was the sign for luck and prosperity. Here are two sevens."

As he spoke, he drew the two figures on a blackboard, then turned to us again. "In runic numerals, the figure seven had, in addition to the form we know, a short horizontal bar across the bottom and to the right.

"There we have," he went on, "the two component parts of the swastika. If we now superimpose one figure on the other, to form a cross, we have the complete swastika. As you see, it forms a twofold good-luck symbol. The actual word 'swastika,' in an Indian dialect, also means luck and prosperity."

All this was most surprising. What came next was even more interesting.

"The Führer," he explained, "got the idea of the swastika when he was wounded, ill and half blind after being gassed. He was undergoing treatment at the Pasewalk Hospital in Pomerania. He tells us that as soon as the Army doctors took the dressings from his eyes, the first thing he saw was a stone swastika engraved on the arched doorway of the room in which he lay. Some months later, on August 8, 1918, when he learned that our front had been broken by the Anglo-French armies, he realized that the war was lost. On that day he swore to avenge this insult to the flag of the German Reich and decided to adopt the swastika as the symbol of his vow."

We all listened with great interest. The SS man turned toward the blackboard again and in a few strokes drew the party symbol.

"However, our Führer has no use for lucky charms or other such ridiculous superstitions. Therefore he reversed the crosses and produced a true swastika; that is to say, the eternal sign of power and destruction among the ancients."

The SS professor came down the few steps which separated his desk from his class, and walked toward us.

"The Hitlerian swastika was later turned aslant, in the Party armbands and banners, to symbolize the inexorable progress of a wheel. This Nazi cross was placed against a white circle, representing purity, and the circle itself was inserted into a scarlet rectangle, emphasizing the proletarian origins of the NSDAP."

He paused for a few moments, foursquare in his perfectly polished boots, as though concentrating.

"The swastika, although of Indian origin, is a purely German symbol. Many castles in Thuringia and Saxony have it engraved in their stonework. The Wandervogel [1] had it as their badge. Kaiser Wilhelm II ordered it to be incorporated in the crest with which he marked his personal effects. To go even further back, the German Emperor Karl the Great had it embroidered on his court robes."

He returned to his place and, suddenly adopting a more serious tone, ended with the words: "That is why you must respect this eternal symbol of the unity and integrity of our country on all occasions and defend it if need be with your life."

The combat training is terrifying.

Yesterday afternoon we watched horrific fights between specially trained Alsatian dogs and the Junkers.

These took place in a large field sloping down to the lake. Four cages containing the dogs were brought out, and at a given signal the doors were flung open. The dogs threw themselves like mad things at the throats of our candidates. The latter had absolutely no protection against the fury of the beasts.

Their special training enables them to overpower the dogs after only ten minutes or so.

[1] Pre-1914 youth movement.

But if they should make a mistake, the dogs certainly won't. One of the men had a torn shoulder, and blood spurted from the gaping artery.

He insisted, however, that nobody harm the dog.

I find this quite normal. These animals are worked up until they are half mad; the consequences must therefore be accepted.

This is the kind of exercise which contributes to the "character-forming" process at Vogelsang.

Another is breaking wild horses.

It's like the Wild West, but with this difference: these horses are only wild because they have been made so.

Very young colts are taken from the stud farms of Thuringia. The right kind of handling quickly gives them back the aggressive qualities of their forebears. And the object of the excerise is to break them in by sheer muscular force, without a saddle. I myself tried this particular form of amusement.

A small Arab horse, as thoroughbred as a Tirschenreuth yearling, was snorting with impatience at the prospect of a future master. Or a future victim.

Franz tried as best he could to dissuade me from this suicidal enterprise. But I had already gone up to the animal, and was trying cautiously to stroke its neck.

With a sudden jerk it threw back its mane and whinnied ominously. But some ten Brown Knights[2] were watching the scene, smiling sardonically. I did not dare face their ridicule. So I suddenly threw myself onto the animal's back, clutching its mane with one hand, trying to catch hold of the wretched brute's ears with the other.

I say "trying"; it was like being seated on the boiler of a locomotive that has been hurtled off a viaduct by an aerial torpedo. Before you could count up to three I was on the ground, wondering how to find the necessary excuses for my inexperience.

I am definitely not cut out to be a trainer of wild horses.

[2] The Ordensburg students were so called because they represented the élite of the Brown Shirts, first members of the Party.

For the past week one thought has been tormenting me: Stuttgart. . . . At all costs I must get to Stuttgart.

It is more than six months since I last saw Brigitta. I have been tortured by the longing to kiss her chestnut hair, with its intoxicating perfume, and to breathe her scent, the scent of a fresh, healthy young girl.

Unfortunately Stuttgart is nearly two hundred miles from Vogelsang. To make matters worse, one has to change trains two or three times. Two hundred miles there, and the same back; it would be difficult to do in a day, especially on a Sunday.

And Sunday is our only free day.

But I must have a shot at it. And I've suggested to Franz that he come with me. I was scarcely pleased with his reaction.

"You're crazy. Four hundred miles, half a dozen changes of trains, and back here for roll call. It's quite impossible."

Impossible or not, I am mad to find out if Brigitta's lips still have that slight taste of ripe currants which I liked so much.

"Don't worry, I have it all worked out!" I answered.

Actually, I don't have anything worked out, and I'll have to get busy very quickly on this problem of cross-country travel.

And so on Sunday, at three o'clock in the morning, we found ourselves on the little forest road leading to Zülpich.

How were we to get to the station more than twelve miles away before the Bonn bus passed? That's another story.

We had left the "Burg" in the middle of the night, after asking someone else to answer our names at the nine o'clock roll call.

We were quite easy in our minds about this. The Sunday-morning roll calls are never very strict.

The most difficult part was to avoid attracting the attention of the sentries guarding the main entrance to Ordensburg. We had to climb up the ramparts and cross the moat by a disused drawbridge, half-buried in briars and weeds. Vogelsang is a genuine medieval castle, perfectly designed for some spectacular film.

The next thing was to strike off through the woods, taking care to go in the right direction, because deep in the forest is the Belgian frontier.

After three hours of cross-country hiking through dense undergrowth and woods and across plowed fields, we arrived just in time to see the Bonn bus disappear over the horizon. There was nothing for it but to flop down on a bench at the railway station and wait for the next train at seven thirty.

Unfortunately at half past seven the platform was invaded by a noisy crowd of local peasants, setting off for Bonn or Koblenz and loaded with packages, clutching baskets full of geese, chickens and even young pigs. All destined, no doubt, for their relations living in town. To board the train amidst this heterogeneous collection of wicker baskets, suitcases and sacks, among this jostling, shouting and laughing crowd, was itself no laughing matter.

The first change was at Bonn. The underground corridors reverberated to the trampling feet of the passengers all running, as we were, to catch the Karlsruhe Express. The latter, with perfect synchronization, left almost at once. We changed trains again a few hours later. It was nearly two o'clock when at last we reached Stuttgart.

The town was quiet. People had obviously not yet set off on their usual Sunday-afternoon excursions, for the streetcars were almost empty. Franz, with his nose against the glass, must have been thinking the matter over, for he turned to me suddenly and announced that he had no intention of accompanying me to Brigitta's house. We arranged to meet again that evening: seven o'clock at the Main Station.

He got out at the first stop, having decided to spend the afternoon at some motion picture or other. Good luck to him. . . . The jolting streetcar went on its way, with an appalling noise of grinding metal, and a few minutes later I too got out of this frightful heap of scrap iron, at the corner of the Charlottenplatz and the Neckarstrasse.

Something which I hadn't thought of until that moment suddenly made me break out in a cold sweat. Suppose Brigitta wasn't at home?

And even if she were, her parents would be there too! How was I to get out of this mess and meet her alone?

The district was a depressing one, with a strange atmosphere, dreary and cold, almost sinister: long rows of mean houses, built to a pattern with ivy-covered porches, and here and there a small and tawdry shop.

37 Urbanstrasse.

I rang the bell, and a few seconds later I heard a shutter bang above my head.

"What is it?"

"Fräulein Halsted, please."

"This is her address, sir. What is it you want?"

"I am a friend of hers. I should like to see her."

I was not, deep down, feeling at all sure of myself. What kind of welcome would I get from her parents? If they only knew! Their daughter's lover coming to visit her as though he were her honest fiancé.

"Come up, sir! Second on the right," said the voice.

The door opened automatically. I climbed the stairs, wondering once again what I would say to them. A second or two later, I was face to face with Brigitta. Blushing and embarrassed, she introduced me to an elderly couple who peered at me suspiciously.

My uniform seemed to amaze them. Strange people. They looked anxious, almost afraid. Then I suddenly realized why.

"Peter Neumann, an old school friend," said Brigitta.

"Pleased to meet you . . . sir," stammered Herr Halsted with difficulty.

"Herr Halsted, I'm so sorry to interrupt the end of your Sunday dinner, but I seldom pass through Stuttgart, and I did want to take Brigitta out for the afternoon. If you don't mind, that is."

The old man turned to his daughter.

"Certainly, if Brigitta wants to go. But I—"

"Yes, Father," cut in Brigitta quickly. "It's all worked out very well. I didn't much want to go with Hanna, anyway. You can tell her somebody's come and invited me out. Just a minute, and I'll be ready!" she added for my benefit, with a radiant smile.

Ten minutes later we went downstairs. From the street Brigitta waved up to her parents, who were watching us walk away. I held her arm rather formally, as befitted a respectable school friend.

When we had turned the first corner I took her in my arms and kissed her.

"Brigitta! My sweet. I've been waiting so long for this moment."

Her lips were pressed to mine. After a moment she broke away and smiled. "Peter, darling! I have been so longing to see you, too. For months I've been hoping you'd come!"

I leaned toward her. "Do you want to?"

She blushed slightly and blinked her assent.

We went to a small hotel in the Olgastrasse. The receptionist looked us up and down with evident surprise, perhaps astonished by our youth, or by my uniform. I felt uncomfortable as I paid for the room. As for Brigitta, she went scarlet and turned her face away to hide her shame.

The woman led us upstairs, and we followed, holding hands. I was almost choking with an insane desire to laugh. We must have looked a thoroughly disreputable couple!

As soon as the door closed behind us, Brigitta took off her shoes and lay down on the bed. I sat beside her. Already she was breathing more quickly.

"Oh, Peter. I do love you so much."

The hours passed incredibly fast.

But as evening approached I couldn't help asking her something I'd been worrying about since early that afternoon.

"Your parents—they're Jews, aren't they?"

She looked fixedly at me for a moment and went very pale.

"Yes, Peter. I was going to tell you anyhow, but what difference does it make?"

Her eyes filled with tears.

I buried my hands in her thick hair and pulled her face toward mine. "None at all, Brigitta. I think I'm in love with you."

It had already struck half past six. There was only just time to get back.

I took her home, and a few minutes before seven I found Franz in a great state, waving wildly from the step of the train that was just about to leave.

We finally got back to Vogelsang at two o'clock in the morning.

Yesterday orders were issued that we were not to use the washrooms any more.

We have to run a mile and a half and wash in an icy stream.

The orders from on high are always designed to strengthen our characters. But the people who give them clearly have no intention of getting their own belly buttons frozen deep in the forest.

According to the veterans, we haven't seen anything yet. They have already been cut off cigarettes for long periods. In July of last year half the meals were eliminated throughout the entire month as a punishment for some breach of discipline. Last winter they were wakened in the middle of the night to go and do exercises in the deep snow.

It is true that the Brown Knights know what to expect before going to the Ordensburg. But all the same. . . .

"Iron discipline. Perpetual obedience," so runs the slogan. It is not for nothing that the Party takes the responsibility for everything that a cadet must leave behind him as part of his civilian past. Everything, even his debts, even any taxes that he may owe. The Party guarantees to pay them all. Its object, in fact, is to release future Junkers from any ties binding them to their past life. Petty material problems must never be a worry or an obstacle to those whose destiny is to govern Germany. Their families also receive a substantial allowance, which varies between one hundred and three hundred marks a month, according to their circumstances.

Today group exercises and firing practice with submachine guns. The instructors stated that live ammunition would be used.

We were issued steel helmets, and our section leaders, having received their orders, distributed the various groups along the forest's edge, ready to attack.

Proper trenches were dug. Our orders made it clear that they must be invisible to possible enemy scouts. They had to be camouflaged, therefore, with special nets and branches which the fatigue party had been bringing up all morning.

To make things even more difficult, there was barbed wire in the theoretical no-man's land. Wire cutters were issued to those of us who would have the job of cutting it.

Under real fire. Quite something!

A flare shot up, then sank down slowly on the end of its parachute. Green. The signal we'd been waiting for.

We began crawling along on our stomachs, headed for Red territory—the enemy.

We hadn't covered a hundred yards, and the barbed wire was still a few yards ahead, when long bursts of machine-gun fire began to whistle past our ears.

"Get down, you fools!" yelled a director with a black armband, at a group of half a dozen morons who were running toward the barbed wire.

Suddenly an enormous roar broke out all about us, shells bursting, others screaming toward us. Artillery!

We gazed at one another open-mouthed. Really, this was going too far! Trying to see where the din was coming from exactly, I suddenly understood. Loudspeakers had been set up in the trees, and we were being treated to the sound effects of a real battlefield. Just like the movies!

We were through the wire now.

Our objective was two small hillocks. We captured one. The other was defended most tenaciously. Two Brown Knights, who had been rash enough to raise their heads, were hit.

Screams of pain, shouting and swearing by the section leaders, an ambulance. . . . For a moment the play-acting was called off.

Later we learned that one of the lads died on the way to the infirmary. The condition of the other one, who was shot through the eye, was doubtful.

It really was bad luck on those two—and on the rest of us for that matter—since they were due to finish at Vogelsang the following week.

Yesterday we had the supreme honor of a visit from the Reich leader Reinhard Heydrich.

He inspected us and announced that he was satisfied with us and with our military bearing.

He looks amazingly young to occupy such a position and is very tall. He wears a pale uniform, and a long sword with a silver tassel hangs by his side.

He made us a terrific speech, punctuated with rather coarse swear words and threatening gestures with his raised fist.

"The time for hesitation is over," he roared. "Very soon, we shall embark upon our war of liberation, our struggle for *Lebensraum*. We must win, and we shall win. Germany is strong enough now to overthrow those nations which have dared to resist her just demands. . . ."

Massed *Sieg heils* greeted this oration.

We marched past, eyes left, singing *Treue und Treue* ("Loyalty! Oh Loyalty") as we went.

6.   Sonthofen

Sonthofen Castle, August 28, 1939. For the last two days German airborne troops have been fighting Polish paratroops who attacked the radio station at Gleiwitz.[1]

The general opinion is that Poland will be wiped off the map in a matter of days.

The Western powers, in spite of their guarantee to the Warsaw government, will certainly not dare to launch an offensive. Once again they will have to try and find a compromise.

Our Führer is definitely a great diplomat.

Besides, the whole of Germany has realized that the pact signed with Russia on the 23rd will give England and France much food for thought.

Sonthofen is very different from Vogelsang.

The castle is situated in impressive mountain and forest scenery, at the foot of the Oberjoch range in Allgäu.[2]

Its tall, gray façade rises proudly above the valley. There is a strange atmosphere here—lofty, stern, majestic, full of grandeur.

But an iron discipline prevails.

About twenty of us arrived by motorcoach from Munich. As soon

---

[1] The SS, who had not received a last-minute countermanding order from the Führer, had been fighting on the Polish frontier since August 26.

[2] A district in southwest Bavaria, near Lake Constance.

as we got out, we were taken in hand by a Party instructor wearing a black armband, who didn't look at all easy-going.

"Fall in here! Jump to it! Come on, get moving!"

When we were formed up behind him, he began shouting like a madman. "To the gate. Left turn! Forward march. Left right, left right, left right . . ."

They showed us where we were to sleep—eight of us to a room, on tiers of bunks. The view from the broad bay windows is magnificent.

Two hours after our arrival, the preliminary questioning began. We are getting used to this by now.

That first evening, Franz and I were leaning with our elbows on the parapet, looking out over the valley. In the distance we could see Immenstadt and the lake. The horizon stretched away to the Schwarzer Grat.

"I've got a suspicion this isn't going to be exactly a picnic," grumbled Franz.

"Oh, you can get used to anything. Anyhow, we've got to make a few small sacrifices if we're to get big jobs in the Party."

September 2, 1939. The panzer divisions are headed for Warsaw. The Führer has ignored the Western powers' ultimatum. It's war.

This is terrifying and wonderful news. The fight to the death against international Jewish capitalism, which is attempting to stop our progress, has begun!

SS Sturmbannführer Griesel, who is acting commandant of the Ordensburg, assembled us all in the great inner courtyard, on the uppermost of three vast terraces.

"Comrades!" he shouted in vibrant tones. "You have heard the news. England and France have been crazy enough to declare war on us. The country is mobilizing. From this day forth all our energies must be devoted to the final victory. But your present duty is not to fight on the frontiers. No, it is to complete the course here, so that when you do go into battle you will be equipped with a political, military and strategical training which will enable you to wipe out your foes."

Raising both arms high in the air, Griesel silenced the great roar which came from all our throats.

"Comrades! You are the future officers of the armies which tomorrow will occupy London and Paris. Prepare to be worthy of the trust which the nation has placed in you!"

Taking advantage of a few hours off duty, Franz and I strolled along the road through the forest that leads to Hindelang.

"It's funny all the same," said Franz suddenly, with a half-smile. "What's funny?"

"France and England deciding to come in," he went on, turning to me. "When you come to think of it, it's really thanks to them that Nazism was born!"

I shook my head, pursing my lips. "Oh. . . . I know, you mean the Rhineland?"

With his hands behind his back he began soliloquizing, as though he were alone. "In 1918, things were going badly for us. The people were at the end of their tether. Revolution was in the air. More than that, there were crippling war debts. Trade was more or less at a standstill."

He thrust out his lips. He was thinking. Then he went on, "Perhaps if the French had played their cards right then, it could have meant the end of this famous traditional hatred."

"But that would have been a pity," I cut in. "Because of Alsace-Lorraine, and a lot of other things, too."

He smiled ironically. "Fortunately for us, France has excellent statesmen. And an enormous amount of farsightedness and intuition. The slightest excuse was enough for them to reoccupy the Rhineland—I beg their pardon—to administer the mines; that's what they said."

I glanced at him with surprise. I myself had studied this subject at length, but I hadn't realized that Franz, the dreamer, was equally interested.

"And so the mechanism is started," said Franz. "On January 11, 1923, the French move in, from Wuppertal to Wiesbaden. On the 26th, the Cuno government orders a general strike. The workers, deprived of their livelihood, mass outside the factories and at the pitheads. To break the strike the French send in troops. Principally, Senegalese troops."

Without realizing it, we were now deep in the Hindelang forest. Above us the trees echoed the songs of the birds. We sat down on a mossy trunk. I took out a packet of cigarettes and offered him one.

"From that moment, the French were defeated." He grinned, reaching for a cigarette. "And yet at the time minds which had been stunned by the war were almost ready to accept an eventual policy of Franco-German friendship."

He leaned toward the match, then straightened up again, blowing out a cloud of smoke.

"But the old hatred was revived. Stronger than ever. Because our people could not accept the humiliation of seeing the Rhineland handed over to black troops. But there was more to it than that. This time the French, who never lose an opportunity of accusing us of bad faith, had deliberately violated the various treaties and agreements. Even his former Allies now condemned Poincaré's action—the Americans, the English and the Canadians. Not to mention Switzerland and the Vatican, who protested."

A cool wind from the mountains sighed through the undergrowth. We got up and walked on again.

"I know the rest of the story," I murmured. "Destitution, and in an attempt to relieve it the printing of vast amounts of paper money. In a word, inflation. With all that that entails, internal, social and economic peril. Germany by now was moving inexorably toward the abyss."

"And Poincaré could celebrate a triumph!"

We had reached the triple barrier of barbed wire surrounding the

Ordensburg. In front of us lay the whole Obertsdorf mountain chain, at our feet the red roofs of Sonthofen village. Further away, emerald-green, the long strip of Immenstadt Lake gleamed in the rays of the setting sun.

Franz said no more. He seemed to be dreaming.

Suddenly he turned to me. "I've been rambling on, as though I were reciting a lesson I'd learned. But it's true, Peter. You remember the conversations we used to have at Schiller? You told me that man must have the strength to pursue an aim in his life, that he must have a mission, whatever it may be. It took me a long time to understand. I've been reading. And I understand now why we must follow our Führer blindly. He alone found the courage to raise himself above the chaos that was Germany. It was then that he really embarked on the struggle which was to lead him to power. It's thanks to that period, and to that chaos, that he got where he is now."

I gave a slight smile. "So you mean that the occupation of the Rhineland by the French was the real starting point of National Socialism? It's they who created the Nazi movement? We owe them an eternal debt of gratitude, eh?"

"I wouldn't go as far as that," he retorted, also with a smile. "But I assure you, there's more than a grain of truth in it."

NSKK [3] instructors are teaching us driving, maintenance and the repair of Benz armored cars, on every kind of terrain.

The enormous machines, roaring and spluttering, force their way down the forest tracks. The ground is often marshy, and we have to use all our limited skill to stop them from becoming bogged down.

The NSKK also teach us how to drive tanks across different kinds of country. With about fifteen tons of steel under us, we plow through woods and up almost invisible tracks which lead to the Oberjoch pass, nearly four thousand feet above sea level. Slopes of thirty degrees are taken in first, engine at full throttle.

[3] National Sozialistische Kraftfahr Korps (Nazi Corps of Drivers and Mechanical Engineers).

Fresh instructions must have arrived from Berlin. The training is getting more and more tough, cruelly tough.

Since September the number of accidental deaths has risen to thirty-two.

· As at Vogelsang, the Sonthofen cemetery is slowly filling up with little flower-strewn graves.

The weak must go to the wall here. Only those who survive will have the right to form part of the National Socialist élite.

When an instructor blows a blast on his whistle, we have to start building dugouts, which must be completed within a given time.

There are about a dozen of us, each with a spade. And we all start to dig like lunatics. Because in front of us there are ten Benz armored cars waiting, their engines slowly ticking over.

We have twenty minutes to dig the hole which will shelter us, which will save our lives. It's every man for himself. We aren't comrades any more.

My eyes fixed on my spade, which seems ludicrously heavy, I toss up huge lumps of earth. Slowly the hole widens, too slowly, horribly slowly. My palms are beginning to hurt. The skin is torn from my fingers by the rough handle of the spade.

Never mind, I must dig and dig and dig.

I can hear the revving up of an engine over there, a sinister and menacing sound.

This is it! They're moving off, advancing straight ahead. The drivers have been ordered to take no notice of anybody clumsy or foolhardy enough to get in the way. Inexorably they thunder toward our foxholes.

With wild shouts the boys jump into the holes they have dug, burrowing into the earth, burying their faces against the damp clay.

In front of me, like some monster in a nightmare, the Benz lumbers forward, its engine roaring, apparently swaying from side to side. It's getting bigger and bigger, and bigger still. . . .

They're past.

Of course, some of our chaps are killed.

But none are cowards.

Thus do we learn courage—at the risk of our lives.

We have been told we shall not be attending the course at Marienburg.

The original intention was that we should go next to Marienburg for instruction in the wider political, economic and strategic problems posed by the neighboring territories of Poland and White Russia.

It is possible that the cancellation of this course has some connection with the signing of our pact with the USSR.

Only the Brown Knights at Sonthofen will now complete their training in East Prussia. Humble "observers" such as we will have to think about our labor service.

And that is a much less pleasant thought.

A month ago we began a new course in biology and organic chemistry, with a smattering of pathology and anatomy thrown in.

They teach us, with experiments on guinea pigs, about the different sorts of war gasses and their noxious effects.

We also learn about the danger from exhaust gas, which is a residue after the combustion of motor fuel. We have watched a dog shut into a glass box connected to the engine of a car; he was dead within a few minutes.

We have seen experiments with different barbiturates, metalloids, paralyzants and other pleasant ingredients intended to dispose of one's fellow creatures.

One thing has astonished us very much. That is the ease with which one can be killed by an ordinary air bubble. An intravenous injection of a few cubic centimeters of air rapidly dispatched another dog to the canine paradise.

Intracardiac injections of benzol, phenol, petrol or turpentine, which all apparently have the remarkable property of sending any living being to his death, now hold no mysteries for us.

It is rather strange that they should force all this information upon us. But I still prefer biological chemistry to the anatomy lessons which we have attended.

Corpses were brought by ambulance from the Bregenz mortuary.

In groups of six, we were taken into one of the rooms of the sick bay, which had been turned into a temporary autopsy room.

It will be a long time before I forget that revolting spectacle. Two bodies, one of a man, the other of a woman, were lying on tables which had been placed end to end.

The woman must have been about fifty, but the man was quite young. Bathed in a pool of yellowish blood, they had been split open from chin to pubis, and their entrails bulged forth. The smell was appalling.

The professor, a young SS doctor who was presumably accustomed to this sort of thing, happily plunged his rubber-gloved hands into this nameless horror, calling out the names of the different organs one by one.

Franz, who was standing beside me, passed clean out and had to be taken outside. Another fellow was sick where he stood, a few feet from the corpses.

The young doctor gave us the full details. The male and female reproductive organs were dexterously opened with his knife. The grinding noise of the scissors cutting the pubic symphysis was disgusting. Or perhaps it was just because we weren't used to it.

With a quick gesture the leg of one corpse was next sliced up, and we were made to put hemostatic clips on the arteries. In cases of serious hemorrhage, this procedure is much more effective than the simple application of a tourniquet, which, our instructor told us, has the disadvantage of checking and even stopping altogether the flow of blood in the limb.

That wasn't the end of it. The SS doctor made us touch the bodies again; we had to prove our ability to give intravenous injections.

The arm of the woman was flabby, limp and very cold. I don't know whether the needle went into a vein or was lost in the brown-

ish flesh. I do know that afterward I spent a good half-hour washing my hands. I imagined that everything I touched smelled,
and felt, like a corpse.

Winter 1940. In the West the war goes on. Or more precisely, it
hasn't yet begun.

England and France, so mad to destroy us, in such a hurry to rush
to the aid of "poor Poland," are waiting patiently behind their
Maginot line.

As for Poland, she hasn't been mentioned for some time.

The commemoration of January 30, the anniversary of the Nazis'
coming to power, was a particularly brilliant affair this year.

We had the honour of parading in front of the Führer in Munich.

The whole town was decorated with flags. Doing the goose step,
we passed by the rostrum where there sat, besides the Chancellor,
Hermann Göring, Goebbels, Admiral Raeder, Doenitz, and several
generals whose names I didn't know.

The band of the Luftwaffe was lined up beside the imposing
saluting base and played the *Horst Wessel Lied*. We joined in the
chorus just before passing in front of the tribunal.

Spring 1940. A few days ago I reported to the hospital.

I had been sent for by the chief medical officer, whom I had
already seen when I first arrived. I came in and stood at attention.

The doctor tidied away the papers that cluttered his desk and
stood up. "I have one or two questions to ask you, Neumann. Quite
—important questions."

He seemed to hesitate. His regular features expressed kindness
and good nature, but his eyes were not smiling.

"We have made inquiries into your background and history. Your
own and that of your family. I congratulate you. You are of pure
Aryan stock. We've gone back as far as the eighteenth century and
we've found nothing but completely Germanic stock in your ances-
try."

He walked around his desk and waved to me to take a chair. I

did so, feeling rather surprised. The officer went across to a filing
cabinet, searched in it for a moment and finally took out a card.

"Incidentally, your blood tests show that you belong to Group A,"
he went on, turning toward me. "That's the pure Nordic group."

He sat down at his desk again, playing absent-mindedly with the
index card.

"You know, of course, that there are several blood groups,
Neumann, the principal ones being Groups A, B and O. The people
belonging to group AB often have Jewish blood in their veins. Group
O is often mistakenly regarded as a universal group, but it can be
used for transfusion to any of the other groups."

What was all this about? Was he planning to use me as a guinea
pig for blood-transfusion experiments?

The medical officer fixed his eyes vaguely on a point above my
head.

"You probably know the basic facts about gentics, Neumann.
. . . You realize that most human characteristics, together with de-
fects and imperfections, are handed down to each generation through
the agency of microscopic elements called chromosomes in the nuclei
of the cells. These chromosomes, or rather pairs of chromosomes,
determine whether the child will have its father's blue eyes, its
mother's mouth and the various other characteristics of its pro-
genitors."

His gaze fell upon me.

"It has been proved that several generations can and do preserve
the same aptitudes—artistic, scientific, or whatever they may be.
Bach was one of a long line of musicians. Strauss, Beethoven,
Richard Wagner also belonged to families of musicians. In another
sphere, the Krupp dynasty, for example, has always given Germany
inventors and technicians of genius. . . . But the examples are innumerable, and it would be tedious to refer to them all."

While he talked the officer kept looking at me through his rimless
glasses. His shrewd eyes seemed to be assessing my powers of com-
prehension, as though to evaluate my intelligence. But he might
have spared himself all these preliminaries.

I had understood.

He sat down now and rubbed his hands together.

"Given these facts, it is easy to understand that two racially pure human beings, of unmixed Aryan blood, have every chance of producing a child possessing their characteristics and their good qualities, or at any rate a good part of them. During the last few years these principles have been given practical application in the breeding of thoroughbred animals. The stud farms have found that a brood mare of pure stock, mated with a stallion also purebred, will produce, nine times out of ten, a thoroughbred. That's the key. Thoroughbreds! You see, it is quite normal to encourage the production of a perfect specimen among animals. Thoroughbreds are admired by all. But people hold up their hands in horror at the idea of applying the same principle to the human species. Why? Surely what is right for the animals must also be right for humans?"

He smiled.

"It's true to say that if we had reached such a degree of evolution as to be worthy to be called civilized, all this would be superfluous. Such unions would take place automatically, as a matter of course. Unfortunately man has not yet reached a state of perfection enabling him to diagnose his own errors objectively. As things stand now, it is quite usual for an alcoholic, after an evening's debauch, to copulate with another alcoholic—or perhaps even with a congenital syphilitic if he is unlucky—who will inevitably give birth to an abnormal child. This imperfect being will in turn produce other imperfect specimens. Think for a moment of the appalling progress. By the third or fourth generation there will be a whole crowd of abnormal human beings. The prisons and asylums will be full, but our morality will not have been offended, so nobody complains. Isn't that a monstrous state of affairs?"

His face hardened.

"In certain degenerate and unprogressive countries it is considered very odd, or even inhuman, that we should try by every means in our power to encourage the perpetuation of a pure Germanic race. But isn't it the governments of these countries who are actually blind and inhuman in refusing to keep their patrimony intact? In accepting the fact that the blood of their own peoples be corrupted, tainted and filled with mongrel strains, is it not they who are deliberately setting about the destruction of their own countries?"

He smiled again, a chilly smile.

"But perhaps the leaders of those nations regard our race purification as dangerous."

An orderly came in holding a piece of paper in his hand, which he placed on the medical officer's desk. The doctor glanced at it and then turned back to me.

"This is about you, Neumann. They've sent me your reports from Plön, Vogelsang and here. Perfect. We shall be able to make something of you. I think you already know what I'm talking about. You've heard, I'm sure, of the Lebensborne.[4] You have been selected with five of your comrades to go to Westphalia. Our Führer, having been advised by Rosenberg and Darré, started these establishments, in which is being produced for Germany that pure, regenerative blood which we need so badly for the future. We require young men like yourself, healthy, intelligent, tried-and-tested Nazis."

I had guessed that this was what it was all about. I knew, as did everyone else in the Hitler Youth, about these Lebensborn places, but I had never thought of myself as a potential stallion. The whole thing amused me, but at the same time it was rather worrying. I was puzzled as to what it would involve.

Before I left, the doctor got up and put his hand on my shoulder in a friendly way. "Neumann, you'd better be a bit discreet about all this. Don't mention it to the others."

Two days later five of us took the train from Munrich's central station.

Franz is not of the party. They must have found that he was not up to standard genetically.

We make so much noise that anyone would think there was a whole regiment of soldiers in the station. Carrying our suitcases and

---

[4] Literally "Fountains of Life"—state-controlled breeding establishments.

wearing our black uniform, we must look like schoolboys setting off for the holidays. It is only our swastika armbands that show how important we really are.

With me there is Albrecht Steiger, Martin Wolf, Curt Allensen and Leonhard Spiselmann. We are all the same age and as excited as kids about what lies in store for us.

"What's your type?" asks Wolf, who is seated beside me. "Mine'll be a blonde, with breasts like this"—he makes an unambiguous gesture—"and thighs like— Wow! Does me good just to think of it."

He is playing the fool, and doing it to perfection. He is almost convincing. But I have no views on the subject. And I haven't any idea how it will be arranged, though I doubt if one will be able to choose one's partner in the same way as in a house of ill fame.

As soon as the train moves off, we lean out of the window, singing at the top of our voices.

Nuremberg, Würzburg, one station after the other whizzes past, and soon we are out of Bavaria and passing through the green fields of the Spessart. It's spring.

At Frankfurt we catch another train for Kassel, where we change again into a local train which jogs along, with many a stop, to Marburg.

Outside the station a little Volkswagen is waiting for us.

"Are you the lads for Schmallenog? Jump in!"

After a two-hour drive we find ourselves deep in the mountains of the Rothhaar range.

Schmallenog is a little village which looks as though it has been recently and completely rebuilt. It consists of either small, two-story cottages with vine-and-creeper-wreathed balconies or large, barrackslike blocks of flats, six stories high and built around horse-shoe-shaped lawns.

Our driver and guide leads us toward a modern building which looks like a hospital. Can this be the headquarters of the Lebensborn?

We are feeling rather nervous. The excitement and enthusiasm of

the journey have been replaced by a considerable apprehension about
the fate that is in store for us.

We are shown into a large hall where a woman in the uniform
of the BDM, seated behind a polished wooden reception desk, asks
for our names and papers.

When the formalities have been gone through, she glances at us.

"Leave your baggage here and go to Room 17. First corridor on
the right, second door."

We do as we are told.

We are met by a nurse in Room 17. She must have been notified
of our arrival by the house telephone, for before we have time to
open our mouths, she jerks out, "Undress, please. Here are your
cards, one for each of you. Go one at a time into Dr. Niewsky's
office. He will examine you."

When my turn comes to report to the doctor, he inspects my card,
looks me up and down from head to toe, and begins his medical
examination. Lungs, heart, X rays, all over again. Then the special
examination relevant to the purpose for which we are here—if one
may so put it!

The doctor must be about forty, a clean-shaven man, without a
vestige of hair on his polished, shining skull.

Presumably quite satisfied, the straightens up and says, "That's
all in order. Now I want a specimen of semen from you."

Semen! What does he mean? And where do I get it from?
Suddenly I understand. I must look completely nonplussed, because
he smiles ironically.

"Here's a test tube. Go into that cubicle there, where you'll be
alone."

God Almighty! What a performance! Here I am shut up in a
cubicle with nothing but a glass tube clutched foolishly in my hand.
I wonder frantically how on earth I'll ever go through with this.

I had suspected that the whole Lebensborn business would be
pretty surprising, but I'd never thought of this! Still, I can't stay
here in a state of desperation all day. Particularly as there's really no
reason to be so upset.

I try hard to think about . . . other things. I must begin the operation.

After long and noble efforts, I finally complete my difficult task. I knock timidly on the door of the consulting room. I hear a drawer being closed as he asks me to come in.

"Finished? Good. Here's a label. Stick it on your jar, and put the jar over there on that shelf."

He points to a small wooden table, where there are other jars and tubes. I do as he says.

"You can get dressed now," he says. "We'll analyze all this. As soon as you're ready, go and see Fräulein Hofdel again; she'll tell you what to do."

When I come out, Albrecht Steiger and Allensen are still waiting their turn to go and see Dr. Niewsky. They start questioning me.

"What was it like?"

I adopt an air of slight superiority. "Just a few formalities. You'll see, it's all very interesting."

That same evening I was told that I could go to the recreation room.

By this I understood that the last examination had been satisfactory, and that I had been passed.

The recreation room, with its great fireplace and its stained-glass windows, reminded me of the assembly hall at Sonthofen. There were about fifty young men and girls there, playing ping-pong or chess, or talking and listening to music. About a dozen were dancing to the radio, which was at the end of the room beside a sort of bar, where I soon learned that they served only milk and various fruit juices.

There was an atmosphere of student life about it all which reminded me of impromptu parties at Wittenberge. There was no trace of any immoral or even free-and-easy carryings-on to indicate that this was anything but a group of ordinary young people enjoying themselves.

I felt ill at ease.

I climbed up on one of the bar stools and ordered an orangeade from the brunette behind the counter.

There were several servicemen in the room, Wehrmacht, Luftwaffe, two sailors and five or six fellows in SS uniform.

Officers and other ranks were talking together with an astonishing lack of restraint.

I didn't see anybody from Sonthofen.

I asked the waitress, "Tell me please, Fräulein, have you seen four fellows in Napola uniforms?"

"There are several halls here," she said. "Perhaps they're in another part of the building."

I had no desire to go into the matter any more deeply, and I got down from my perch after thanking her. But without paying, because one doesn't have to pay here.

I had caught sight of a blonde who was looking through some magazines, seated at a little round table. Everything about her was perfect—her figure, face and teeth—apart from one small blemish which I noticed at once: her eyes were a clear china-blue, but almost totally without expression.

I went up to her. "Good evening, Fräulein. I hope I'm not disturbing you. I was rather bored over at the bar. It isn't much fun talking to a waitress."

She looked up and smiled. "You must be new here. Only a new arrival would be so apologetic about speaking to a girl. And so polite, too. But do sit down."

I sat down beside her in an armchair. She laid her magazine on the table. "Did you arrive today?"

"Yes, from Bavaria, early this afternoon." I leaned toward her. "I'm sorry. How awful of me; I never introduced myself. My name's Peter Neumann, and I'm taking a course at Sonthofen."

With a little, ironical smile, she replied, "Lotte Pflingen. Liselotte to you."

"Tell me, Fräulein—Liselotte, if I may call you Liselotte—you seem so charming, and kind, and sympathetic. Do you think you could initiate a poor, ignorant new arrival into the mysteries of this place? What happens here? I mean, in general. Naturally, I'm not just referring to the genetic part of it, but—"

"But you're dying to know how we all go to bed together according to National Socialist regulations?" she broke in, smiling again.

I was rather embarrassed. I must have blushed. "That isn't quite what I meant. I want to know the organization at Schmallenog."

She became more serious. "I don't know any more about it than you do. I've only been here three days. You can bet your life that if I'd been here any longer we shouldn't be talking together at this moment. Perhaps I'd have already been . . . booked! All I can tell you is that we live—the girls, you understand—in dormitories of six or twelve beds, supervised by Jungmädelführerinnen[5] of the BDM. The girls who are . . . chosen are taken off the dormitory roster and moved to another section, which deals with the legal details of the union, and of course with any future births which may result from it—because we must remember that that's what we're all here for," she ended quietly, looking away. "A strange thing for one's country to ask of one. Don't you agree?"

I shook my head and stood up. "It's all a bit too complicated for us to understand! Shall we dance?"

She nodded, and we went onto the floor.

The radio was playing blues or something of the sort. Her forehead was very close to my lips, and I smelled the sweet perfume which came from her blonde curls.

"Actually, it's all quite stupid." She sighed. "We could have met in the ordinary way at a party, and become good friends, without its being a certainty that we would end up in bed together."

I held her closely. We were dancing slowly among all the other couples.

"Do you really think it's very different when a boy and girl meet—in the ordinary way?" I asked. "Unless one wants to be hypocritical, I think it's exactly the same as it is here. After the first few minutes the man has taken the measure of his prey, and the woman is ready

[5] Officers of the Bund Deutscher Mädel who are in charge of 150 other girls.

to be caught—on condition that one pays the price, whatever it happens to be, and that one sticks to the rules of the game, or the moral code, if you prefer to call it that."

She shrugged her shoulders.

"Why are we talking like this? I'm sure you're right. It's better this way. Anyhow, I like you," she whispered in my ear.

She looked up at me. "I'm not going to ask if you like me. You've chosen me. I hope not just out of boredom."

I didn't reply; anyhow, the music had stopped and we went back to our seats.

For the rest of the evening we sat side by side and chatted about all sorts of things.

About midnight she glanced at her watch and suggested, "Shall we go up to your room? I've had enough of this music and chatter and din. Haven't you?"

Smiling, I agreed.

We got up, and suddenly I felt like a little boy being led off by the hand. And yet I had come several hundred miles just to play the man.

Before going up to the second floor of the building, which was reserved for this purpose, I remembered something. "I believe we have to get our cards stamped first. It says so on the paper they gave me."

It was Liselotte's turn to blush now.

After this indispensable formality, which is a sort of express marriage—very much so!—we went to my room.

As we climbed the stairs, I suddenly thought of Brigitta. But a moment's reflection convinced me that I had not come to the Rothhaar Mountains to amuse myself, but to serve my country.

As soon as we entered the room, Lotte casually threw off her coat and sat down on the bed, crossing her legs.

"Well, here I am. Mr. Peter Neumann, your baby-making machine is at your disposal." Her laugh sounded false. "Don't you think it's pretty horrible, this business of selling one's body as an instrument of procreation?"

I sat down beside her. "Quiet, Liselotte. You aren't selling your body. You're giving it to Germany, which is a very different matter."

I stroked her hair, and gradually my hand slid down onto her shoulders, brushing against her thick blonde curls and moving across her body.

She gave herself to me with a sort of desperate fierceness. But I had the feeling that she didn't belong completely to me. Her eyes never left mine. Her expression was almost one of defiance. It was only after some time, when she could no longer restrain herself, that she really let herself go.

Later, her body pressed to mine, I pillowed her head in the crook of my arm.

"Peter, do you think if we have a son he will really look like us?"

"A son—or a daughter, Lotte. I should like her to have your eyes, your mouth, your hair— And also a little bit of me. So that you'll always remember your Peter."

"How funny it all is. Just once like this. Then the operation's over and you go away. And I'll never see you again."

"Why do you say 'never,' sweetheart? Life is full of surprises."

Without opening her eyes, she ran her fingers over my face, like a blind person.

"Tell me, Peter, are you engaged? Have you a girl friend? Will you tell her?"

"Let's talk about something else, Lotte. Why don't you tell me how you happen to be here? Are you all volunteers?"

She snuggled closer to me and made a *moue,* like a cat.

"Volunteers—if you like to put it that way. We're mostly from the BDM, where they exert pressure of various kinds to persuade us, going on about patriotism all the time, of course. Anyhow, it can get you in a lot of trouble if you refuse, endless fuss."

She drew away a little.

"Don't make me go into it, Peter! It's all so silly, and there's no point in it. Anyhow, I'm not really very sure how it was that I let myself be talked into coming here. I think I only really understood what it all meant when I arrived at Schmallenog. But by then it was too late."

She raised her lips to mine, and I took her in my arms again.

For the next few days we lived as though we were really married.

When we felt like it, we lunched at one of the little inns down in the valley or deep in the forest, and we explored the neighborhood from Willingen to the banks of the Ruhr or the Eder.

All over the Rothhaar there are these little villages, their houses painted different colors and flowers growing on the walls, with roofs of shining red tiles. At Altenhunden, Berleburg, Winterberg and Erndtenbrück are other Lebensborn establishments. Every now and then one sees a tall, modern building, painted white, a hospital or maternity home; or maybe just an ordinary house, recently built, for the use of the mothers and babies, where they stay for a few months, or even years, after the birth, depending on circumstances.

And the Third Reich foots the bill.

Liselotte seemed rather depressed when we passed these tall houses, built like barracks. She was doubtless thinking of the time when she would have to live alone in one of those concrete cells with her child—our child.

One afternoon as we lay in the spring grass, looking up into the sky and watching the wild, billowing clouds, she suddenly asked to see the chart which they had given me on arrival at Schmallenog.

On this card it said, among other things, that having once chosen our partner, we were not allowed to go back on our decision. Also, and rather surprisingly, on the cards marked "Men" it stated that in very exceptional circumstances we might be asked to attend other voluntary breeding establishments.

Lotte pouted as she read this.

"So if they ask you, you'll have to go off and sleep with another girl? My God, they are disgusting, these people!"

I smiled. "Don't worry, silly! There's no question of that for the time being. And don't forget that unfortunately we only have two more days together."

There was a tense expression on her face as she looked at me.
"Will you write to me, Peter? Afterward?"

"I promise."

And then we went away.

The other fellows from Sonthofen, who had also discovered the only girl in the world for six days, found it as hard to end this amazing experience as I did.

Lotte had sworn that she would write to me as soon as the tests had proved the fulfillment of our artificial love affair.

"Artificial"—that was not quite the word. We had known a little happiness together, Liselotte and I.

An astonishing experience in a man's life.

Tears, kisses, promises. And the train moves off.

Tomorrow it's Sonthofen again for a few more weeks.

7. Victory

Wittenberge, June 24, 1940. In the train which brought me here from Sonthofen, I learned that France had capitulated!

In Leipzig station there was extraordinary activity everywhere, and Franz and I saw people running in all directions, asking questions and embracing one another for no apparent reason.

Suddenly a woman opened the door of our compartment and, seeing our questioning faces, shouted, "The armistice is signed. The war is over!"

Yes, the armistice was signed the day before yesterday, in the old railway carriage in the forest of Compiègne, scene of Germany's humiliation in 1918.

General Keitel had made General Huntziger initial the twenty-three clauses of the French surrender.

And so the shame of the Treaty of Versailles is wiped out.

The whole of Germany is shouting for joy. Every town, every village and every house—everywhere the flags are out and every heart rejoices.

Sieg heil!

We owe an eternal debt of gratitude to our Führer, Adolf Hitler, who has led the Third Reich to victory and triumph.

Against the advice of the High Command, Hitler concluded the *Anschluss* of Austria.

Against the advice of the diplomats and politicians, he annexed the Sudetenland.

Against the advice of his generals, who believed France to be powerful and invincible, he gave the order to attack, and he conquered.

Sweeping aside all secondary considerations, hesitancy and delay, ignoring the colossal difficulties which they alleged beset his offensive projects against the Western powers, the Chancellor of the Reich maintained his faith in himself and in the nation.

Germany must henceforward have blind confidence in her Führer, for he is never wrong.[1]

Nevertheless, it all leaves one feeling quite stunned.

We Germans believed that France was a great country, with vast military forces at her disposal, ready to defend herself to the last ditch.

We were certain of victory, but we had never dared to hope for such an overwhelming one in so short a time.

Rosenberg was right when he said that the plutocratic Western powers are completely decadent as a result of their enslavement to Jewish Communism.

It is this Jewish Communism which gave rise to the political party struggles in France, and which allowed corrupt politicians to pullulate in the filth and anarchy it created.

This victory has proved once again that the Jews, the Communists and the Freemasons are the mortal enemies of all order and civilization.

We Germans must never forget this lesson.

We all three went to Berlin to take part in the Victory Parade.

The enthusiasm was indescribable, and in spite of the rain the crowd never stopped shouting its delight to the troops returning from the West.

Thousands of flags floated over the capital, and a hurricane of excitement swept through the streets.

[1] Since 1938, most of the German generals had thought that the war in the West would end with the annihilation of Germany. Von Fritsch said, speaking of Hitler: "This man is Germany's destiny; he is running into the abyss and will drag Germany with him."

To the sound of trumpets and drums, the men of the Army, the Air Force and the Navy goose-stepped past the crowd, which cheered them without a break. In front rumbled the tanks which had made the breakthrough at Sedan.

Next came the units of the SS cavalry and the panzergrenadiers, then the Alpine troops.

Behind them marched the infantry, the reservists, the police and SS defense units.

Field police, in light armored cars, completed the parade.

On the official platform, in front of the Brandenburg Gate, the Führer, flanked by Göring, Goebbels, Rudolf Hess and the generals, seemed transfigured with pride and saluted the troops with upraised arm.

That afternoon we went to visit the historic railway carriage, which is on view in front of the new Chancellery. It is an ordinary carriage, formerly belonging to the Wagon-Lits Company. But for us it represents revenge.

We went inside. It is extraordinary to think that at this very table the other armistice was signed, between the French general Foch and the traitor Erzberger.

In the evening, still together, we took the subway to the Kroll Opera in Berlin because we wanted to see all the Party and Army higher-ups, who were going to celebrate the victory with an impressive ceremony presided over by the Führer.

We were lucky enough to see the Chancellor pass within a few yards of us, followed by his closest colleagues from the Brown Shirts or SA, the Old Campaigners, as they are called. They will all, now, form part of our country's history.

About thirty generals came next. Royal-blue dress uniforms, and trousers with red stripes. They seemed to be marching in a sort of unreal fog, borne along by the acclamations of the crowd.

Two hours later, twelve of them were made marshals.

Out in the streets the loudspeakers brought us the Führer's voice calling them up, one by one, to receive their marshal's batons.

Toward midnight we set off through the streets of Berlin and joined in the general celebrations.

On the Unter den Linden, the Pariserplatz and the Kurfürstendamm people went past singing and waving flags, shouting their excitement and enthusiasm until they were hoarse or utterly exhausted.

Our steps led us to the embankment of the Spree, just beside the Friedrichsbahnhof bridge. We were also quite exhausted by this unforgettable day and sat down on a bench by the river.

The waters of the Spree rolled past, silver beneath the lights of the victory celebration. We could hear, faint and muffled, the voices of the crowd, fireworks going off and the blare of military bands. We sat on our bench for most of the night, talking endlessly, about the war, the future of Germany and ourselves.

Karl was of the opinion that the war was not yet over by a long shot, that the collapse of France was only the first stage in the program mapped out by the Führer. Up to now, the prophetic plan outlined in *Mein Kampf* had been fulfilled point by point. The West, on the point of surrender, was clamoring for mercy. The annihilation of England was only a matter of weeks.

The High Command knew that Great Britain was so completely beaten that a last-minute order from General Reinhardt, who had commanded at Saint-Omer and Dunkirk, had allowed the encircled British troops to re-embark. Von Grieffenberg had ordered von Kleist's armored units, when they were actually much nearer Dunkirk than the Allied troops, to stop at the Aire Canal.

The Wehrmacht had shown itself chivalrous in not wishing to destroy an already defeated enemy.

The Führer wished to show the English that he was completely confident of victory, that he was giving them an opportunity to avoid useless slaughter. Perhaps the English would understand the significance of such a gesture and would sue for peace before it was too late. . . .

I found Karl's reasoning very sound. Personally I thought, as he did, that with France and England defeated, there remained only one more large item to be dealt with—the Eastern territories.

A dull mind might be misled for a moment by the provisional pact signed in Moscow. But this pact, after all, was only a truce. And truces don't last forever.

In fact the struggle was only beginning.

So far we had been too young to participate in the glorious battles in which we had seen the German eagle soar triumphant. But now we were old enough to think about joining up.

The three of us, sitting on the bench by the Spree, talked eagerly. Suddenly I got to my feet.

"Listen, fellows. It's all very well to think about joining up, though I can't really see myself on some barrack square in East Prussia doing rifle drill under some miserable sergeant. In any case, it's pretty certain that we have to do six months' labor service before we join the Army."

Franz turned and looked at me. "So what? Anyhow, there's no way we can get out of it."

"Yes, there is. Join the Schutzstaffel." [2]

Now Karl too stood up. "I thought of that myself. With our diplomas, and having been at the Ordensburgen, we can apply to go to Bad Tölz. A year from now, we'll be officers."

Franz said nothing. I put my arm around his shoulders.

"Well, Franz, what do you think? Already two of us are agreed. We were together in the Pimpfe, and in the HJ. Then we had the luck to be together again in Bavaria and the Eifel. You're not going to back out now, are you? Listen to them singing and shouting about the victory. This is all reflected glory, which other people gave their lives for, not us. We've got to go and give a hand to the men who have been fighting for us, who have suffered to make our country great. The more I think about it, the more certain I am about one thing: we must serve in a crack regiment, a front-line regiment, the first one to go into action and to shed its blood in order to raise our flag up from the mud."

[2] The SS. Literally, "defense squadrons."

Franz got up, and smiled. "What a speech! Must be the fifes and trumpets that have worked you up."

I looked at him, a little disconcerted. "What do you say, then?"

"Well, I've got nothing to say, really. Except that I agree. Funny if I didn't agree after that long lecture! No, I'm only kidding. You're right. It's the best thing we can do. Anyway, the war won't last forever! And probably those who've fought for their country will have special privileges when it's all over, get the best jobs. . . ."

I realized that he was looking for arguments with which to convince himself. This merely emphasized the seriousness and merit of the decision he had just taken.

We shook hands, the three of us, almost solemnly. It was ridiculous, maybe silly, but we couldn't help it, we were so carried away.

Obviously we had no idea of what was to happen in the next few years; but that night, by the shimmering waters of the Spree, we were all three united in this wave of enthusiasm, and we accepted, in advance, all the uncertainty, the risks and the dangers that fate held in store for us.

Berlin was asleep, and the last of the victory torches were guttering. Already behind the Lichtenberg hills dawn was beginning to lighten the sky.

The sun of a new day would soon be rising, on Germany, and on our future.

8. SS Officers' Training College

SS Junkerschule, Bad Tölz,[1] September 1940. Just two years ago I went through Tölz for the first time, on Sedan Day. I never thought at that time that I should return here as an officer cadet.

I had a strange impression of the place when first I passed through the school gate at the end of last month. The entrance to the building, which is ultramodern, consists of a gigantic porch roofed by an arch and flanked on each side by a majestic white tower with a pointed roof of varnished tiles.

Inside the gate one is surprised to find a vast stretch of turf, planted with rare, gnarled trees, around which are single-story buildings of normal barracklike size and shape. It is as though the architect first planned to build a sort of castle and then changed his mind and decided to create a modern functional building.

Behind the Junkerschule, the high peaks of the Karwendel Alps tower above a dense forest of black pines, through which the roaring waters of the Isar pour down in a series of waterfalls.

A few days after our arrival we were issued all the twenty-seven pieces of equipment which constitute the complete SS uniform. Trousers and tunic of black cloth, helmet and cap—also black—with a silver death's-head. Two lightning flashes, which have the same

[1] One of the SS officer cadets' training units, situated in the Bavarian Alps, south of Munich. Other SS officer cadet schools were at Brunswick, Posen-Treskan, Klagenfurt and Prague.

significance of power and destruction as the swastika, form a threatening double *S* on the right lapel of the regulation tunic.

It is unbelievable how the black uniform changes one's personality, hardening the expression of one's face and defining one's features.

The first weeks of training have passed with amazing speed. We don't have time to notice whether we are tired or not. It's as though our instructors wish to draw a crude line across our past lives, to brutalize us, to prove to us that in the SS everything is different.

"Stand up. Get down. Stand up, get down, stand up, get down, forward, get down, forward, stand up, get down." And so on for hour after hour. In mud, in water, on concrete, in the snow (during mountain exercises), in the middle of the night or under a burning sun.

Just to give us a little rest, we are given four hours of the goose step. At the end of the fourth hour the recruit must thrust his legs forward as rigid and straight as at the beginning of the exercise. After this, very often there is rifle drill with present arms in three motions.

After the evening meal, often there is saluting practice, just to fill in time. Right hand raised six paces before reaching a superior officer, eyes left or right according to circumstances, the arm not to be lowered until three paces after passing the officer.

In the evening, there are also lectures on the origins and history of the SS. The Schutzstaffel was originally created in 1926 as the élite unit of the SA.[2] From the very beginning the first regiment to be formed was called the Leibstandarte AH.[3]

As the years went on and the NSDAP became more and more powerful and needed increasing numbers of specialized units, other regiments were formed. Today they amount to several divisions.

At the beginning of the war, in 1939, the combat units of the SS were sent into action on the Western Front. These units were at

[2] Sturmabteilung—assault troops. The SA consisted of the Brown Shirts, Hitler's original supporters before his accession to power.
[3] LAH life guards, the Praetorian Guard of Hitler and the NSDAP.

first called Waffengrenadiere of the SS, later abbreviated to Waffen SS.

The non-combattant SS were given the distinguishing name of the Allgemeine SS, that is to say, SS who perform general duties.

Certain sections of the Allgemeine SS were used to form the SS Totenkopf Verbände[4] engaged principally in police work and in guarding the prisoners in the concentration camps. The Totenkopf men undergo a special training, and have quite a different course of instruction from the other SS.

I have noticed that here at Bad Tölz the Death's-Head Units are not highly thought of, and are even rather despised. I have heard it said that they are taken from all walks of life and are not a very decent lot.

But in rapidly developing countries such as ours, there must be men who will do the more menial tasks which nobody else wants to handle.

"Well, my lad, so this is the great day, is it?"

A Junkerschule veteran, who had been watching me dress up in full regalia, was speaking to me.

I stood up, and seeing the silver on his lapels, brought myself sharply to attention. It was a sergeant, and he was very young. Perhaps even younger than I.

He smiled at me.

"Take it easy, soldier. Only one question. You're obviously one of the *Kröne* class—about to be sworn in?"

"Yes, sergeant, I think about a hundred of us are taking part in the little show."

His face suddenly hardened.

"It's not quite a 'little show,' my lad. It's a very important day for all of you. Swearing an oath to the Führer is a very solemn and very serious occasion, and you don't want to take it lightly."

I stood to attention again quickly, and saluted. "Sorry, sir. You're quite right, of course."

[4] Death's-Head Units.

Two hours later, most of the school was lined up on the big parade ground.

The commandant, SS Sturmbannführer Richard Schultze, head of the Junkerschule, gave the opening address:

"Soldiers. You are assembled here to swear an oath of fidelity to our Führer and to Germany. I'm not going to make a long speech, but in a few words I will tell you that we believe you are grown men, and as such you will know that to break the oath you are about to swear would be worse than death. Remember that the motto of the SS is *Meine Ehre heisst Treue*.[5] You must never forget your motto, and it must never be out of your minds. Remember that you have sworn obedience and loyalty in all circumstances. I repeat, in all circumstances and under all conditions. Nothing must stop your determination to carry out an order, no matter what it may be. You are all volunteers. No one has asked you to join us. You are here of your own free will. That is a further reason never to forget that you have voluntarily accepted our discipline, and that you must always respect it."

The loudspeakers echoed the commandant's words from one side of the courtyard to the other. Between each sentence there was an impressive silence. High above our heads buzzards were circling over the treetops.

Standing to attention in six ranks the *Kröne* class, rigid and motionless, listened to the earnest voice with its deep Silesian inflections booming from the loudspeakers.

"In a few minutes you will be true SS men! In a few minutes you will have given yourselves body and soul to our Fatherland. Remember that your country can ask anything of you, can expect everything from you, including your life; and you must obey, without a murmur of protest or the slightest misgivings about the orders that your country may give you. *Heil Hitler!*"

Like a roll of thunder, the band struck up with *Deutschland über alles*.

Two standard-bearers now marched into the center of the parade

[5] "My honor is loyalty."

ground. The first held the black SS banner, the other the national flag with the swastika.

Two officers with drawn swords marched toward them and held their swords crossed at arm's length so that the points touched the flagstaffs.

Next two Sturmmänner of the *Kröne* class advanced in their turn, goose-stepping in slow time, to the accompaniment of a prolonged roll of drums. They came to a halt in front of the group formed by the standard-bearers and the officer.

A brief command rang out.

"Present . . . arms!"

Only those who had to take the oath had no rifles. The others, in an impressive mass movement, raised their Mausers in three movements and presented them, held before their chests.

The two Sturmmänner placed the middle and index fingers of their right hands on the officers' swords and spoke the words of the oath.

With forearms held vertical, and the two fingers of the right hand raised, we repeated with them:

"I swear to you, Adolf Hitler, my leader, fidelity and courage. I promise you, and all those whom you choose to command me, obedience unto death, so help me God."

A moment of silence, and the loudspeakers shouted, "Order . . . arms!"

With the band in front, we then marched past Commandant Schultze.

October 7, 1940.

"Come on, get going. Rise and shine!"

As an alternative to reveille by trumpet, it was very successful.

They oughtn't to pull honest and virtuous SS men like us out of bed in such a hurry.

The deputy NCO, Doltzmann, is standing in the middle of the room.

He says something that I don't grasp immediately. Anyhow he

always speaks fantastically fast. One has to snatch what one can from his flood of Pomeranian gabble.

He comes across and leans over me.

"Well, Neumann?" he sneers. "Lady's maid, chambermaid or valet?"

With a quick movement, he pulls back the sheets.

"State your preference, Neumann! Anything we can do . . ." Idiot.

I get up and dress rapidly, firing questions at the fellow in the next bed, a fair-haired Berliner covered with freckles.

"What goes on? Remobilizing? Have the English landed?"

"Nothing of the sort! The sergeant just told us that it's tattooing this morning. He says they never tell you in advance. I think it's true all right."

Tattooing—that's all we need! However, it's got to be gone through, I suppose.

An hour later we are in the sick bay, handed over to the expert hands of medical department specialists.

My turn comes, and I am told to lie down on a sort of operating table. The orderly says I must lie on my right side.

The delicate operation is performed in the left armpit.

The orderly starts by disinfecting the whole area with alcohol, then wipes a clear brown liquid on with absorbent cotton and my skin absorbs it immediately. I am holding my arm high in the air, which is most uncomfortable. It would be better, I think, if I can remain standing up. I mention this to the orderly, who shakes his head.

"It's because of the circulation. Anyhow it'll be so quick you won't notice it."

A moment later some sort of vibrating electrical apparatus—I don't know definitely because I have shut my eyes—punctures my skin, an unpleasant sensation. This lasts for a moment or two, and then the pain becomes bearable. And soon it ceases.

The orderly says with a smile, "You can get up now. It's all over."

His manner suggests that he couldn't care less about me, and I decide I dislike him.

I ease myself up awkwardly, throwing black and bitter looks in his direction.

There is a mirror in the room. I go across to it. Lifting my arm I see a reddish Gothic *A*. It looks quite hideous.

"Don't worry, it'll be more decorative in a day or two," says the orderly consolingly.

I shrug my shoulders. It's too late to complain.

On the other hand it's certainly true that this little operation, though a nuisance, has its practical uses. In cases of wounds or a serious hemorrhage, it is much quicker and easier to perform a transfusion if it is known to which blood group the wounded man —and the blood donor—belong. If this is not known, then a preliminary blood test must be made, which often means precious time lost.

Franz comes across, resplendent with a large *O*.

Karl, however, is permanently branded with an *A*, like me.

There are lots of *B*'s too. Each of us looks curiously at the other's tattoo marks. Comments and jokes abound.

A little later the orderlies swab us all down once more with alcohol. We are finally thrown out of the sick bay at about midday.

November 4, 1940. Ready for action. Heinrich Himmler, Reichsführer of the SS, is coming to inspect us.

They give us polished black helmets, and heaven knows what in the way of whitened belts and crossbelts.

Once we are rigged out in this mass of steel and leather, which of course has to be adjusted to fit us, we look quite presentable. The black helmet is particularly impressive. It gives us a martial air, very menacing. To tell the truth we also look slightly sinister.

Through the window overlooking the great central lawn, I suddenly see a great rushing about, and men running. Almost immediately there is a stampede down the corridors, and blasts on whistles inform us that the approach of Uncle Heini has been signaled by telephone from Holzkirchen.

It always happens like this. When an official visit is expected, patrols are sent out all over the surrounding country, with orders to warn the commandant of the VIP's imminent arrival.

"Fall in! On the double! Get moving—quick!"

We're all doing our best. There's no need to panic.

A little later we are formed up as a guard of honor, at right angles to the central porch. Turning my head slightly I can see the whole road in perspective.

About fifteen motorcyclists appear, changing gear as they turn the corner; they are followed by an impressive convoy of black Mercedes. Our Great White Chief must be in one of them.

"Present . . . arms!"

The cars come to a smooth, perfect halt, and Commandant Schultze hurries toward the third one, from which Himmler steps, looking rather disagreeable and sullen. He is followed by a Standartenführer, whom I recognise as Rudolf Brandt, his aide-de-camp.

The brass hats talk briefly while we remain rigidly at attention, chins up and rifles held before our chests.

I hope that they aren't telling each other the latest Berlin jokes, because the position we have to hold isn't exactly comfortable.

"At ease!"

And about time too; I was beginning to get pins and needles in my arms.

This is the third time I have seen Himmler, and each time he has made the same odd impression on me. He never looks people straight in the face and always seems ill at ease, embarrassed and nervous. He has a twitch which slightly affects his jaw, and he continually turns his head from side to side while talking.

And then there is his thin, unimpressive figure and his little pince-nez like a village schoolmaster's. He definitely doesn't look the part.

It has been decided that he will inspect us. Followed by Brandt,

the commandant and about a dozen Gruppenführer and Brigadeführer, he marches between the ranks, with almost mincing steps,
painfully trying to smile. A photographer from Propaganda Unit,
appearing from heaven knows where, takes a picture of him at the
precise moment when Himmler has succeeded in looking almost
human.

Tomorrow there will be a photograph in the SS magazine with the
caption: "The Reichsführer among his men . . ."

They all disappear into the building. The big clock on the concrete wall tells us that they stayed in there for more than an hour.
We spend that hour waiting for them to reappear.

At last they all drive off, without so much as making us an address. We then go in to eat.

December. For the past fortnight we have been attending lectures
on strategy given by a professor from the War Academy in Berlin.

The battle of Cannae and the rest of Hannibal's campaign, the
wars of the Byzantine emperors, Tannenberg, the siege of Sedan—
we've been through it all.

All day long we are crammed with Clausewitz and the more
modern theories of war as penned by von Blomberg and von Moltke.

After the theoretical, we try the practical—field exercises, or using
sand tables with very well-made scale models. Thus, we have a
Maginot line and a Siegfried line, both in miniature, with their
deep installations, pillboxes, even the ammunition elevators.

Another professor, a strange fellow, gives us very violent lectures
on racial theory. His name is von Arensdorf, and he's about forty,
completely bald, with thin lips and small, steely blue eyes.

There is a rumor that he taught German at a school in Paris, but
was expelled in 1938 for subversive propaganda. This must account
for his hatred of the French. It is apparent in his every sentence,
and is only equaled by his frightful detestation for anything that
has any trace of a Jewish origin.

A few days ago he talked to us about what was happening in
France. According to him, the French are biding their time while

pretending to collaborate with us. In fact, they are only waiting to stab us in the back at the very first opportunity.

Pétain, he says, is a sly and crafty man. With honeyed words he offers his right hand to the Führer, while in his left hand he grips a cudgel behind his back.

When he talks about the Jews he hisses through his teeth, and his eyes grow even smaller.

"For Germany the Jew is the very incarnation of annihilation and destruction. If we don't neutralize them, it is they who will destroy *us,* for we must never forget that they are fantastically powerful. Their tentacles encircle the entire globe. They are always to be found close to the seat of power: in Wall Street, as well as at the gaming tables of Macao or in the sordid shops of Hong Kong. It is our national duty, it is a matter of life and death, to exterminate the Jew. We must either strike him down or he will murder us."

We emerge from his lectures in a daze, our minds confused by a thousand contradictory thoughts.

April, 1941. The SS is getting ready to fight. The 2nd Division was given the title of *Das Reich* a few days ago. The former Leibstandarte regiment is the 1st Division.

The Schutzstaffel has been fighting in Greece since February, at the side of the Italians. The 1st Division, which was in Metz, has gone to Bulgaria and is now occupying Sofia.

On April 6—that is to say, four days ago—the LAH under the command of Sepp Dietrich crossed the Yugoslav frontier and occupied Monastir and Skoplje.

On the Cyrenaica-Libya front, Erwin Rommel and his men are pressing on toward Alexandria.

Everywhere the flag of the Reich flies victorious.

In the east, too, great events are in preparation.

Russian single-engined Tchaikas and SB2's have repeatedly violated the skies of the new Government-General, which used to be called Poland.

According to the *Völkische Beobachter,* important troop movements have been noted east of the Bug, the river which serves as a temporary frontier with Russia. One hundred and fifty Timoshenko-Voroshilov divisions are said to be massed between Insterburg near the Baltic and the Dnieper, south of Lvov.

Bad Tölz, May 1941. An impressive ceremony took place on the main parade ground, attended by all the Junkers of the *Kröne* class.

Great black SS banners and swastika flags flapped against the walls gently in the soft spring breezes, redolent with the woodland scents of pine wafted from the Lenggries forest.

The sky was clear and bright. The birds of prey swooped majestically above the roofs of the Junkerschule, as always happens when there is some unusual activity afoot. Any departure from the normal routine seems to attract them. At Bad Tölz the eagles, buzzards and falcons form an integral part of the countryside. They take part in all the ceremonies there.

One by one we climbed the steps of the tribunal.

With a word of congratulation for each man, the commandant handed us our brevets as Fähnrich (ensigns).

We were officers now.

Preceded by their banners, the new cadets who were to take our place marched past us, singing the *Marching Song of the SS*.

Part II

AT THE ZENITH

9.   The Attack

June 27, 1941. Six days ago German troops entered Soviet territory. On a front of one thousand miles, stretching from the Baltic to the Black Sea, the Wehrmacht and the SS panzer divisions are forging eastward.

In the north, von Leeb's Army Group, which is pouring toward Leningrad, has already swept aside many of Voroshilov's divisions.

On the central front, von Bock's Army Group has besieged Bialystok and is making for Moscow. His panzers are moving fast.

We ourselves are a few miles from the frontier of Galicia, in the Przemyśl district. Day and night hundreds of trucks and tanks belonging to von Manstein's southern divisions pour across the San.

We went straight from Bad Tölz to Lublin, where we were assigned to the 5th (Viking) SS Division.

I was not even granted a few days' leave in Wittenberge. The orders were strict: "You will report immediately to the Standartenführer of the Nordland Regiment, of the 5th Waffen SS Division."

There were seventeen of us who arrived together at Lublin. The regiment was about to leave for the Eastern Front; whistle blasts and orders rang out on all sides. In the courtyard of the old barracks of the 27th Polish Hussars, the tank engines were revving up and equipment was being distributed. So our reception was on the cool side.

When my turn came to report myself to the regimental CO, he didn't even look at me as he snapped, "From Tölz, are you? Which

means you know nothing. Until further orders you'll be attached
to the regimental HQ staff."

Franz and Karl had been given commands in a tank squadron
of the Nordland Regiment. Why was I treated differently? I
wondered a lot about this.

During those last few days, while awaiting our marching orders,
I wandered all over Lublin, learning about the regiment.

It consists of two squadrons of light tanks, four squadrons of
medium tanks—Mark I, II, III, and IV—a company of motorized
infantry, a company of antitank gunners and a battery of regimental
artillery. In addition, there are the auxiliaries of the NSKK, the
supply troops, the antiaircraft gunners and the medical, gas and
signals units. Not forgetting, of course, the regimental staff, to which
I am attached.

June 28. All night wave after wave of Dorniers, Focke-Wulfs and
Junker-Stukas have been flying eastward. The deafening drone of
the engines was like a huge throbbing, the sinister prelude to
destruction.

Sleep was impossible. I chatted with Franz and Karl until dawn.

At about four o'clock the vibration of the heavy artillery firing
outside Rawa Ruska began to make the ground shake. Hundreds
of guns were firing at the Red positions some six miles from the San.

It was so exciting that we stopped talking, impressed in spite of
ourselves. The veterans tell us that we haven't seen or heard anything yet, and that this is only the artillery filling in time.

A fortnight ago a lot of our tank boys were with von List's army,
somewhere between Athens and Belgrade. Traveling at a steady
thirty miles an hour, by day and by night, they raced along the roads
of Thessaly, Macedonia, the Balkans and Bohemia, finally reaching
the Russian frontier still white with the dust they'd picked up in the
southeast of Europe.

A little before noon, the colonel called together all the officers
and the sergeants of platoons and sections.

We had been standing around him for a few minutes, in a sort of large hanger exposed to the four winds, before he started talking to us. His voice was serious, and we soon realized that we were going to see what the Russkies were up to from closer range.

"Gentlemen," he began, "we advance on Krements! We move off at dawn tomorrow. We are attached to von Kleist's right wing, which has already been fighting for the past week as part of Army Group South, under von Rundstedt, in the outskirts of Lvov."

He bent down and pointed to a large map spread out on the floor.

"The direction of the attack is east-southeast. The first objectives are Rawa Ruska, Kremenets, Newieskaya. We shall be faced by a corps of Budënny's army."

He looked up.

"Further orders will be issued in due course to squadron and company commanders."

He suddenly straightened up and faced us. His face seemed set, and his jaw hardened.

"According to the orders I have received, I am to remind you of the order of the day issued on the solstice of the 21st.[1] I shall only quote you a short passage from it: 'The Führer-Chancellor of the Reich, and with him the German nation, are certain that you will do your duty, and that you will pursue the struggle against the enemy relentlessly until he is destroyed. The SS, picked troops of the very finest quality, will always be sent to the most exposed positions and will show the German nation that it can count on them.'"

He bent down and picked up the map, which he began to roll up slowly, as though wishing to gain time. Finally he said, "And another thing. Supreme Headquarters in East Prussia asks me to make known to you the following order. It concerns the line which we are to follow in occupied Russian territory. In no case are we to concern ourselves with civilian matters, all of which come under the local commandants. We have no right to question their decisions"—he looked at us fixedly—"except in cases of absolute ne-

[1] On the night of June 21st (summer solstice), Hitler made a solemn proclamation announcing to the troops the opening of the Russian campaign.

cessity, or when it is a question of actions directed against the Army! I think, gentlemen, you understand what I mean. . . . We have also received special instructions concerning the Russian People's Commissars captured in action or arrested in the occupied territory. In no case are we authorized to take them prisoner. The order is explicit! They must be killed at once, but in front of our own lines or of the regimental command post! This is very important. If necessary, they must be moved to the combat zone and there shot as terrorists, not as soldiers."

He attempted a smile and made a vague gesture with his hand. "That's all, gentlemen."

Killed at once.

It was only then that I realized I was in the SS, and that we were at war.

June 29. It is three o'clock. H-Hour is fixed for 0415.

We are on the bank of the San, huddled in our armored troop-carriers. We are waiting for the signal from Division which will tell us that it's time for us, too, to set off for Moscow.

Moscow. . . . Perhaps that's aiming high. We mustn't expect everything, to begin with.

Fears about the first battle, the baptism of fire, fear of the unknown, and the cold of the early morning. . . . I don't know. I only know that I don't feel too comfortable.

In the white, blurred dawn, the massive silhouettes of the tanks and troop-carriers begin to stand out.

The technicians are busy with their steel and concrete monsters, which will go ahead of us and cover our advance.

On the far side of the river all is quiet. Behind a clump of trees is a little village, Newieskaya, which according to the regimental intelligence section is completely destroyed. The whole population cleared out a week ago, and there is nothing to stop us moving in. We shall probably meet no resistance until we get to Wisnia.

I catch a glimpse of Franz, who must be looking for me. I wave to him. As soon as he sees me, he comes over.

"A soft job, being on the staff, from the look of it."

But his serious face belies the lightness of his words.

"So it's all set for half an hour from now," he says jerkily. "Good luck, Peter."

"Good luck, Franz. Same to Karl, if you see him."

He shakes his head and does not reply. With a tight smile he walks slowly away. All of a sudden I realize that it's I who dragged him into all this, that he might not come back.

But I have no time to worry about this. Whistle blasts are rending the air. I see the commanders climbing into their tanks, followed by the gunners and drivers. There are the muffled sounds of engines starting up.

I look at my watch. It is barely 0345. Has the time for the San crossing been put forward?

Seeing my expression of surprise, the young lieutenant beside me says dully, "The regiment's getting into position for the attack. It won't be long now."

A few moments later the artillery opens up.

The dull rumble from the depths of the forest rapidly becomes a terrifying, apocalyptic din, which makes the ground tremble and everything vibrate. The sharp crack of the light-caliber guns is soon drowned by the deafening, powerful roar of the big railway 600's.

For us, this is the first moment of war. It is also the most impressive.

The dawn is slowly breaking, scattering the trails of mist that hang above the San and float among branches of the trees gashed by the bursting shells.

Suddenly we hear the violent screech of a rocket flare, shooting up with a long *who-o-osh* into the gray sky. An enormous green flash, and the flare floats slowly down, hanging from its parachute.

Green. . . . That means attack!

Heavy rumblings like thunder. The first tanks move across the pontoon bridge. Our troop-carrier follows. We travel some two hundred yards, jolting along a smashed road. Our driver tries as best he can to avoid the shellholes, twisting and turning all the time.

Then we cross the San, and now are on a fairly wide road, which, however, is also three parts destroyed. The Field Police, equipped with red and white discs, signal to us as we go by that everything is all right. For the moment.

The eastward advance has begun.

The 5th SS (Viking) Division thrusts forward as fast as possible, toward the Ukrainian plain.

We pass through Wisnia: impressive piles of rubble, burnt-out buildings whose blackened framework is still smoking, others as hollow and empty as stage sets, metal skeletons, twisted ironwork, electric cables hanging down over the street, perhaps a woman on her knees beside a dead body, weeping loudly.

One of our troop-carriers runs over a dog which vanishes, howling, beneath its tracks. Apart from the din of the artillery, all is quiet in the town. Strangely quiet. A pitiless sun shines down on the ruins, lighting up every little corner and recess, so that the full horror of it looms up out of the shadows.

At one street corner a body dangles from a smashed truck, the tires of which are burning. The face is half charred. The teeth stick out like an animal's tusks in the blackened face. It is a Russian; he is still wearing a khaki cap with a red star.

We move on through the countryside.

The heat becomes intolerable as the sun rises higher into the sky. The dust kicked up by the tanks and trucks clings to our sweat-drenched skins. I take off my cap and wipe my face with a handkerchief, which is immediately stained with long, black streaks.

I shall give up this habit soon, when the dust has caked on my face to form a hard, thick mask and only my eyes are visible. Around my mouth, dust and saliva mix to form a sort of black paste.

The smell of hot oil and gasoline is asphyxiating, and I lean right out of the carrier in my effort to breathe a little fresh air.

All the wheat and corn fields have been burned. The little farming communities have been razed to the ground. The telegraph poles are cut down. Even the signposts and milestones have been destroyed.

The "scorched earth" commandos of the NKVD [2] have been through here.

The convoy pulls up suddenly. I can see the leading tanks grind to a halt, six or seven hundred yards in front of us.

A motorcyclist in a crash helmet dashes through the column, hooting furiously to clear a passage for himself.

The tanks open fire. The sharp crack of their guns provides a contrast to the dull rumble of the artillery, still spitting death toward the east.

"Battle formation! On the double!"

Orders ring out on all sides. I jump down from the troop-carrier, completely bewildered, trying to stop the erratic thumping of my heart.

"Look out there, Ensign! Get down! Can't you see they're firing at us?" shouts a voice in my ear.

Without knowing exactly what I am doing, I find myself running behind a group of antitank gunners who are making for the tanks which are in trouble.

And all at once I am in the thick of it.

I have put my *MP Feuer*[3] to my hip, and I pull the trigger, sending long bursts toward a little wood which is on fire—a fire started by our artillery. Several enemy antitank guns must be hidden among the trees, for a number of our Mark II's already show deep gashes in their armor.

Lying on my stomach in a field, in the cover of a fold in the ground, I try to pick out something to aim at, some object, whether a man or a gun. But in vain. I can see nothing but pine trees.

---

[2] Special units, trained in the Lake Ladoga region, for purposes of sabotage and destruction. The NKVD, *Narodnii Kommissariat Vnutrennikh Del* (Peoples' Commissariat for Internal Affairs), controlled several regiments, each with a complement of twenty sabotage commandos. As the Red armies retreated, these units were charged with the destruction of roads, railways, works of art, bridges, factories, electric power stations, dams, etc.

[3] *Maschinen-Pistole Feuer*—submachine gun or machine pistol.

Suddenly there is a helmet in the grass. Two helmets. Men are running in short bursts, trying not to be seen. I press my finger hard on the trigger. I empty the whole magazine at them. A man falls, and I distinctly see his head burst open.

My God! They must have shoved explosive bullets into my magazine.

A click and I slip on a new magazine. Too bad for the *moujiks*.

Suddenly I notice that I am in the middle of a group of infantry-men who are staring curiously at me, at this ensign who fires away like a madman, as though he were only a simple private.

They jump up and start to run toward the wood, and I follow them. Without knowing quite why, I begin to shout. Perhaps because all the others are shouting too.

I remember the maneuvers at Vogelsang, and I run in short bursts, dropping flat on the ground every few yards.

Now we are all firing at once. There must be a nest of machine guns over on the left, because I see several men fall. Fall, and perhaps die. I suddenly realize that I have not been afraid—that I am not afraid now.

A hundred yards ahead of me, on the far side of a narrow stream, I can make out a gun carriage, then the mouth of the barrel.

Grenades. I have forgotten about grenades.

I fling myself down hard on the ground and take a hand grenade from my belt. I am just going to draw out the pin when I notice that the tank boys are there ahead of me. A burst of their fire has done it for the Red gunners.

Now the infantrymen are chasing some fifteen Russians who are trying to escape. Is it possible that this ludicrous handful of men has caused such havoc? Counting the dead, I reckon the number must have been about thirty in all.

From where I am I can see the Russians throwing away their rifles far in front of them and raising their hands in surrender. Several well-spaced bursts send them sprawling, face down. Two try to get away, but the bullets are faster than they are.

I stand rooted to the spot. They were prisoners, weren't they?

The tank men are soon back, each with a captured rifle slung over his shoulder. They are as happy and as excited as schoolboys who have just played a good lark on somebody.

Seeing me, they shout, "You were all right, Ensign!"

That is all very well. But my legs are trembling as I climb back into the carrier.

So that's what it's like, a baptism of fire. It's so easy to kill a man. Oddly enough, I feel no remorse. It was either him or me. And if I hadn't been around, the others would have killed him. My God, that's what we're here for.

My first Russian. And the first man I'd ever killed.

The Nordland Regiment moves off again, a little more cautiously now, and armed men are seated beside the drivers of the trucks.

The lieutenant who had already given me the information earlier this morning now tells me that a correspondent from the Propaganda Unit told him that less than one week after the Russian campaign began these little parties of guerilla fighters began to appear everywhere, shooting up our convoys.

No major battles so far, except outside Bialystok and at Brest Litovsk, where the fortress is defended by a female battalion of the NKVD and has not yet surrendered. The Reds do not seem to be trying to hold on in the Polish plains, which are difficult to defend. They are probably withdrawing to either side of the Pinsk Marshes, which form a natural defense line, covering White Russia and the wheatfields of the Ukraine.

The convoy stops again. After a moment I jump down and try to see what's happening. At the front of the column, I catch a glimpse of our colonel, deep in conversation with a group of officers. He sees me and beckons me to come closer.

"Here's the Junker. Seems you got on all right in your first skirmish. Or so I hear. Carry on the good work, we may make something of you yet. Meanwhile, stay here and listen, it's the best way to learn."

At this point I notice a Brigadeführer whom I hadn't seen before. I had not saluted, but he seems too preoccupied to give a damn about that sort of thing. He is pointing out something on the map which I can't see. I listen while he goes on talking.

"Lvov is here, east-northeast. The 3rd is on the Kremenets road. The 2nd and 4th are going round by way of Yavorov. In two days we'll all be in Lvov."

He turns to the colonel.

"For the time being get your vehicles off the road. Put them in the field on either side. Then the tanks of the Westland Regiment will be able to pass through."

This order is sent on at once by dispatch riders. With a loud whine of engines the trucks and troop-carriers start up, and one by one they back gently into the fields. It's not going to be so simple getting them out again.

I glance at my watch. It is nearly two o'clock.

We have not come very far since morning. Thinking that we will be here for quite a while, I go off and look for Franz.

The men have all quickly realized what is happening and look as though they couldn't care less. They are sitting beside the road, playing cards. Some are sunbathing, stripped to the waist. Good luck to them! Personally, I have a horror of frying in the sun for hours at a time, simply for the satisfaction of seeing my skin become a little less white.

Soon I catch sight of my two inseparable companions, sitting quietly on the tracks of a Mark II, chatting happily as though this were a picnic. Talking of picnics, I am beginning to notice some rather sharp pangs of hunger in my belly. I walk up to them.

"Heil Hitler! Well, you old warriors. It's all very fine, this war, but do you happen to know if there's any chow about?"

"Chow? We're famished too. But we know how to wait."

Franz starts laughing.

"It must be all the fighting that's given him an appetite. Playing the hero, rushing hell for leather to get his head shot off at the first sound of gunfire. For God's sake, man, you should have kept down.

It wasn't your job to run after the Russkies like a greyhound," he adds in more serious tones.

I shake my head. "I think I must have been a bit crazy. I saw everybody jumping out of the trucks, and I thought the Reds were making a mass attack."

"Poor old Peter! Look at him feeling sorry he wasn't in a big battle," Franz says, to tease me.

A dull rumbling that starts far down the road becomes a deafening din of engines in low gear and a horrible grinding of tracks tearing up the tarred surface. Pieces of asphalt and gravel fly in all directions. I feel that once the Vikings have all gone through, this road won't be a very pretty sight.

The tank commanders are almost all standing in their turrets and shout at us happily as they go by.

"Hi, there, Vikings. Taking it easy? Waiting for Lvov to be served up to you on a gold platter, eh? Don't worry, pals; once we get in there there won't be a *moujik* left for you to worry about. Not even a girl for you; you'll have had it, you bunch of loafers."

For a good half-hour the tanks go on rolling past us, raising clouds of dust and digging steadily deeper into the road.

Between each column, trucks loaded with troops try to edge through. Probably men left behind by the 1st Division.

It is nearly three o'clock and the field kitchen still hasn't turned up.

At last, to keep us quiet, they pass out hunks of bread and meat paste in tubes. The old hands call this "monkey's arse paste." It certainly isn't very appetizing. Brownish black, with white streaks of the most revolting aspect embedded in it. But we haven't eaten anything since six o'clock that morning, and we squeeze the last bits out of the tubes. I have to admit I did the same.

The afternoon goes on and we're still squatting on our backsides in the fields like a bunch of mangel-wurzel pickers.

Then colonel comes around to see us.

"Well, boys," he says, "it looks as though we'll have to get organized to spend the night here. Platoon leaders had better pick their men for guard and fatigue duties. Two SS per platoon, reliefs every two hours. I'll also want air sentries posted by the ack-ack guns. One never knows."

He strides off to join a group of officers.

"Waker! Light company Jena forward, on the Sokal road. Heavy squadron Herzog to act as rear guard! Tell me, anyone seen van Kolden?"

A lieutenant, looking surprised, pops his head out of a tank.

"Yes, sir?"

He is a Dutchman that I've already seen several times. Barely thirty years old and a very nice fellow. They say he won the Knight's Cross which glitters around his neck when he was with von List down in the Thessalian campaign.

There are a lot of Dutchmen in the Viking Division. Dutchmen, and also Flemings, Walloons, Finns, Danes and Norwegians. The Viking is the first division of European volunteers.

As we are walking along Karl suddenly turns to us. "Let's have a look around if we've got to spend the night here. There's plenty of time."

I'm game, but Franz says he's tired. Tired by what, I can't imagine. So the two of us set off across the fields. A bit dangerous, perhaps, because though it looks peaceful enough hereabouts the skirmish this morning has shown that the Reds, without wishing to meet us head-on, will shoot us in the back if they can. Obviously they're entitled to act this way, but it certainly isn't playing the game as we see it.

We have been told that the early battles which took place beyond the Bug and before Kovno were rather unpleasant, and in any case quite incomprehensible.

It seems certain that the Russians knew all about our plans, probably for months. Just as we knew all about theirs. Still, they appear to have been surprised by the rapidity of our advance. It looks as though the forecasts of the High Command—as happened in France —will be left far behind by the speed of our eastern advance.

According to information given out on the German radio yesterday evening, the High Command hopes to reach Moscow within the next fortnight.

It seems that some Dornier 215's—reconnaissance planes—have reported unusual activity around the Kremlin. The pilots said that barricades are already being erected in certain streets of the Russian capital.

Anyhow, for the moment we are not yet in Moscow. We are wandering about the fields of Poland, and a damned fool idea it was, too.

"I must say I wonder what we're looking for here!" grumbles Karl, dragging his boots with difficulty up out of the deep mud.

I turn to him. "Don't you start beefing now. It was your idea. Besides, we can't just sit on the hood of a truck with nothing to eat till morning!"

We find a narrow path, pitted with deep ruts. Obviously carts often pass along it. And if they do, it must be with the object of getting somewhere.

Soon a little farm comes in sight. It has been hidden by a tall hedge.

Silently we approach it. Dogs start barking. Perhaps people still live here.

Carefully we walk on.

As we turn a corner, a little wizened man with a black beard appears, waving a gun. I reach for my Mauser pistol. Evidently this is enough, for he drops his rifle and puts up his hands.

Who is he? He jabbers away volubly and beckons us to come into the house.

Karl has also gotten his long-barreled Erstalt at the ready, as we follow the joker inside.

The house is dark, stinking and filled with smoke.

In the gloom we finally make out two women and a snotty-nosed boy of about ten, hiding timidly behind the skirts of the younger woman.

I ask them, "Who speaks German here?"

"*Nie Zruzumiee pan Niemisk,*" the man replies.

As far as I can make out this must mean, "I don't speak German." That's not going to make our conversation any easier. My knowledge of Polish is sketchy, to say the least.

Food, sausage, butter. How does one say it in Polish?

"Have you sausage and butter?" I ask.

I point toward the cupboard.

The women are looking increasingly terrified and the man more and more half-witted. We're beginning to be thoroughly annoyed by their stupid gaping.

Karl suddenly starts to shout, and he too points at the cupboard.

"*Heilige Sakrament vom Teufel!* "What have you got to eat, damn you?" he roars, scarlet with anger.

All of a sudden the Pole seems to understand this charming language. He goes up to the younger woman and starts stroking her shoulders. "*Piekny Kobieta, dobry Kobieta . . . Czy Masz!* [Isn't she pretty? She's a good girl, you can have her if you like.]"

I am absolutely astonished and it takes me some time to understand.

Suddenly, I get it. We have been pointing at the cupboard for a quarter of an hour. But in front of the cupboard is the woman. His wife.

The bastard! Obviously it has been the custom for the occupying Russians to see a good deal of his very accommodating better half.

The offering gives us a languorous, seductive smile, which shows her blackish, toothless mouth. What a pity. Perhaps we should not have said no otherwise.

Now the wretched man is at his wit's end. And we can't spend the rest of the Russian campaign trying to make him understand.

In three strides I am in front of the famous cupboard.

I wrench open the door so violently that it nearly falls off its hinges.

Inside there is bread and bottles. Not much.

I sniff at a square bottle that looks as though it might contain some drinkable vodka. I confiscate this miserable piece of loot and signal to Karl that it's time we got back to camp.

Proudly we walk out amidst the indescribable hubbub put up by the Polish peasants, who will presumably spend hours asking each other what on earth it was all about. And who were these two strange SS men who threatened them, armed to the teeth, for the sole purpose of rifling a kitchen cupboard? Half an hour later, we are back in camp and night is falling. Our first day at the front, and a very surprising one.

June 30. This time it's serious. The armored troop-carriers are carrying us at full speed toward a small village outside Lvov where we are told there is an important pocket of resistance.

The colonel has decided that I shall be attached for the day to Lieutenant Scholtzberg, who commands the light company of panzer infantry. While awaiting a definite posting, I must familiarize myself with different forms of combat. Thus spake our regimental CO.

About fifteen tanks are ahead of us. We can see them lumbering along a few hundred yards in front. Suddenly they make a right-angle turn and head off into the fields. The village is there, very near. Soon we hear the din of their .50's and 75's firing, followed immediately by the angry barking of the Russian antitank guns.

About two hundred yards from the tanks the troop-carriers stop. We immediately jump down.

The tanks fan out across the whole countryside and fire all their guns at the buildings.

The lieutenant looks at his watch. Just before starting, the squadron commander had given him the exact hour at which the tanks were to cease fire. Only then could the armored infantry attack.

With machine pistols at the ready, we crouch behind the trucks. Nervously our fingers stroke the triggers.

A sudden burst of shooting from the Reds.

The tank gunners cease fire.

It's up to us.

Shouting like madmen, we jump up and start racing toward the nearest houses.

I have two sections under my command, those of Sergeant Diekener and Corporal Libesis.

They know I'm from Tölz. They won't spare my feelings if I make the slightest foolish mistake.

My twenty men go forward, throwing themselves down between each advance behind any cover that's available, lengths of collapsed wall, piles of rubbish, scrap metal.

The Russians are firing at us now, point-blank.

Several of their antitank antiaircraft guns are located in the middle of the main street. Perhaps they thought that our tanks would go straight through the village.

Rat-tat-tat-tat. That's the heavy Voroshilov 12 mm MG. In spite of the frightful rattle it makes, it's terribly dangerous.

We have already been taught about all sorts of guns at Tölz and at Sonthofen. We've even had the opportunity to handle them on maneuvers.

The men are forcing their way through the doors of the houses, kicking them open or smashing them in with the butts of their rifles. The Russians are quickly mopped up. Those still inside lift up their hands to heaven. Too late.

I go into a large wooden building from which about half a dozen Russians have just been firing. Grenades and carbines have taken care of these savages, or they've vanished out the back. I thought it wise, all the same, to make sure for myself that there was nobody left inside.

On the threshold, two dead bodies.

Heads blown open, gaping wounds, glassy eyes. They'd had it, these two.

I climb up to the first floor by a shaky staircase made of planks, crudely joined. A young SS I haven't seen before follows me. I turn

around and smile at him. He has obviously come because he saw
me going into the house alone.

With my finger on the trigger of my MP40, I slowly walk up to
a closed door.

The lock yields to a hard kick.

A man suddenly looms up out of the darkness, shouting. I fire,
a simple reflex action, sweeping the muzzle across from left to right.
This time I'm frightened, and with clenched teeth I go on emptying
the magazine, terrified.

The black mist which had surrounded me like a leaden cloud the
moment I began firing is suddenly dispersed. At my feet lies a
Russian, literally cut to pieces.

I realize suddenly that I am trembling with nerves and that I
have been in a real blue funk. That'll teach me to think of myself
as a seasoned warrior! Very dangerous to go alone, or even in pairs,
into any building where large numbers of the enemy might be
hiding.

Outside, the barrage goes on. It sounds as though it's growing
more and more violent. As a result of this escapade I have lost my
two sections who are doubtless getting on just as well without me.
But all the same they must think I'm a lousy platoon commander.

The advance continues, and nearly half the village has been
cleared. A lot of Russian corpses, but some German dead too. Two
antitank guns have been put out of action by hand grenades.
Sergeant Diekener is particularly expert at this game.

He takes out the pin with his teeth in one rapid movement, waits
a second or two and then hurls the death-dealing charge more than
thirty yards.

Some houses are on fire. The incendiary grenades are also doing
first-class work.

A group of Russians appears around a corner of the street,
dragging a 76 behind them. They're a bit too cocky. They are
greeted, as they deserve, by four or five simultaneous volleys.

One of them, clutching his stomach, comes on, staggering. We
let him come closer, not understanding; then suddenly we see him

drop to the ground and roll over, screaming like an animal.

A Mauser bullet through the head puts an end to his sufferings. On that occasion it was an act of charity to finish him off.

Rat-tat-tat-tat . . . Rat-tat-tat-tat . . .

The Voroshilov is still spitting out its deadly venom.

And one can't even see where the stuff is coming from. This filthy machine has already killed a dozen men. I calculate that if one spots the angle of fire and the points of impact there's a chance of finding out at least the direction from which it's firing. There—I've seen it! A window on the second floor of a tall, square building. Certainly a public building.

"I want four men! Come on!"

Like Indians, one behind the other, we creep forward from wall to wall, tree to tree, making the most of all natural cover and of all the obstacles we come upon.

The swine have seen us coming, and they're firing like madmen. We'll never get there.

A long-drawn-out scream ends up as a horrible gurgle. His jaw broken and his throat split open, a young private falls down, choking on his own blood which fills his mouth. We have to leave him behind. To fetch him would have meant death for one of us.

The Russian machine gun goes on firing insanely at the wounded man. When hit by the first bullets his poor, agonizing body twitches spasmodically. Now he doesn't move any more. He's had it, too.

Suddenly I understand that it will be impossible to knock them out this way. There are not enough of us. I signal to the others, and all four of us set off back again, under cover, to where the rest of the company is.

Lieutenant Scholtzberg is there, talking to his men. On seeing me he turns around quickly.

"Oh, there you are, eh? Listen, my boy, you're going to get it in double-quick time if you go on like this. You don't have to fight as if you were a knight in the Crusades; just kill Russians, that's all. I've sent a signal to Division, asking them to send up two tanks to help us. Meantime, you stay put, and don't budge from here."

There's a noise of running feet, and an SS man comes up to the lieutenant and stands at attention.

"Sir, we've caught about ten Bolsheviks, and two of them are civilians. What'll we do with them, sir?"

"Bring 'em here," orders the officer.

The Russians arrive almost at once, their hands above their heads. Prejudice apart, they are certainly not very beautiful to look at. Shaved heads, Mongoloid faces, waxy skins and convict's beards. A pretty lot of ghetto sweepings. I notice a gold star on the sleeve of the two civilians.

Commissars!

Scholtzberg has seen me looking at them. He understands, too, and nods to me.

"They're all yours, Neumann! You deal with them."

I can feel myself breaking out in a cold sweat. They've got to be shot! Yes. But I don't want to do it.

My hesitation, brief as it is, has not escaped the lieutenant, who says quickly, "You'd rather not. Relax, Neumann. Libesis will handle this little formality."

He signals. Quietly, casually, with deliberate movements, the corporal gets up and goes toward one of the commissars.

"You are a People's Commissar?"

"Yes! Why?" answers the man, surprised.

Libesis slowly takes his Mauser from its holster, loads it under the suddenly bulging eyes of the Russian, aims it at the shaved head and squeezes the trigger.

There is now only one People's Commissar.

A moment later, there are no People's Commissars at all.

The first man slid to the ground, crying out, not knowing what had happened. The second tried to bolt. The bullet must have gotten him in the spinal column, for he rolled on the ground for quite some time, kicking with his legs in all directions but not moving his body. Then he went rigid once and for all.

Meanwhile, the prisoners, terrified and covered by the SS machine pistols, don't look too pleased with the turn events have taken.

Probably they are wondering just how and when they will be dispatched to join the other two *moujiks*. They don't, however, want to find out just yet.

But this is war.

It's war all right, and we haven't the time to worry about their sad plight.

Two 30-ton Mark IV's are coming up, their 500 hp engines roaring, and they stop a few yards from us. In brief, clipped phrases Scholtzberg explains to the tank gunners what is wanted of them.

The monsters grind off, their armor jolting and shaking as they move on, and a few minutes later they start firing at the house in which the dangerous Russian Voroshilov gun is probably hidden.

The job is soon done—without a hitch.

About a dozen 75 shells have gone through the front of the building, and the tanks' heavy MG's have done the rest.

Some panzer infantry now run into the building and reappear a moment later, waving their machine pistols in the victory sign.

A final patrol to make sure that there are no Bolsheviks hiding in the ruins, a few rounds from our Mausers to finish off the wounded Russians decently and thus relieve them of useless pain and suffering, and we are back again in our armored troop-carriers.

I haven't seen the prisoners again. Obviously we have spared them, too, the tortures of a long captivity.

On the road to the camp we sing wildly, perhaps as an outlet for our feelings of great joy that we are still in the land of the living.

July 3. The advance continues at a thundering pace. In the north Kovno and in the south Bialystok have fallen. Von Bock's armies and Guderian's armored divisions are driving for Moscow.

On the 30th von Stülpnagel's divisions seized Lvov.

I went to this last named town yesterday, with Major Deurne, who was sent on a liaison job to the headquarters of Army Group South.

We came from Dubno, which we had captured from the Russians after a terrifying battle lasting two whole days. Budënny's armored forces were equipped with a new tank, the T-34, an almost perfect job. The tank battle went on day and night, swaying back and forth, a grim struggle of giants, fought with tracer shells by night. In this area the Russians are hanging on with all their strength, and fighting to the last man. We didn't even have to bother about prisoners. Each new district that we enter is already deserted.

The Russians carry away their dead and wounded, and even used shell cases and cartridges. They leave nothing behind, not a sign that they have been there. Except death and destruction.

At Lvov we saw a frightful scene.

Before leaving, the Russians burned and pillaged everything, took everything away. Not being able to move their prisoners eastward, they simply massacred them.

In the NKVD prison where the Russian and Polish political prisoners were housed, there remained only about a hundred survivors. The other prisoners must have been machine-gunned in the courtyards of the jail, because the bodies were all heaped up, at times to an impressive height.

The population of Lvov didn't escape the massacre either. It seems that the Reds were thrown into disorder by our advance and went quite mad. They fled on foot, in carts and trucks, in complete chaos, firing like lunatics at everything in sight.

They never stopped firing from the moving lorries, aiming their MG's at the houses as they went by.

It was the political commissars who ordered the Red troops to shoot all the prisoners, men and women alike. These people had all been arrested during the last few weeks on the most ridiculous pretexts—persistent lateness at work, unintentional bad work construed as sabotage or nonexecution of requisitioning orders.

The smell of filth and decay in the streets was indescribable. The Army crematory trucks were soon found to be inadequate, and enormous piles of wood have been built outside the town on which the corpses are being burned.

Before the bodies were taken away, many people tried to identify the remains of friends or relatives. Handkerchiefs pressed to their mouths, they rummaged about among the dead, turning over the bodies from which rose clouds of flies.

Silence envelops the town, broken only by the horns of our vehicles and the loudspeakers on the propaganda trucks issuing urgent instructions in Polish to the civilian survivors.

After seeing these horrors I won't feel so much remorse in future about liquidating Russians, as Scholtzberg says.

Major Deurne finished his job and we drove back. He has a French 5 hp Citroën which goes like the wind. In two hours, despite the wretched state of the roads, we reached Dubno.

July 10. Over the dusty roads of the Ukraine, the tracks of Panzer Division Viking's tanks roll on.

From Dubno to the outskirts of Zhitomir the advance has been relatively easy, apart from a few skirmishes with isolated pockets of resistance or groups of guerilla fighters. Actually many of the encircled units scatter as soon as we attack, and the men hide out for days in the neighboring farmhouses. Then, quickly reformed into sections or companies, they attack our lines of communication again.

Everywhere we go we see the same scenes of destruction wrought by the special commandos of the NKVD. And we meet the same endless columns of Soviet prisoners from the Lvov pocket marching toward the rear. There are more than a hundred thousand of them. In addition, nearly two thousand tanks and fifteen hundred guns have been left behind by the Russians.

July 11. Troops of Budënny's 6th Army are blocking our advance and are defending a forest to the southeast of Zhitomir.

Since this morning we have been in line of battle, waiting for the tanks to finish their job before we attack.

Their tactics are as follows: Once arrived at the enemy position, the tank squadrons spread out fanwise so as to outflank and encircle the opposing forces. Then with a pincer movement they gradually close up again, thus forcing the Russians back into a progressively smaller area.

Our panzer infantry then attack the pocket thus formed and methodically clear the area. . . .

The terrible uproar of the artillery, which has been spraying the Russian positions since dawn, has just stopped. We receive a message that forward HQ has ordered us by radio to start advancing.

I signal to the driver that he can move off. A little while ago we were issued new half-tracked armored vehicles, very fast over any sort of surface. A .50 is mounted in front, and two gunners are ready to fire it.

The vehicle stops suddenly. We jump down.

Three hundred yards ahead the battle is in full swing, or rather we see a confused mass of men among whom we occasionally recognize a Russian or a German uniform. The Reds, however, look as though they intend to hang on here.

Bullets and shells whistle past on all sides.

Some of our men are very stupidly advancing standing up.

"Get down, for God's sake! Where do you think you are? On maneuvers?"

In front of us is the wood and a few broken-down shacks from which comes the violent banging of the antitank guns.

Scholtzberg starts to shout, "Deploy! Objective—Neumann's platoon: the nearest huts! The others, into the forest!"

He raises his arm. "On the double!"

I run, half bent, at the head of my men. I deploy my platoon in an arc, and we go forward fairly quickly, without too much difficulty.

The other battle groups have already reached the line of the first trees. The flame-throwers are spewing out long red tongues of fire and the pine trees begin to burn like torches.

The Russians are firing without a pause in our direction.

A terrible screeching like the end of the world. . . . A horrifying din. The ground seems to open as though forced up by a giant spade. Clods of earth fly in all directions.

The heavies! They are firing at us, with 400's at least!

Are they our guns or the Bolsheviks'?

Whichever they are, about ten men have been hit by fragments of a shell which bursts right among them.

And now a battery, which must have been hidden, God knows where, has all fired at the same time. Muck rains down on my helmet, tossed up by the explosions. My face is completely buried in the earth, and I think at this moment that I'd happily swallow enormous mouthfuls of it if only this abominable shooting would stop.

But we must go on at all costs and get out of the Russian barrage, if we don't want to be turned into nitrogen fertilizer.

This time there's no doubt about it. It's the filthy Reds who are firing at us. We can hear the guns in the near-by forest.

We run like fury, through this belt of death, flattening ourselves against the ground every twenty yards or so. About ten more men have been hit, hacked to pieces by enormous hunks of jagged steel as big as soup plates. One of the wounded men is dragging himself along the ground, swearing at the stretcher-bearers for not being there to fetch him immediately. And a lot of good it does him!

The first houses. A few bursts. Incendiary grenades. The thatched roofs flame like torches.

Russians run out, yelling. One with his clothes on fire rolls on the ground, screaming like a pig in a slaughterhouse.

We fire into the crowd of Russians. Suddenly I am overwhelmed by anger. They've loused us up with their idiotic resistance, haven't they? We've got to wipe them out. Wipe them out. . . .

I fire and reload again and again, straight ahead. The men are hurling grenades into the huts that are still intact. Roofs collapse amidst clouds of sparks.

Green shadows, glimpsed vaguely through the smoke, trying to escape toward the wood.

Grenades.

Fragments of torn flesh fall to the ground among bits of wood and stone.

A final mopping up of the huts with bursts from our machine

pistols, and then we, in turn, plunge into the thick undergrowth
where the other platoons are already heavily engaged.

We spend the rest of the day sweeping the thickets and clearings
and hunting out the Reds, who emerge on all sides with their hands
above their heads. We send them off, with kicks, toward the trucks.

They will go to swell the numbers at the camps hurriedly built
in the Carpathians and Galicia.

Zhitomir, July 28. We occupied the town some days ago. Perhaps
I am exaggerating when I call it a town, because all we have seen
are miles and miles of ruins, and again ruins.

Fresh orders have reached the division.

In addition to People's Commissars, we are to shoot, without trial,
all Jewish functionaries we find, whether civil or military.

Liquidations, executions, purges. All these words, synonymous
with destruction, seem completely banal and devoid of meaning
once one has gotten used to them.

It is a vocabulary which has become general usage, and we use
such words just as we talk of swatting disagreeable insects or destroying a dangerous animal.

These words, however, are applied to men. But men who happen
to be our mortal enemies.

The order also stipulates that each SS officer will be held personally
responsible if these directives are not carried out—even if one of
his subordinates is actually at fault.

That is to say, our own lives are dependent on the death of
others.

At Dubno I saw Karl shoot down with his Mauser a group of
civilians belonging to the local Russian ITO.[4] These characters
were by no means saints, and probably had no hesitation in sending
any poor devil guilty of some minor offense off to the mines in
Siberia. But all the same I stopped for a moment, rooted to the spot

[4] *Issipravitelno Trudovnoie Upalvelnnie* (Central Administration of Corrective
Training), department concerned with sending people to labor camps (concentration
camps), attached to the People's Tribunal.

by Karl's amazing cold-bloodedness. His hand didn't even tremble.

Is it possible that this is the same fellow I once saw, in short pants, playing ball on the sands down by the breakwaters of the Aussen-alster in Hamburg?

August 4. The Stalin line—that is to say, the Vitebsk-Mogilev-Gomel-Kiev position—has been broken through in several places. The upper Dnieper has been crossed.

Von Leeb's Army Group North, after smashing the fortress of Polotsk, is outflanking Luga and advancing on Leningrad.

Smolensk has been seized from Timoshenko's men by von Bock's central armies.

The road to Moscow is open.

August 6. The Viking has passed through Zhitomir and occupied Belaya Tserkov, one of the strongpoints of the famous Stalin line, almost without fighting. Tirelessly the squadrons of Dorniers and Junkers, under Air Marshal Kesselring and General Loehr, are smashing the enemy's positions in the Kiev sector and all along the Dnieper.

The town is encircled from north to south, and crushed in a pincer movement by von Kleist's troops and the armored divisions of von Reichenau.

August 8. Budënny has fallen into the trap!

Traveling without a break by night and day, our entire division, together with the regiments of the 1st Leibstandarte Division, has finally linked up with the Hungarian troops at Pervomaisk.

The 6th and 12th Red Armies, and part of the 18th, are surrounded in the Uman pocket.

This is the first time since the beginning of the campaign that we have been involved in such an important battle.

The Hungarians, who are about to attack, say that a fantastic concentration of artillery has been bombarding the Russian positions for four days and nights.

Indeed all along the road we noticed hundreds of heavy batteries, their guns raised skyward at forty-five degrees, camouflaged by protective netting and piles of branches.

The infernal thundering of thousands of guns makes the ground tremble. For miles and miles there can be nothing left standing in the sectors held by the Bolsheviks.

At dawn all the tanks which are not taking part in the encirclement of Kiev move off and advance toward the southeast.

We are ready to go at nine o'clock.

The ground is marshy and progress made more difficult by the fact that all the bridges have been smashed. Built by the Russians to carry peasant's carts, they collapse as soon as even a light tank tries to cross them. At each smashed bridge the engineers have to build pontoons, until they can rebuild new and more solid structures.

The Russkies must have had very strict orders because they suddenly begin to fight like madmen. Very different from the early battles at the beginning of July.

The liquidations ordered by the Red General Staff and the directives issued by the bigwigs of the Supreme Soviet must have had something to do with this sudden access of heroism.

A few Red bombers drone overhead, flying very low. It is their classic method of avoiding the Messerschmitts, which are much faster. But they probably won't get far.

We are now the advance guard, and we have to be extremely careful.

The Luftwaffe doesn't know our positions exactly, and we have already been fired upon by German fighters under the impression that we are Russian troops.

There have been a lot of Germans killed by bullets from Stukas or ME109's. From now on we have orders to carry a swastika flag at the head of our column.

As our advance goes on, we occupy half-burned villages which we have to clear house by house.

Often Russian soldiers, hiding in the ruins, start peppering us with bullets or grenades several hours after our arrival.

Furthermore, one has to be very careful where one walks since the entire countryside is mined. Incautiously opening a door may set one of the infernal things off. In some places everything is a booby trap. The magnificent pistol lying on the floor conceals a wire connected to an explosive charge. In the harmless interior of a samovar, pounds of cordite are hidden, waiting to blow up. Jam jars, vodka bottles, even a well the rope of which one is tempted to pull in order to get a drop of fresh water—they are all death traps to be steered clear of.

Sometimes it's easy to spot the wires leading to the acid cartridge or the percussion cap. The difficult thing is to dismantle the contraption without being dispatched to a better world in the process.

The simplest system is, from safe cover, to toss in three or four hand grenades before entering any building. The explosion sets the booby traps off at the same time.

August 10. Everywhere, from Novo-Ukrainka to Golovanesk, lie tens of thousands of Russian corpses.

They have fallen on the hillsides, on the banks of the rivers, on both sides of the bridges, in the open country. They have been scythed down as they fought, by divisions, by battalions, by regiments, by sections.

Often the piles of interlaced bodies are a yard or more high, as though a machine gun has mown them down, wave after wave of them.

One has to have seen this monstrous mass of decomposing corpses to realize fully what war is like.

At certain times of day, when the sun is hot, gas dilates the ballooning, distended bellies, and then one hears the most horrible and unbelievable gurgling sounds.

Wherever we camp, we first have to spray all the carrion in the vicinity with quicklime or gasoline.

August 20. This morning the colonel sent for us.

The regimental HQ is in a small and isolated house beside the

Pomonskia-Vyskie road. When I came in, the colonel was surrounded by a group of officers listening to what he had to say.

"Gentlemen," he said, "Intelligence tells us that for almost a fortnight the Russians have been demolishing the giant dam installations at Dnepropetrovsk. Several 62,000-kilowatt turbogenerators have been transported eastward. Furthermore, reports from a reliable source reveal that special NKVD commandos are standing by ready to blow up the rest of the Dnieper dam installations."

He pointed to the map which lay on a rough oak table.

"Since July they have been rapidly building pillboxes on both sides of the river. Also, still according to Intelligence, thousands of antitank/antiaircraft 76.2's have been installed all along the valley. The job we've got to do isn't going to be easy. . . ."

He straightened up and faced us.

"The High Command has decided that if we are to capture the dam intact, there is not a moment to lose."

His face suddenly hardened.

"The orders are explicit. We shall attack in the direction of the Dnieper immediately. Our rendezvous with von Kleist's leading units is Chigirin, on one of the tributaries of the river."

August 22. The Dnieper lies at our feet, vast and majestic.

The cliffs on the western bank dominate the whole industrial plain, flanked by the Kobelyaki and Samara rivers. The far bank, just visible through the low-lying mists, is quite flat, however, and this will obviously facilitate our offensive.

For the time being the sector is almost quiet, apart from the continual artillery duel and the usual bombing raids.

If the sky were not gray, and if it stopped raining, one might be able to make out away to the east the tall chimneys of *Kombinats-Industriels*, the pride of the Soviet Five-Year Plans.

It is to be hoped that within a few months all the factories in this valley and in the Donets Basin will be manufacturing German munitions.

But for the moment, it's raining.

If it can be called rain. More like a liquid cascade, a permanent curtain of water pouring down from an eternally black sky.

Actually we are lucky, because on the northern and central fronts mud is holding up operations completely. One hears of whole regiments bogged down in it after only an hour's rain.

In any case, the rain along the Dnieper doesn't stop the Red artillery from spraying us with shells and high explosive with a generosity and perseverance that is in extremely bad taste.

Luckily for us a number of shells bury themselves in the mud without bursting.

Wumph. . .ph. . . .

Death passed us by that time.

August 24. An enormous explosion, amplified by the silence of the night.

A hot wind, as though the door of a blast furnace had been opened, sweeps over the dark plain.

There's just been a second explosion at the dam.

We won't find the hydroelectric works intact, that's dead certain.

Into the attack.

The tanks of the Viking tank regiment slither down the steep roads leading to the banks of the Dnieper. Behind them at full speed come the armored troop-carriers, filled with troops and performing a veritable *slalom* in their efforts to avoid the innumerable shellholes and carcasses of men and beasts that block the road.

The Reds, from the far side of the river, are desperately trying to stem this formidable onrush of tanks and infantry.

Turning a corner, we already see the first rubber boats of the Combat Engineers setting out across the river under machine-gun fire.

A continuous barrage, extending for miles, of ack-ack guns being used as antitanks is firing ceaselessly at our panzers. The latter are regrouping, awaiting the moment when the pontoons will make it possible for them too to cross the Dnieper.

As for us, we cling to the iron uprights of our armored carriers as we head for the bank. We are waiting to get within range before we open fire.

Hundreds of Stukas with their infernal screeching go plummeting down on the Red batteries, which are partially camouflaged by netting and branches.

A hundred yards in front of us a truck has just overturned and rolls over and over, probably eliminating one platoon of the antitank company. Thirty men, and not one escapes. A wounded man with both legs crushed begs us to finish him off. There is no time. The ground shakes, everything seems to disintegrate and disappear.

A blinding flash. A fiendish din.

A shell has just hit the front of our vehicle head-on. It is a miracle any of us is still alive.

There is death on every side. A hurricane of steel beats down on us as we painfully dig out the remnants of the truck. Several men are trapped between torn bits of metal. But it's too dangerous here; we can't help them—we are less than five hundred yards from the Russian batteries.

I suddenly notice that I haven't got my MP40 any more. It's obviously buried under the wreck of the truck.

I snatch another machine pistol from the dead hand of a corporal, whose glazed and staring eyes can no longer see the terrible, mortal struggle all about us.

It seems that the Russian fire is increasing in intensity.

Shellbursts, explosions, rain down on every side. I no longer dare to lift my head. Lying flat on my stomach on the ground, I try to see whether the rest of the regiment is advancing. We can't afford to stay in this inferno for long.

My God, if I ever get out of this I'll grovel on bended knees in the church at Wittenberge and say a prayer.

Someone must take charge. I raise my left hand.

"Platoon! Advance!"

The MP40 seems terribly heavy. I must have bruised my arm when the truck turned over.

While running forward something suddenly occurs to me. I have no ammunition. God, what a fool! A few minutes later, taking advantage of a lull, I see a private who carries an impressive cartridge belt slung across his shoulders, and I help myself to a handful of clips.

I am now fully equipped for the Dnieper crossing.

The Russian fire is gradually diminishing in volume. One by one the Red batteries are being silenced by the Luftwaffe and the gunfire from our tanks.

Engineers, deployed all along the bank, are getting their first pontoons into position.

A few hours later, crouching behind the armor of the tanks, we too cross the Dnieper on a pontoon bridge.

The rest is nothing but a mopping-up operation of isolated pockets of enemy resistance.

August 27. Dnepropetrovsk has been captured after terrible fighting.

But one side of the gigantic Zaporozhe dam is breached for a length of nearly two hundred yards. Of the nine turbogenerators, with a total output of more than half a million kilowatts, five have been taken away by the Russians.

The others have been deliberately burned out by the NKVD engineers, simply by working them at full throttle—without oil.

An enormous, useless mass of concrete, huge chunks of stone and iron destined to go rusty. So much for this gigantic product of Soviet genius.

Lieutenant General Thomas's scouts have already arrived to check on the extent of the damage. Technicians of the Todt organization will have their work cut out if they are to get the dam working again during the next few months.[5]

---

[5] In the radius of Dnepropetrovsk, the electrical power capacity was 800,000 kilowatts in 1938. By 1943 the hydroelectric plant had been put in working order again by the Todt organization. But production never exceeded 38,000 kilowatts, less than 5% of the normal output.

This operation certainly will not be accomplished without difficulty and trouble.

Meanwhile we have a whole week out of the line. We have certainly earned it.

Franz has been slightly wounded in the arm, but his condition was not considered serious enough for him to be evacuated to Hohenlichen.[6]

Scholtzberg was not so lucky.

A shellburst cut his head off just at the moment that he set foot on the east bank of the Dnieper.

September 16. Novo-Georgiyevsk is nothing but ruins. . . .

For mile after mile there, nothing is standing. There are no more streets. Only trenches cutting straight through the rubble and fallen masonry. Everywhere the frameworks of the gutted houses are still smoking slightly. Occasionally one hears the dull explosion of a shell or a grenade touched off by the fires which are still smoldering.

At the four corners of what was the town they have put up signposts with arrows, showing where to find the different supply dumps, the regimental aid stations, the divisional HQ's and so on.

In the daytime, the town is weird, silent, almost deserted.

The rare citizens who venture into the streets walk with their eyes straight ahead of them, pretending not to notice us, and looking utterly dejected and miserable. In the other towns we have captured, the Russians appeared to accept the occupation with a sort of fatalism and resignation. But around Novo-Georgiyevsk there are quite a few partisans.

All the same, groups collect around the notices put up by the Propaganda Unit. These list the destruction for which the NKVD commandos were responsible. There are others which explain the plans for reconstruction and distribution of land as defined by General Thomas's people. The Russians shake their heads thoughtfully and go on their way.

The nights in Novo-Georgiyevsk are more lively.

[6] German hospital reserved for SS.

"Lively" is an understatement. For three days we have been pestered by groups of partisans constantly attacking trucks and isolated detachments of soldiers.

Some of the partisan groups hide by day in the ruined houses in the town. Or perhaps they walk about disguised as honest workmen, equipped with papers to prove that they have jobs. So it is difficult to catch them.

Others hide out, it seems, in the near-by Gradizhsk forest and infiltrate back at night to places where they know they have friends.

The curfew is fixed for seven o'clock in the evening, by order of the local commandant. After this hour patrols go through the town arresting all those who are out without a pass. They are then put in the municipal prison as hostages.

In spite of this, according to the soldiers of von Stülpnagel's divisions who occupy the town, the partisans' attacks are becoming more and more numerous. Again and again officers and men are shot down in the streets, bridges are blown up, trains derailed, supply units traveling over secondary roads are machine-gunned or peppered with grenades. And nobody who is arrested will ever admit having had anything to do with it all.

To all questions the Russians simply reply that they know nothing, have seen nothing, heard nothing.

And the murders go on. Soon it will be more dangerous to stop in a town than to take part in an attack under artillery fire. Two Finnish sergeants of the Nordland Regiment were assassinated tonight.

September 23. We leave at dawn. Direction Karasnaya, on a reprisal operation. This time they've overdone it, hitting two gasoline trucks, which blew up. Six dead and three wounded, appallingly burned and certain not to recover.

It is impossible to allow these terrorists to continue their crimes. Some peasants informed us that certain suspected groups are hiding near Karasnaya, and the colonel immediately ordered the Dutch

lieutenant, Kolden, to take command of two platoons and go and
see what was up in Gradizhsk forest.

One armored troop-carrier per platoon. We set off at about six
o'clock. It is barely daylight.

I have with me as section commanders Sergeant Diekener and
Corporal Libesis. One is the direct opposite of the other. Diekener
is a big, quiet, tacitiurn Wurttemburger, a man of few words and
stiff manner, and is not, it appears, very popular with his section.
His men regard him as a slave driver, but he seems quite indifferent
to their opinion and controls them by means of threats and punish-
ments. He is a one-time SA man who got into something of a jam
in 1934, at the time of the Röhm affair. Libesis, on the other hand,
is a cheerful Tyrolese peasant. He shouts like a wild bull if his
orders aren't obeyed, but off duty he goes and pinches the bottoms
of the Russian girls and gets drunk with his men like any ordinary
second-class private. His courage in action has won him both Iron
Crosses and the silver SS *Ruhne*. For all his faults, the SS of his
section say he's first-class.

Once again we cross the Dnieper on a pontoon bridge. But this
time without an accompanying storm of shells and bombs.

Without that storm, but in torrential rain.

The engineer who designed the armored troop-carrier is a smart
operator, I've no doubt, but he could at least have given us a tin
roof, or even a canvas one. With our rifles and machine guns
between our knees, and with our shoulders hunched against the
deluge, we must look a sorry band of terrorist-hunters.

We pass through villages where people watch us go by with
terror, then run and lock themselves in their houses. They have
already learned the difference between the *Armvogel* and the
Brustvogel. They are probably saying to themselves, *"Armvogel—
very dangerous. Let's get out of their way."* A distinguishing mark
of the SS is that we wear the Nazi eagle on the left sleeve. The
Wehrmacht wear it on their breast, and on the right.

An interminable forest—Karasnaya.

Kolden jumps down first. Following him, I make for the Starosta's house, recognizable by the rusty remains of a hammer and sickle, which has been completely torn away. Carbines at the ready, our SS men have also gotten out of the trucks.

The lieutenant kicks open the door.

An unsavory-looking old man is in there, with two women, frozen with surprise and terror when they see us come in.

Kolden knows a few words of Ukrainian, and he asks the man, "Are there any unregistered men in the village or hereabouts?"

The Starosta apparently finds some difficulty in answering. He lifts his head and looks at each of us in turn, confused and very frightened. Finally he stammers, "No, there's nobody you don't know about here."

I turn to the lieutenant. "I don't think we'll get anything out of him, Untersturmführer. It would probably be better to ask the ordinary people. Women in particular are more ready to talk."

"To hell with that! This one will talk, or else he'll get a bullet pretty quick, the filthy bastard!"

The Dutchman has drawn his Mauser and he points the muzzle against the Starosta's chest. Livid with rage, he forgets to speak Ukrainian, and starts shouting at the fellow.

"All right, you bastard! If you don't say where these filthy partisans are, as true as I come from Groningen I'll fill you full of lead."

He grabs the man by the shoulder and shakes him furiously.

"Terrorists! Do you understand? Terrorists! Do you know anything about terrorists?"

The man slides to the ground, quite limp, and clutches at the hem of Kolden's cape. "Have pity, little father. Don't kill me!"

He is deathly pale and trembling. He drags himself along the ground trying to avoid the powerful kicks the Dutchman gives him full in the solar plexus.

"Have pity!"

"Damned swine!" roars Kolden suddenly.

He fires three times.

The man falls over gently, and his eyes roll up to reveal the whites.

The lieutenant watches the small patch of blood spreading over the floor, as though he doesn't understand what has happened.

All of a sudden, and I don't know why, I want to fly at the throat of this vile Dutchman. The poor old man! But we are on active service. And an SS man must have no heart.

As we come out, Kolden, white as a sheet, turns to me.

"I know I've been a fool! I let myself lose my temper. But that old bastard knew something. They all know something. And they won't talk. So much the worse for them! There are too many of our men getting shot!"

Nobody in the streets. The little town looks quiet, but we can see people watching us fearfully from behind their windows. Everyone has heard the shots and must have guessed that we are looking for the terrorists.

Warrant Officer Martin, in command of the second platoon, walks up to us. "What's up? The Russkies are all looking scared!"

Martin is a veteran of the Leibstandarte. He spent more than a month at the Wolfsschanze[7] in East Prussia, then asked to be sent back to the front. He still wears on his sleeve the silver stripe with the Führer's name on it, and he is very proud of having been part of Adi's personal bodyguard when he was in France. Apart from this, he is always quite contented and phlegmatic. He comes from Lübeck and is rather a simple fellow.

"Not in the mood for talk, eh?" he now says.

"Cut it out, Martin," snaps Kolden. "We're not here for the laughs." The Dutchman turns to us. "Your men must seal off the whole area. And nobody is to leave their houses."

The orders are passed on to the sections, and we move off toward the center of the village. As we go the lieutenant gives us his orders. We shall first question the local inhabitants, and if they won't talk

[7] Name given to Hitler's main headquarters in East Prussia.

we'll search the forest. But we haven't much chance because the odds are that the partisans have already been warned of our arrival by the peasants.

We split up.

I call over two SS men who are near at hand and order them to follow me. I pick quite a decent-looking house and we three burst in there.

A gnarled old peasant dressed in rags, with a bushy beard, gets up as we come in. A woman who seems paralyzed is seated in a deep armchair close to the fire. She doesn't move, but her eyes are bulging out of her head with terror.

Actually, in spite of my threatening appearance, I feel very uncomfortable. What am I supposed to ask these people? If they've got terrorists hidden in their cupboard? A silly question, for if they say yes, I shall be bowled over by the shock.

Another, younger woman, attracted by the noise, enters through a door at the far end and stares at us without speaking.

I say, "Any terrorists here?"

I feel I must look extremely foolish.

"No, sir, no!" the old man assures me.

In spite of his air of innocence, I sense immediately that he's playing daft and that he actually knows something. But what can I do? He looks sullen, and his hands are nervously clasping and unclasping. He won't say anything.

The two SS men are looking at me strangely, questioningly. They obviously think I am putting up a pretty poor show.

I force myself to speak in more assertive tones, more sharply, when I address the young woman. She, too, cannot say anything but no, always no.

All this is beginning to make me very angry. I start shouting and waving a menacing fist. "Damned bunch of savages! Are we going to have to kill every one of you before you'll agree to talk?"

But confronted by the silence of the Russians, I see it's useless to go on, and I signal to my two SS men that we might as well go.

I slam the door behind me as violently as possible and hear the tinkle of broken glass. Poor consolation.

We haven't taken more than ten steps outside when we hear a tremendous burst of firing. We hurry in the direction from which the noise is coming. I see a dozen men running away. I stop, and then I realize what has happened.

Beside our trucks the sentries we had left there are lying on the ground, one of them still groaning.

The partisans!

They must have crept up close to the trucks when they saw us move off. But the village is surrounded. How did they manage it?

There is no time to lose. Men are running up from all sides, attracted by the firing. I shove about twenty of them, any old how, into the truck. No time for explanations or details. The urgent job is to catch the bandits.

We move off at full speed. The armored troop-carrier dashes toward the forest at fifty miles an hour. Suddenly we pull up. The driver has spotted a German uniform in the undergrowth.

I jump down and recoil with sudden horror.

It is a private of my platoon, a Berliner of about twenty, who joined up just a month ago.

His face is nothing but one hideous great wound. There is an enormous branch rammed into his mouth, which is appallingly distorted. I can see that they have beaten the poor fellow with sticks and then bayoneted him. His stomach is covered with blood. The filthy bastards!

But I don't understand it at all. They have only now run off.

Obviously they must have murdered the poor kid some time ago, silently, while he was on sentry duty.

They'll pay for this.

I climb back into the truck, thoroughly shaken.

"Come on! Let's go. We've got to step on it if we're going to catch them!"

Catch them. Yes, but how? The forest is vast. According to the map it stretches as far as Korel and Miolgorod.

Hours of search, on foot, through the impenetrable undergrowth, produces no results. All the roads within a radius of twenty miles are covered in vain. As always the partisans are invisible and seem to have wings.

Reluctantly I give the signal to go back.

The men don't say anything. With clenched fists and rigid faces they are thinking about their comrades, who must somehow be avenged.

At Karasnaya, the whole population has been assembled in the market place before a sort of war memorial, a bronze soldier brandishing a rifle over some object or other.

It is Kolden who has given the order to assemble all the inhabitants. In front of them, covered by blankets, the dead bodies are laid out on the ground. The German dead. . . .

I go up to the Dutchman. "I couldn't find them, Lieutenant!"

After a moment's silence, I add, "Have you found the body of the private, near the pond?"

"A private? No, the only ones are over there"—he points to the dead bodies—"the men killed beside the trucks. I'll give orders about the other fellow."

Several SS men have already heard, and they hasten off toward the edge of the village.

Kolden turns to me, his face hardening. I can see the veins in his forehead throbbing.

"The damned swine! They'll pay for this. As I told you, they all know what's going on! All this Ukrainian filth hates our guts. Their régime reduces them to slavery, but in spite of that they're trying to stab us in the back. They love this Russian soil of theirs, they love it. Well, they're going to get their fill of it! Their mouths'll be stuffed up with it," he ends, with a laugh.

Ten minutes later two men come back, carrying the dead body of the young Berliner on a strip of canvas. One of them is sobbing.

"Appalling!" hisses Kolden as he draws back the greatcoat which has been thrown over the body. "Let the Russians see that. Go on, go on, walk them past it; let them smell it and touch it, so that they can see what might happen to them too," he says to the two men.

Suddenly he grabs a machine pistol from the hands of a corporal standing beside him.

"Bastards! What *is* going to happen to them, more likely," he roars as he fires into the crowd.

Screams and shouts. The Russians in front fall to the ground. The serried ranks of local inhabitants suddenly break up. The people in terror attempt to flee into the houses.

The SS guards try at first to hold them back. Then, seized by ungovernable fury, they too begin firing into the mass of people and hitting out at them with anything to hand.

And so it is carnage.

The Russians run away in every direction, screaming with terror.

A woman, wild and disheveled, dashes toward a big pond, clutching a small baby in her arms. She is whining with fear, just like an animal. A burst of fire knocks her over. The blast sends the baby rolling over and over on the ground. I rush forward. I pick up the bundle of swaddling clothes and run with it to the shelter of a cottage. At least one human being will be saved.

The SS are now quite out of hand.

All the accumulated fury of the last few days spent in the occupied villages, under ceaseless attack by the partisans, has suddenly burst its bonds.

They have gone mad.

Blood flows on every side. Blood lust has taken possession of these men. They are no longer disciplined soldiers, obedient to any command, but brute beasts, that nothing can control.

It is all quite horrible. Blood. Wild shouts. Fierce hand-to-hand fighting.

A suffocating black smoke is spiraling up above the miserable hamlet. Incendiary bullets must have set fire to the thatched roofs.

Corporal Libesis is leaning against a wall, looking stupefied.

"Libesis, you must help me to stop this horror!"

I have to shout in his ear.

The din of rifle fire, the screams of the Russians and the shouts of the SS make an appalling uproar.

"Nothing to be done, Neumann!" he says, staring at me as though he were almost out of his mind.

His head is swaying from side to side as if he were drunk.

"You can't stop men who've suddenly got a thirst for blood," he mutters painfully. "They don't care about their own lives. So what can the deaths of others mean to them? Destruction comes terribly easy and natural to them."

He gestures vaguely toward the market place.

"Look, Ensign! Look at those men who were laughing and joking like kids only yesterday! They've suddenly become wild beasts, simply because they're angry and yearn for revenge."

"But these people didn't kill the men on guard duty, or the private."

"Doesn't matter, Neumann. They could have saved themselves by giving us information. They must pay."

"But what about you, Libesis?"

He starts to tremble. His expression is terrifying, the face of an idiot.

"I'm scared all the time, just scared," he says, his manner suddenly changing. "Scared of dying, of blood, of war—the whole business. But right now I'm in a blue funk. I've got the jitters, Ensign. I really have!"

I suddenly turn away from him. We're all going crazy. The screams echo and re-echo in my head. All this blood—and smoke.

There are women lying on the ground, in the mud.

It's too much.

Grabbing my Mauser, I rush up to Sergeant Diekener, whom I see near at hand, his uniform covered with mud, standing with his feet apart and grasping a long-barreled Erstalt. His face is stained with reddish streaks, the scars left by fingernails.

"Diekener, I order you to call your men to order. This frightful butchery is unworthy of the uniform we wear!"

He looks at me. At first I think he has not understood what I said. Then he gives a nasty grin.

"Are you trying to make a monkey out of me, Neumann? Where do you think you are? A Sunday-school picnic? You're an SS man now, Ensign. It's your pals that have been butchered, as you call it!" He shrugs his shoulders. "Anyhow, Kolden gave the order. Go and see him about it."

"I'll have you sent to Tarnow,[8] Diekener. For refusing to obey an order. You're swine, Diekener!"

He has gone suddenly pale, and he clicks his heels sharply. "I'm sorry, sir. As you say, sir!"

He takes out his whistle and blows a long blast on it.

But the men don't seem to hear.

Kolden comes toward us with long strides.

"What's that about? What's up, Neumann?"

"What's up is just this, Lieutenant. If you don't give the order to stop this massacre immediately, I shall take over command of the company. And, believe me, my report won't make pleasant reading as far as you're concerned!"

He turns to Diekener.

"He's out of his mind! What's biting him?"

The Dutchman suddenly looks at me.

"Report? Massacre? What are you squawking about? You haven't seen anything yet, you sniveling little Ensign. Go on, get the hell out of here or I'll be the one that sends in a report about you for insulting a superior officer and for insubordination. What do you think this is all about? You imagine we're amusing ourselves? You think the soldiers are playing Jack the Ripper just for the hell of it? What about your dead comrades? Ah, I suppose you think there'll be tribunals which will decide by law who's guilty and who isn't. Listen, you silly little so-and-so, if we wait for that sort of thing, and don't teach these damned *moujiks* a few sharp lessons they

[8] One of the punishment camps reserved for the SS, situated east of Krakow, in Poland.

won't forget, the partisans will have knocked off more of our people than the whole of the Timoshenko-Budënny armies put together!"

He leans toward me, his voice suddenly quiet.

"Listen, Neumann. Calm down. You're young still. In a few years you'll understand that all men, whoever they are, are more or less brutes when they have power or—which is the same thing— guns in their hands and a reasonable excuse for using them. They all have the same latent bad streak, well tucked away, even the so-called decent ones, the Good Samaritans—only, in peacetime this bad streak shows itself simply in hating the next-door neighbor or somebody who's more successful. In war a soldier kills, and enjoys killing!"

Meanwhile, the SS have calmed down, and the few Russian survivors have reassembled on one side of the market place. People are crouching beside the bodies of the victims, weeping noisily. One woman is on her knees by a corpse, her arms raised, howling terribly, like a dog.

Before we move off, Kolden says to me, "Actually you're right, the lesson has been pretty severe. There's nothing more to be done here."

He goes toward one of the trucks and starts sounding the horn for minutes at a time.

I sit down on the edge of the pavement, my head in my hands.

Too many contradictory impressions are confused in my mind in an infernal, shouting, mocking cavalcade. Life, death, murder, life, death. . . . Why had we chosen the SS? But it's too late. We are now inexorably dragged into these jaws of steel, which will never let us go. My childhood, all my studies, Wittenberge, Brigitta—these drift across my brain like phantoms from a past that is over and desperately far away. Whom am I to reproach the others? I, too, have become the slave of Death. But perhaps such was my destiny.

Blasts on the whistle, brief orders barked out, men running along the pavement, the sound of boots being sucked up out of the gluey mud in the streets.

And the trucks move off.

A guard of honor stands upright in the leading vehicle, guarding the murdered soldiers laid out on canvas.

Somehow or other, we all pile into the second truck.

Most of the houses of Karasnaya are in flames. The whole village is burning. The frameworks of the houses crash down amidst enormous showers of sparks, leaving only charred and blackened skeletons outlined in a most sinister way against the background of heavy cloud.

The incendiary grenades have seen to it that nothing remains.

September 24. All night I was haunted by the scenes at Karasnaya.

We of the SS may be ruthless. But the partisans also wage an inhuman war and show no mercy. Perhaps we cannot blame them for wishing to defend their own land; but all the same, it's clearly our duty to destroy them.

Where does true justice lie? If such a thing even exists.

The surprising fact is that our High Command pretends to know nothing about these SS reprisal actions. It shuts its eyes to them because it, too, knows that only mass executions will force the terrorists into submission. When the wives and children of those bandits are killed, because their menfolk are guilty of the cowardly murder of some German soldier, perhaps they will stop and think.

Unless, of course, repressive measures only increase the number of partisans, and their thirst for vengeance.

Then we shall have a vicious circle of death, ad infinitum.

It is quite incomprehensible, all the same.

A few months ago, when we entered the Ukrainian villages, we were hailed as liberators. Triumphal arches were put up in practically all the villages we passed through. Whenever we stopped, a delegation of local women, led by the Starosta, would come up bearing flowers and the traditional offering of bread and salt. It is impossible to believe that all these people were traitors to their country or even potential collaborators. The enthusiasm was general, and the obstructions caused by crowds of people pressing toward our tanks showed that it must have been genuine.

The situation is now quite different. The people have suddenly withdrawn within their shells. The liberated populations now look coldly on us.

There are, in my opinion, several reasons for this.

To start with, one fact is quite certain. General Thomas's units have slipped up in organizing their system for getting industry and trade going again in the occupied territories.

In 1936 Lieutenant General Thomas was put in charge of the economic section of the General Staff. Since that date his contribution has consisted of publishing four dossiers known as the green, red, yellow and brown dossiers, in which he gives his program for the rational exploitation of the future occupied territories, both in the east and the west.

Russia was to be split up into twenty-five areas, from the Baltic to the Caucasus and the Urals. There is a school at Zehlendorf, in the Berlin suburbs, where future specialists are instructed in the principal branches of industry, trade and crafts.

These groups of General Thomas's, responsible for exploiting the occupied territories, have found themselves faced with almost insoluble problems.

Most of the factories and power stations were destroyed by the Reds as they retreated. And the few factories which remained intact were dismantled and the plant sent off to Germany.

The population was thus reduced to unemployment and beggary. The Russians in the occupied territories lost no time in blaming the Wehrmacht for this state of affairs. Clandestine broadcasts and tracts printed in Moscow served to aggravate the situation, of course.

At the same time, during the first weeks of the occupation, our German propaganda repeated over and over again that the collective-farm system was to be done away with. Lieutenant General Thomas, however, was satisfied with renaming them "Communal Farms," which did not altogether suit the peasants.

And the result?

The people felt terribly deceived; they listened more carefully

to Moscow Radio and fell headlong into the trap set by the Kremlin
—busy playing its own little game.

Last July Stalin addressed an appeal to the Russian people in very
clear terms:

> With the coming of war to our country, a pitiless fight to the death
> against our most mortal enemies, the Germans, has begun. It has be-
> come for us a matter of life and death to fight the invader with all our
> might.
>
> All the States of the Soviet Union must unite to repulse the Nazi
> hordes. Our policy of destruction must be carried out according to the
> prearranged plan, which was made known in advance. Nothing must
> fall into enemy hands. In all occupied territory, groups of partisans
> must be formed immediately. The Russian people must rise up in a
> body to hound the German invader back across the frontiers of the
> Soviet Union, and to destroy him forever.

In this proclamation there was no suggestion of pity. We are
the enemy. We must be beaten.

What is one to make of all this?

Such frightful scenes as the reprisal at Karasnaya are undoubtedly
not humane.

But the question is, Can they be avoided?

It is war itself which is appallingly inhumane. And this war can
presumably only be ended by the annihilation of one or other of the
combatants.

Woe to the conquered!

10. The Partisans of Odessa

January 4, 1942. Since mid-December operations have been more or less at a standstill on all fronts.

The icy winds from the distant Urals sweep over the plains, from the Don to the Moskva. The intense cold is in control of the situation. There is nothing men can do but submit.

The Reds themselves admit it; we are going through the hardest and bitterest winter Russia has known in forty years.

A black, sinister winter, with sharp talons, that seems to reflect this colossal and pitiless struggle between giants. Nature now is Russia's most effective ally.

In our sector, somewhere along Kalmius between Stalino and the sea, the cold, though intense, is bearable.

But on the central front and outside Moscow, it seems there is terrible suffering among our troops.

Men coming back from Smolensk or Briansk tell us that the German divisions, in their zigzag entrenchments, lie buried in the snow and the frozen ground.

Thousands have died from the cold in a single fortnight. The hospitals are filled with wounded suffering from frostbite, and the ambulance trains moving westward are endless and full.

Everything is covered by a thick layer of ice. The tanks and trucks are frozen to the ground and are therefore no longer of any help to us.

We learned that on December 5, after battles of an intensity beyond belief, the survivors of one company of the 258th Infantry Division which reached the outskirts of Moscow were simply massacred; they had no means of defending themselves at all, for their weapons were frozen and useless. Workmen from a local factory simply slaughtered them with picks and shovels.

In the forests of Leningrad or Kaluga, Guderian's armored divisions and the troops of Hoth and Hoepner are holding their ground against the Russian counterattacks. Our men up there live as the Emperor's veterans must have lived during the Napoleonic campaign.

Their rations do not arrive regularly. The men scour the country-side for dead horses, killed by the cold or by exhaustion, in order to have a bit of fresh meat to eat.

We are fortunate enough to be rather better off. In our sector our sufferings are more bearable.

January 19. I have been promoted.
Second Lieutenant.
Yesterday afternoon, presumably because there are few entertainments hereabouts, they handed out an impressive number of Iron Crosses.

I myself collected a *Korps-Tagesbefehl* [1]—hot stuff—as well as the Iron Cross, First Class.

". . . Distinguished himself during the action at the Skosyrskaja bridge on the river Krinka, by wiping out a Red artillery battery forming part of an assault-gun regiment. Eight 122 mm guns, four 150 mm, and a 400 mm rocket-launching mortar were destroyed within a few minutes by means of explosive charges. . . ." the citation read.

January 21. On the strength of orders from on high, we are billeted in a small village near Rjazenoie on the banks of the Kalmius.

It's a miserable hole, as they all are in the Donets. One main

[1] Mentioned in dispatches at Corps level.

street, flanked by low single-story houses. In the center a church
built of rough boards and planks, surmounted by the eternal onion-
dome, covered with multicolored porcelain mosaics. The town
hall is the only stone building and adds a vaguely modern note to
all these anachronisms.

The streets are not paved. In summer one walks almost knee-deep
in a thick, viscous mud, the terrible Russian *rasputitza*. The old
people tell about a Cossack messenger of Catherine the Great's time,
sent with an important order to Tsaritsyn, who got stuck in the mud
on his way through a Don village and never got out again. Legend
has it that even today, whenever a young Cossack passes through
the district, he never fails to say a prayer for that unhappy fellow
Gesporovich, buried forever under the main street.

In winter all this mud freezes, so that it is like walking on a
rough sea that has suddenly frozen solid.

The inhabitants are as wretched as their surroundings. All the
men young enough to fight have gone away, or were moved out
by force before our arrival. Only old people, women and children
remain.

All these people, dressed in tattered bits of sacking, pass their
time squabbling over scraps of food around our field kitchens, which
seem to be everywhere.

January 22. Snow has been falling heavily all night. This morning
a pale sun makes the roofs glisten, giving an almost cheerful and
friendly air to the little town.

The women are gathered around the communal well at the far
end of the village, talking volubly and gesticulating. At this moment
they look like the eternal mother-figures to be seen in every country
throughout the world.

Karl is with me, and we stroll quietly down the only street the
place possesses. Our boots crunch on the immaculate white carpet.
We enjoy the spectacle of all these Russians living their daily lives.
We pass by the blacksmith's forge. The man is hammering with all

his might at a red-hot horseshoe. He gives us a friendly smile and carries on with his work.

Karl suddenly turns to me, without stopping. "It's incredible luck that we three have managed to stick together all these years," he remarks.

I smile at him. "Not such luck as the fact that we've managed to stay alive till now. Let's hope we shall see the end of this bloody war without—well, any hitches."

We pass a group of Finns who have recently joined the regiment. Eyes left and arms raised, they salute us very stiffly. They have extraordinarily light, almost transparent eyes and blond hair with a silver gleam in it. The Viking Division had heavy casualties last year, and new drafts of recruits arrived at the end of December.

"It's amazing," says Karl dreamily. "Who would ever have thought that we should have such a lot of trouble with these damned Russkies? If only the bastards wouldn't resist the way they do!"

"Listen, Karl, I couldn't care less about the war. Let's go and see Niastia; that'll give us something else to think about."

Niastia is the manageress of the local *Soldatenheim*. It is an old inn converted into a soldiers' club. A few minutes later we walk in, to be greeted by shouts and wisecracks from the other officers already installed behind their pints of beer or little glasses of vodka.

We go over to the wooden bar.

"Let's have something to drink, sweetheart," says Karl.

Niastia wears her blond pigtails turban-style, above a small, triangular, freckled face. She has a nice, well-filled bodice and is altogether quite a dish. Besides, she is not difficult about letting one enjoy her charms, if approached in the proper way. Preferably with the added attraction of five roubles.

She gives us her most gracious smile. "Vodka, raki, Vinodgradnoie?"

"I go for that light Crimean wine. What do you think, Peter?" asks Karl.

"Yes, okay. Let's try the Vinodgradnoie."

He turns to me. "I could do with some fried fish and a little of that Biryuchia caviar. I tried it the day before yesterday and it's terrific! All right with you?"

Without waiting for my reply, he leans toward the waitress.

"Listen, sweetheart, can you fix us some fried fish with caviar?"

She disappears into the kitchen and half an hour later we are seated in great style in front of an enormous dish of Don pike and Caspian caviar, which would cost at least one hundred marks in Berlin.

Russia has its points.

An *arraba* stops in front of the inn. Franz, cheerful and jaunty, steps out of this magnificent vehicle, hands some change to the driver, who is dressed in greasy old rags, and makes an impressive entry into the *Soldatenheim*.

He comes straight across to us.

"I knew I'd find you with the enchanting Niastia," he says, sitting down without ceremony at our table. "Stuffing yourselves, I see. You might have invited me along too, you old gluttons." He turns to the waitress. "Niastia, love of my life, a plate for me!"

The young woman immediately brings a pewter dish onto which Franz piles a considerable portion of our pike. Scowling, we watch him gobble up the crisp golden fish. He is fantastically greedy. He may be our friend, indeed a brother to us, but at this moment he has a dangerously insatiable appetite.

Half choking over a fishbone, he suddenly shouts, "Oh, I forgot! I accepted an invitation for you. Someone I've just got to know. He's an ex-NCO of the Czarist Army, who was at Odessa last month. He speaks perfect German and he told me all about the siege of the town. No joke, I can tell you. We're going to go see him right away."

Vasiliev Ukarin is a strange character. He is all bones and whiskers and looks as though he only shaves every three or four months.

He is almost six feet tall, and can't weigh much more than a hundred pounds.

When we entered his house, he bowed almost down to the ground. I was afraid that he might break in two.

"Gentlemen, you do me a great honor by coming into my humble home. The lieutenant here"—he pointed to Franz—"has already listened to my tale with great understanding and kindness. I feel quite embarrased that he should have mentioned me to you, so unimportant a person as myself."

He speaks a rather stilted, old-fashioned German, which is somewhat irritating. Obviously the kind of language they must have talked at the court of Nicholas II in 1914.

Drinking tea and little goblets of vodka, we listened while he told us of the events at Odessa.

". . . early in July, the German-Rumanian troops, under the supreme command of the Rumanian Generalissimo Antonescu, were closing in on Odessa.

"The huge Black Sea port now embarked upon a struggle which was to last for months. Day after day, Stukas bombarded the town, first destroying the port and the defense installations, then, as resistance grew stronger, the town itself. During this time the railway 600's were firing night and day, reducing the city to ruins with ton after ton of steel. And the ruins themselves were wiped out next day by further tons of high explosive.

"On the Russian side, the enormous guns of the fortress, with barrels twenty feet long, fired ceaselessly at the enemy troops. The warships anchored offshore fired salvo after salvo over the rooftops of Odessa, so that all the windows in the town shook.

"The old cruisers, *Priiezjii* and *Krasnii Aktiabar,* gallant survivors of the Battle of Port Arthur, though ceaselessly bombed and machine-gunned by the Luftwaffe, continued valiantly to bombard Ovidiopol and Akkerman, where Antonescu's troops were dug in, until these poor, battered ships, rusty and exhausted, had at last to give up the struggle.

"The *Priiezjii* was sunk, but the *Krasnii Aktiabar* succeeded in reaching Yevpatoriya, and from there went on to Novorossisk in the Kuban. Thence she returned a little later to assist in the defense of Sebastopol."

Old Vasiliev has a remarkable talent for telling a story and we were rather moved as we listened to this amazing epic. Three SS hanging on the words of a Russian as he recounted the misfortunes of his fatherland. Surely a unique scene.

The old man went on:

"When, after two and a half months of siege, the first Rumanian troops entered Odessa, they did not find a single Red soldier. Neither dead nor alive.

"Our troops had all gone. Also all the old, rusty carcasses of the trucks and cars burned out during the bombardment. Also all the signposts and the other junk that an Army usually leaves behind as worthless when retreating from a battlefield.

"Nothing but the tall, shattered walls of the ruined buildings and the electric cables dangling across the streets showed that Odessa had been the scene of a battle.

"Silence hung over the town. The howling of the wind in the ruins and in the toppling chimneys seemed a sinister omen to the German and Rumanian troops as they goose-stepped through the deserted streets with bugles and fifes playing.

"All the shutters were down, and the inhabitants were shut up in their houses, for they preferred not to see their poor city crushed beneath the boots of the enemy."

Vasiliev glanced at us quickly, then, as we remained impassive, continued:

"It was only after some days that General Antonescu's troops began to realize Odessa was not dead.

"At night, strange noises were heard at ground level. Patrols, going about the town, thought they heard sounds, shouts, military commands. They found nothing.

"Then the assassinations began.

"At first it was isolated soldiers whom the bandits struck down."

It suddenly seemed to us that the old man didn't dare to look at us, and that his voice shook. Especially as he said the word "bandit." But he went on:

"Then the Wehrmacht trucks were attacked at night, shot up by machine guns, and the soldiers in them disappeared completely. None of them were ever seen again.

"And one day, during a staff conference at which about a hundred officers were assembled, the building which served as GHQ for the German-Rumanian forces was blown up. Some thirty survivors were dug out of the ruins. The others were buried beneath tons of stone and gravel.

"Next day the reprisals began.

"Eighteen thousand Jews were shot in two days.

"The Germans had very properly already taken a census during the previous weeks of all Jews or people with Jewish blood in the town."

The atmosphere in the little room where we sat became suddenly tense, as though charged with electricity. We felt that the Russian had difficulty in finding words which would be acceptable to us. "Very properly" sounded wrong; it didn't ring true. We waited now to see how far his servility would go. If it was genuine. One couldn't by any means be certain.

"After the GHQ affair, the Jews were all taken into the slaughter-houses and the warehouses down by the docks. An order was issued to exterminate the lot.

"The Rumanian and German soldiers opened the doors of the warehouses as though to let everyone go. The Jews came out, de-lighted by this sudden freedom which they had given up hoping for, and were met by a crossfire of dozens of machine guns. Screaming and fighting like animals to escape death, they were shot down in heaps, cut to pieces by the bullets.

"Some tried to throw themselves into the sea, but were killed by bursts from the Germans' machine pistols, not any pleasanter a death.

"In the slaughterhouses hand grenades were used. Presumably a whim of the officer commanding the extermination detachment. But this made too much noise, and they found it better to finish the job quickly and thoroughly with the good old Skoda machine guns."

Vasiliev suddenly got up and went across to the engraved copper samovar which was standing on a kind of sideboard. He turned on the tiny tap and made a new pot of the green, scented, peppermint tea which the Russians drink. Ceremoniously, with affected gestures and interminable remarks of the "Oh, pardon me," "Please excuse me" and "Won't you allow me?" variety, he poured us each half a cup of the steaming, amber-colored liquid.

He then sat down again, breathing more easily, and leaned toward us with a conspiratorial expression, as though to conceal the fact that he had a delayed-action bomb hidden in the pocket of his overcoat.

"But it is very difficult to kill such a large number of people at one blow. There were 128,000 registered Jews in Odessa. A pronouncement by the High Command said that all the Jews in the town were to be expelled, and marched 'under escort' of the Rumanians to Poland, where camps were ready for them. The order specified that they should march 'under escort,' but it didn't state what they were to eat.

"It was already beginning to be cold and there was snow on the roads of Bessarabia and Moldavia leading to the Carpathians. The column moved on, mile upon mile of it. For mile after mile one could hear the cries for mercy and the screams of those hungry, cold creatures. Sometimes there was the sharp crack of a rifle among the mountains through which the road wound. There were thousands of such sharp cracks. When they finally arrived in Bukovina it was obvious that the camps would not be needed."

Vasiliev gave us a sidelong glance before continuing.

"At Odessa, the Germans had suddenly discovered why it had been impossible hitherto to arrest the terrorists guilty of the assassinations.

"The whole subterannean system under the town had been put to use.

"I must tell you that since Roman times immense catacombs stretch beneath the city, old subterranean passages built for purposes of defense or something of that sort, nobody knows exactly. Real streets, squares, enormous halls exist, some of them thirty or even fifty feet below ground level.

"And it was here that the partisans were installed; their ammunition and guns were all stored underground. In addition there was a complete organization which was set up before Antonescu's divisions ever entered the city. Baker's shops which produced fresh bread daily, butchers, food shops of all kinds, printing presses, a miniature prison and armorers' workshops. A radio station, with both reception and transmission, kept them in constant touch with the garrison at Sebastopol, which gave them their information, passed on orders from Moscow and news from the front. Wireless aerials were skillfully hidden in apparently harmless lead pipes.

"To begin with, the Germans tried to send armed patrols down into the underground. But it proved impossible to advance along narrow passages six feet wide, defended at each end by men with machine guns entrenched in steel and concrete blockhouses.

"The High Command was informed. Specialist engineers were sent from Bucharest and they tried every trick to get the better of the rebels.

"During this time the assassinations and the blowing up of ammunition depots and supply stores continued. The officers of Antonescu's staff tore their hair in despair, enraged at their inability to achieve anything.

"They tried everything. Charges of dynamite blocked the subterranean exits wherever they were found. They flooded the galleries. But many of them sloped down to the sea, so the partisans merely got their feet wet. They tried to establish a ruthless blockade. Guards were posted at all the entrances and in front of all the known exits from the catacombs. But all the same Moscow Radio continued to rejoice publicly every evening over the exploits of the heroic partisans of Odessa.

"In desperation they decided to use poison gas.

"Every kind of shell, grenade and cylinder containing poison gas was sent down into the underground passages. But lacking pressure the gas did not reach very far. This final effort was destined to be as unsuccessful as all the others.

"Repressive measures against the civilian population became more and more brutal. They hoped that by such means the partisans would be persuaded to abandon the struggle. But with no such result."

Vasiliev Ukarin got up again and gave us each a large glass of vodka. Then he smiled, somewhat vaguely. "It was at this point that I asked the commandant for a permit to come back to this little village where I was born," he concluded.

He gazed at us in a friendly way, mechanically rubbing the long fingers of his skeletonlike hands together.

I suddenly wondered why he should have told us this story. I felt uneasy without knowing the reason for this.

Karl was the first to speak.

"And when did they finally eliminate the partisans?" he asked.

"When?" murmured the old man in a changed voice. "At this very moment the struggle is still going on." [2]

We left shortly after this, and the Russian thanked us a thousand times for the honor we had done him and invited us to visit him again.

We did not discuss it, or make any decision, but I think it's unlikely we shall go to see him again. He was disquieting in an indefinable sort of way, that fellow, and I can't help feeling that in spite of his air of humility and his deferential attitude, he only told us what he wanted us to hear, what he wanted to tell us.

And what he told us has given us a great deal to think about.

As we walked silently through the dusk toward the camp, Franz said, "You know it's just subversive propaganda put out by the partisans, all that stuff the old man told us."

Neither Karl nor I replied.

[2] It was not until the end of 1943 that the Germans finally neutralized "the underground partisans of Odessa."

February 24. The mail, presumably held up somewhere or other as so often happens, has all arrived at once, in an enormous pile. Letters from everywhere, some of them posted last November.

The Field Post Office overdoes it sometimes.

Klauss wrote on behalf of the family. A short letter, straight to the point and without any subtleties.

Everybody is well, except that Mutti still has her rheumatism and Father his angina. As for Lena, they have had no word from her for several months.

He tells me that they have moved. I think I know why. Since Father was in prison people have been avoiding him, for reasons of caution or for fear of the Gestapo. He has had to apply to the railway administration to be sent back to Hamburg.

Another piece of news, slightly surprising.

Liselotte writes that our child is just a year old. She has called him Peter. The Lebensborn administration has authorized her to keep him for a little longer. According to her letter, he is blond, as plump as he should be and looks like me.

It's funny, but I don't feel at all like a father.

March 6. The winter is ending. One sees a thousand signs that nature is being transformed, is changing its skin.

"How clear flows the river when the snow is gone."

This line of verse, the rhythm and evocative power of which reveal the hand of a master, is by me.

The snows have not exactly gone, but it is thawing—and high time too.

We hope that operations will be resumed before long.

April 4. General Gille, who is on the staff of the SSFHA,[3] came to visit us this morning. It is the first chance I've had of seeing him at such close quarters.

He breakfasted in our mess. He struck me as being extraordinarily

[3] SS High Command.

simple and friendly. They say that on duty he's a hard man. But he did not strike me as at all severe.

Quite tall, carrying his fifty-odd years lightly, slightly balding, he has the red face and nose of a *bon vivant*. His tortoise-shell glasses increase the impression of infectious good nature he seems to exude.

Around his neck he wears the Knight's Cross of the Iron Cross with Swords and Diamonds. The star of the Military Merit Decoration gleams on the right breast of his tunic.

I had once before seen General Gille, at an investiture ceremony somewhere on the plains of Pricher-Nomorsk. He was accompanied on that occasion by Field Marshal von Kleist and the commander of our First Division, Sepp Dietrich.

At that time we were quite content to gaze at all these big wheels from afar.

I do remember, though, that the Field Marshal had a rather haughty manner. His thin lips never moved, except when this was strictly necessary. Fat old Dietrich, on the other hand, waved his arms about and talked a lot. He looked like a shopkeeper driving a bargain with a customer. Which isn't surprising because, according to what they say, he was a butcher's boy once.

April 29. Fall in! Partisans!

Men climb up quickly into the armored carriers, which immediately set off northward.

Only a few minutes ago some vehicles were attacked when bringing back a fatigue party along the Volnovakha road. Two sections of No. 1 Company were immediately detailed to try and catch the terrorists.

On this occasion the peasants of the district told us that we might surprise them in the Grunau plains, where it seems they are hiding. It is rare for the Russians to denounce their own partisans. But I have the feeling that they are not highly thought of in this district. They loot the farms, fleece the villagers and are dangerously quick on the draw.

Also the peasants are beginning to get tired of being paid with the partisans' famous requisitioning slips, the so-called ISIKBK.[4] The pieces of paper accumulate, but the money to redeem them never arrives. And for a good reason. The villagers know that the mere possession of ISIKBK coupons is a capital offense, punishable by immediate execution.

This makes them think twice.

These sinister red and white coupons are becoming more and more detested by the Russians in the Donets area as the months go by.

Hours pass and the two sections sent after the terrorists still have not come back. Kolden was detailed to command this anti-terrorist detachment. Actually it is almost always he whom they choose to direct this sort of operation since Scholtzberg was killed.

His orders are: for ten drops of German blood, ten dead Russians.

We have never liked each other much, but a sort of status quo has been implicitly agreed upon between us. Since he was promoted to Captain a month ago, he commands the company. He leaves me in peace, and for my part I shut my eyes to his little eccentricities when I am on duty.

"Little eccentricities" is putting it mildly.

Two days ago he half-killed a local girl who resisted his advances. As a result the girl's mother came to regimental HQ and kicked up the most awful fuss. It happened that the colonel was not there, and it was I who received the full fury of her indignation. I tried to make her shut up by threatening that if she went on shouting at me her daughter would be shipped off to a soldiers' brothel within three days.

Not very pretty, but it was the only way to put an end to her fearful screechings.

My threat was actually meaningless because in the first place I have no power to carry it out, and in the second if Russian women

[4] *Isentialmi Ipollmtelmi Komitetpartia Bilet Koupets*—the coupons of the Party Central Executive Committee.

are sent to the brothels, it's because they've volunteered, as profes-
sionals you might say.

Loud blasts on the horns. The crowd of peasants fall back to
clear the way through the main street.

Kolden's men are back in the village at last.

Russians, their hands tied behind their backs, are standing up
in the troop-carrier. They are guarded by SS with their Mausers at
the ready.

I go forward.

The vehicles stop. The prisoners are made to get down with blows
from the men's rifle butts. They are covered with blood. They are
dressed in long uniform greatcoats made of a coarse yellow worsted,
canvas boots, and fur hats with ear flaps and red stars on the front.
They look just like the prisoners of the Regular Army whom we
have captured.

There are three women among them.

I am not greatly surprised by this, for I have known for a long
time that women are fighting in the ranks of the partisans. This is,
however, the first time I have actually seen them.

One of them is young. She jumps down from the carrier, looking
sullen and contemptuous, and gets a brutal push from a private of
No. 1 Company.

The other two are older. You have to be very close to them to
see that they actually are women. Their faces, or rather physi-
ognomies, are bloated and bestial, with snub noses and prominent
cheekbones. They look as though they are direct descendants of
some Outer Mongolian tribe.

Walking along the pavement I meet Kolden, who is returning
from the regimental HQ where he has been to make his report.
I shout out to him as I pass, "Hi, Kold, everything okay?"

"Everything is fine, Neumann," he says happily, "apart from two
wounded. This is the first time I've been able to get my hands on
any of these partisans. Believe me, I'll make them talk."

I follow him into the hut where the interrogation of the prisoners will take place. I am not on duty, but I am curious to see how the captain will do it.

He sits down at a small table on which there is a portable typewriter and some sheets of paper with the regimental letterhead. I know that orders have been issued to the effect that a written report must be sent in, containing all possible information that can be extracted from the partisans before they are shot.

"Let's have the first of these swine in," barks Kolden, getting to his feet. "It doesn't matter which. I couldn't care less," he adds for the benefit of one of the SS guards who seems to be hesitating.

A man is pushed in front of him. They have stripped him of his greatcoat and vest. He is incredibly thin and is visibly trembling, from either cold or fear. His face, with its deeply sunken eyes, is half hidden by a straggling gray beard. His cheeks are filthy and bloodstained. They have obviously tried to make him talk already during the journey in the carrier.

The interrogation begins. Within a few minutes Kolden is scarlet with rage and begins shouting in German. This is characteristic. When he loses his self-control he always forgets his Russian.

"You filthy bastard, you'll talk or you'll die!"

He siezes the first object at hand. It is the wooden lid of the typewriter. Mad with rage he suddenly begins to beat the partisan violently with it, while the man tries to shield his head by bending double. He can't move his hands, which are tied by a cord, the end of which is firmly held by a private.

The prisoner rolls over onto the ground. Kolden kicks him. His jaw now broken, the man drags himself along the floor, howling like a dog. "Swine! Let's have another!" shouts the Dutchman, straightening up.

He takes a handkerchief from his pocket and wipes away the sweat and blood on his face.

"These so-and-so's never talk! Another two years in this job, and I'll be completely crazy." He turns toward me.

"Reports! What do they think they're going to get in their reports, these headquarter bastards? Let them come here and try to make these damned *moujiks* talk when they don't want to!"

He suddenly goes up to one of the prisoners, his face distorted with fury, and begins shaking him violently while shouting, "Well, you swine, are you terrorists or aren't you? Not much doubt about it. Caught with your guns in your hand. You'll be shot. That's the usage of war!"

Obviously the man doesn't understand any of this and keeps his terrified eyes fixed on Kolden.

His interrogation, punctuated by blows and kicks, goes on for a quarter of an hour—after which the Russian is seized by two SS and thrown without further ado to the far end of the room, where he lands among the other partisans, guarded by panzer soldiers of No. 1 Company.

Now it's the turn of one of the women to be interrogated, the youngest one, the one I noticed earlier.

Kolden lifts his head and stares at her for a moment. He says in Russian, "What is your name?"

Looking more and more contemptuous and fierce, she eyes the Dutchman up and down, a disdainful smile playing about her lips.

The captain walks up to her.

"Do you despise us too? Well, well, my pretty *moujika,* you're only human, you know. If you don't talk, just wait and see what's coming to you! Your pretty body will go green and rotten when you're buried under the earth; next it will turn brown, and finally black, until it has all been eaten up by millions of tiny maggots!"

He is speaking slowly, in German, and an unpleasant smile twists his face. The Russian woman looks at him in silence.

He takes a step nearer to her, and suddenly rips off her coarse canvas shirt.

Losing her balance, the woman falls to the ground. Her hands are tied in front, and she is having trouble getting up again. Half naked, she tries to support herself on one elbow, her eyes flashing at Kolden, who walks over to her.

"You look more comfortable there, *Barichnia,*" he snarls.

He turns to two SS who are guarding the prisoner.

"She's still two warm, poor girl! Go on, strip off the rest of her clothes."

The soldiers come forward, but before they can lay a finger on her the Russian woman begins to scream and roll about on the ground, kicking out in all directions.

Two men finally seize her, but only after a struggle, and their faces are marked with deep scratches and bites.

Kolden leans over the partisan woman once more. "So you still won't talk?"

The woman gets up. Suddenly, before Kolden has time to get out of the way, she spits full in his face. The Dutchman lets out a terrible roar of fury. Drunk with rage he rushes at her. Throwing himself on her defenseless body he begins pummeling the prisoner's face and body with his fists. The Russian girl, who has been silent up to now, screams like an animal. It must have been a particularly violent blow. A trickle of bloodstained saliva reddens the corner of her mouth. I watch, horrified. It is impossible for me to intervene. Impossible to intervene. Impossible.

Kolden is in command. The orders are specific. Make the prisoners talk by all and every means.

After a final kick directed at the woman's prostrate body the Dutchman straightens up. He seems calmer.

Suddenly he grabs a bucket of water held by a private who was apparently intending to wash away the blood spattered all over the floor, and throws the cold water brutally over the Russian girl, who has fainted.

Fainted? I am not so sure. I notice there is a sort of croaking sound coming from her split lips. Her body is a mass of bleeding cuts and is shaken by long, regular shudders. Too regular. Her fingers claw the ground.

She is dying.

The captain does not seem unduly concerned. He sits down at his desk and raises his head.

"Rhedi! Come here," he orders.

The warrant officer comes forward and springs to attention, his right arm shooting out like an uncoiled spring.

"Sir!"

"Rhedi! Get rid of this lot for me. In the market place. All ten of them. As at Lublyasya! That'll teach them."

Is this what the SS has made me? A coward? Afraid to shout aloud my disgust and horror?

And yet there was nothing I could do. Kolden was fully protected by his orders. My intervention would obviously have been interpreted as insubordination. A report by the Dutchman would send me to prison or to Tarnow. And Tarnow means death, in the long run or the short.

So I too am clinging to life. We have only one life, and we hang on to it.

If Kolden was cruel, didn't he have good reason to be? Nobody asked these women to become soldiers. Nobody asked them to stab us in the back. They put themselves on the same footing as the men. They must suffer the same consequences.

It can't be denied that it's essential we make them talk.

So what am I beefing about? Basically, why should the death or suffering of an enemy worry me, even if it is a woman, when that death or suffering, even of a woman, means the protection of my fellow Germans?

Are we really monsters to try to exterminate those who, after all, only wish for our own destruction?

No one can pretend any longer that they are merely defending a fatherland which has been treacherously attacked. Perhaps a few ignorant bourgeois, decadent people may still persist in closing their ears and eyes.

Who can still maintain that it wasn't absolutely essential for us to destroy the Soviet Union before it was strong enough to set about annihilating us?

We simply forestalled the Russian plan.

Russia constituted a terrible danger for us and for the whole of Europe. It was our plain duty to make it harmless.

To achieve this end, all and every means have to be employed.

These thoughts were all mixed up in my head. But it was too complex a problem for me to attempt to solve on my own.

Since yesterday evening they have been swinging there gently, hanging by their feet from the low branches of the trees around the little market place.

Some of them took hours to die, screaming endlessly the whole night through, filling the whole village with their sobs and prayers for mercy.

When dawn came, the population of the little town came out to watch this hideous spectacle at closer quarters. Without apparent emotion, it seems.

They're a queer lot, these people.

I've seen peasants laughing as they watched the final, appalling convulsions of the dying. Ridiculing the final death rattles. By their faces I could see that they were making cruel comments on the way each one died.

Maybe the partisans did make life difficult for them. All the same, they were of the same blood.

The Russian soul is certainly a mystery.

I find myself thinking of something I read one day at Wittenberge, written by one of their compatriots—I don't remember his name:

"The Russian is like the steppe—savage, violent, cruel, mysterious. He recognizes neither God nor the devil. For him neither life nor death has any meaning."

Nitchevo!

They have only one master— Destiny.

11. The Advance Southward

July 24. The cannons are roaring outside Rostov.

From our forward positions we can see the Stukas spitting death from five hundred feet at the Reds and can hear the terrifying din of the screamers attached to their wings.

The heavy artillery has been hammering away at the railway and the Taganrog-Rostov road for four hours. But the Russians seem to be holding on desperately, and our armored attacks have been repulsed almost everywhere.

We are entrenched in a defensive position on a little hill which dominates the extreme southermost point of the Gulf of Taganrog. From here we can see the white line of the surf breaking on the shore and the extraordinarily blue water of the bay.

The Bolsheviks are facing us three hundred yards away. They pepper us ceaselessly with shells and mortar bombs.

If this goes on, the sector will become untenable.

Everybody wonders what the High Command is waiting for and why it doesn't commit the main strength of the armies toward the Novocherkassk-Rostov pocket.

Three times this morning numerous Mark and Panther squadrons have tried to force a way through the Red lines.

But the redoubtable 76.2's have driven them back with heavy losses. The armor of our tanks has been thickened and is of better quality. But what they have gained in security, they have lost in performance. The technical boys maintain that the engines now react badly, since they are not built to pull such a weight of steel and concrete.

The first Tigers, which are actually only a variant—larger and with thicker armor—of the Panther, have appeared on the southern front. Their long-barreled guns make them easily identifiable from a distance.

As the sun climbs toward the zenith, the heat becomes more and more unbearable.

The dust kicked up by the bombing of the railway line swirls all around us and makes the atmosphere unbreathable. There is no wind to blow it away.

This is the first time the Russkies have forced us to adopt the tactics of trench warfare. All their reserves must have been sent to Rostov to try to stop our advance. Facing us must be many regiments brought across from the Far East, for most of the prisoners we take are Mongols, Oirats or Kirghiz. Really savage-looking brutes. Despite their appearance they become cringing cowards as soon as they are captured.

The extraordinary thing is that one now sees exactly the same types in German uniforms, thousands of them, all captured last year. They wear on their left sleeve a sort of crest marked "R.O.A."[1] with an *X* above—which means I don't know what, unless it is the cross of Saint Andrew—blue on a white ground. I have a pretty good idea that if any of them should fall into the hands of their old comrades on the other side, they'll have a hard time of it.

The frightful din of the artillery never lets up. It's enough to drive a man mad—this continual bombardment, the barking of the machine guns and automatics—and the whole thing merges into one colossal roar which frays the nerves and destroys the will.

"I'll settle their hash!" Goebbels said.

For the moment they seem to be busy settling *our* hash!

It's strange, all the same: the blue sky, the azure sea, the gentle curling of the waves on the distant beach, the pines swinging softly

[1] *Ruskaja Oswoboditelnaja Armija* (Russian Army of Liberation).

in the breeze. Down there, peace and life. Up here death, and killing steel.

Still, we prefer this to the endless guerilla warfare which we had to fight against the partisans on the Kalius. Week after week we spent, chasing shadows which always eluded us, disappearing without trace.

When the order to attack came, not a single Viking had any regrets, and our gear was packed in double time and with a light heart.

"Hurrah, Stalin! Hurrah, Stalin!"

Waves of Russian soldiers rush upon us, shouting like savages.

Some of them are stripped to the waist and carry no equipment apart from their caps. With fixed bayonets they charge, unheeding, through the machine-gun fire that mows them down by the hundred, leaving great gaps in their assault groups.

"Hurrah, Stalin! Hurrah, Stalin!"

The Reds despise death, according to their propaganda leaflets. They don't even think about it.

But when a bullet hits a man or a shellburst splits open his skull, he rolls on the ground crying like a baby.

"Hurrah, Stalin! Hurrah, Stalin!"

The third wave of assault troops is upon us at full gallop.

The Bolsheviks all have twisted mouths; is it hate or fear? Who knows? And still the corpses pile up. A regular carnage, dead and wounded all in one great heap.

When the bulk of the assault force is decimated, the survivors hesitate and stop; then suddenly overwhelmed with fear, they turn back, only to meet the next assault group which is advancing with shouts of "Hurrah, Stalin!"

Rat-tat-tat-tat, answer the machine guns.

And so on, for hour after hour, until they have learned their lesson.

And God knows their heads are thick. But they have astonishingly large reserves of manpower. Still, this time it will take them several hours to bring up their reinforcements.

Meanwhile the German tanks attack and rapidly break through the disorganized enemy units.

Thundering at full speed across plowed fields and roads, knocking down any buildings that are in the way, crushing the dead and the wounded in a single bloody mess, they forge straight ahead with sirens screeching horribly. They are preparing the way for the panzer infantry and the SS.

The Vikings run behind the tanks, mopping up with machine pistols, hand grenades, incendiary shells and of course our invaluable SS daggers.

July 26. A new contingent of volunteers just arrived from the training camps in Bohemia and Moravia.

Walking through the little groups of men being issued their equipment, I suddenly caught sight of Michael Stinsmann.

Stinsmann! Incredible.

I went up and tapped him on the shoulder. "Michael, old pal! What the hell are you doing here?"

He turned around quickly. "Peter Neumann! Well, well, well."

He gave a long-drawn-out whistle when he saw the silver square on the lapel of my tunic. He couldn't stop shaking his head.

"Second Lieutenant! What do you know? I'd heard from Klauss that you were an officer and in the Viking, but all the same I never thought I'd run into you here."

I put my hand on his shoulder. "It's really good to see you again, Michael. How is old Wittenberge? And tell me how you got in this outfit! I always thought the SS didn't attract you."

He looked at me, smiling slightly.

"People change, you know. I decided in December. After Papa Roosevelt began to show his teeth. Anyhow, I thought all my pals were at the front."

He offered me a cigarette.

"Besides, I'm not the only Wittenberger here. For weeks the propaganda department of the SSFHA bombarded us with lectures at Schiller. Having thought it over, I decided I'd rather go to Brunswick than fool about with a pick and shovel in the Labor Service."

I felt that he deliberately checked himself from adding, ". . . and be left in peace."

We were outside the supply stores of the 2nd Company, where I knew I should find Franz and Karl.

With his foot on the staircase, he added, "They didn't waste any time at Brunswick. It was an SS armored training school. We never went back to Wittenberge. To Posen-Treskau, and then the Anwärterlager [2] at Neveklov, south of Prague. And here I am."

An idea flashed like lighting through my head. What was it he had told me all those years ago—about his Jewish mother?

A little pale, perhaps, I now turned to him. "Tell me, Michael— it's nothing to do with me—but how did you get out of . . .'"

"Out of—?" he asked, suddenly going rigid.

There was a moment's silence between us; then we made our way up to the guardroom on the first floor.

As we reached the door, Michael said, "I know what you mean. I only ask you never to mention it to a soul."

He pronounced the last words in a tired voice, then shrugged his shoulders. "Anyhow, it doesn't really matter! Suppose I get myself thrown out? Sent to Tarnow? Do you think I care?"

I caught hold of his arm, roughly. "But, good God, man! What made you choose the SS?"

He pursed his lips. "I haven't a clue! A gesture of defiance, perhaps, or for the experience, or maybe to sh— on some of 'em!"

After asking at the guardroom where we could find Franz, we went down to the tank-repair shop on the ground floor. The mechanics were busy working on damaged armored troop-carriers and Marks.

We found Franz after a few moments' search. As soon as he saw Michael, he threw his arms in the air.

"Stinsmann! Good heavens, man! So you've decided to take a holiday on the shores of the Black Sea, eh?"

[2] Training camp for SS cadets.

While they slapped each other on the back with the greatest enthusiasm, I looked around to see if Karl was about.

"You won't find him here," Franz said, seeing me gazing around the shed. "He's gone off on a mission with one of the boys from the 3rd. They're at Krivoi Rog. I don't think they'll be back before evening."

"Anyhow, it's wonderful to see you two again," said Michael happily.

He took my arm.

"Come on. There must be a bar of some sort in this one-horse dump. Come and have a drink to celebrate the reunion of the four of us, or rather the three of us—the ancient order of the Knights of Wittenberge!" He added, laughing, "But who am I to give the orders? Me, a poor little private with a couple of lieutenants!"

July 28. House by house, Rostov has been seized from the Reds. All over the town the battle rages.

For two days we have been attacking a sort of gigantic factory which, they say, once made jam. A whole Soviet company, which has the railway-station area and part of the marshaling yards under fire, is entrenched inside it.

The position is terribly dangerous for us. All around Daroga Square, which we hold, are buildings that haven't yet been cleared. From the windows come repeated bursts of fire from the Red machine guns and the sharp crack of their new Dektyarov rifles, which have very great powers of penetration.

"If this goes on, we'll all have had it, to the last man!" Libesis shouts in my ear.

But there's nothing to be done except hang on. At least until the bulk of the regiment has encircled the factory and the station.

There are not many of us here to occupy all the buildings on Daroga Square. Two platoons holding an entire quarter, it's not enough. Libesis is right. We're in a spot.

The orders are explicit. Hold on—and if possible force them out.

Force them out. Easily said. We haven't a single tank, not even one with a miserable 37. If we don't get reinforcements soon, it's going to be us who'll be forced out by them.

I have made my platoon dig a trench of sorts with their spades. A narrow communicating trench more or less links it with the positions on Torgulitsa Street, held by von Reckner's platoon, that is, Karl's platoon. A trench which, incidentally, has already cost us the lives of three men. It's not deep enough, so we have to crawl along on our bellies to get across the square.

The three men, who were on a fatigue detail, had the bad luck to stand up too soon. One of those damned snipers—they're concealed on nearly all the rooftops—didn't give them a chance.

The battle is still raging. Rostov is disappearing beneath an apocalyptic bombardment which will certainly not leave one single stone standing on another. The German artillery, the Stuka dive bombers and the heavy guns of the Russians are reducing the town to smoldering ruins.

I don't hear Karl come up to me. I jump when he shouts in my ear.

"The station's been captured! I've just had a message to say that half of Ulkijaj's company have by-passed the square by the level crossing and are moving up to reinforce us."

Soon about a hundred men arrive, in single file, running in fits and starts. They creep along beside the walls, making the most of the smallest cover, a tree or a building. The Dektyarov rifles are doing quite a bit of damage, though, and several SS are hit.

The Finnish lieutenant, Ulkijaj, tumbles breathless into the hole in which we are crouching.

He has some difficulty in getting his breath as he gasps, "We are to attack immediately! The whole regiment is advancing on the factory and then the pipeline pumps. I'm in command."

After a moment, seeing our stupefied faces, he adds with a smile, "Don't worry! The tanks will attack from the south."

Fifteen minutes later we begin to advance on the factory. The

Reds realize what we are up to and greet us with long bursts of fire from their heavy MG's.

Somehow or other we manage to move forward, yard by yard, but at the cost of heavy losses. I expect every second to be hit by a small piece of steel which will finally solve for me the tactical problems of an advance in street-fighting.

All around me bullets are splattering against the walls, kicking lumps of brick and plaster into the air. I am suddenly reminded of the cowboy movies of my childhood. The way the bullets used to whistle past, with a wonderful whining noise. But now I don't hear the bullets whistling. Has Russian steel the peculiar quality of killing in silence?

Enormous wooden sliding doors, and then suddenly we are inside the factory. I see several huge vats, and quantities of rusty metal boxes.

The first shed is not defended now. That's good. It means the Russians are withdrawing.

We advance cautiously. There was a huge glass roof above the shed, but not a single pane is now intact. We walk on a sort of bed of broken glass.

Suddenly there is a terrific explosion. The wooden doors facing us are wrenched from their hinges. Another thunderous roar, then a third.

The Russians must have a big gun trained on the shed.

The men lie flat on the ground. The Russian fire is intensified. Stones and chunks of concrete and metal rain down on us from all sides.

We must either retreat and go back, or else press on. If we stay where we are we run the risk of being buried under the ruins of the shed, which is obviously about to collapse on top of us.

I am lying flat on my stomach in the broken glass, and tiny splinters, which the explosions send flying all over the place, sting my face. I run my hand across my cheek. It is wet with blood.

Ulkijaj starts to shout, his arm raised.

"Vikings! Forward!"

A sudden wild stampede takes us to within a hundred yards of the Soviets. The swine are still firing, and the crossfire of their machine guns causes heavy casualties among our men.

Fifty yards, thirty, twenty, ten.

The Reds are stripped to the waist and yelling like pigs.

Grenades on the first battery. Blows with rifle butts, bursts of fire, an appalling din, dull explosions. Dust, heat. A sudden rush. Grenades. Bodies wet with blood. Faces torn off, bellies gaping open. Another burst. Grenades . . .

Corpse upon corpse, our machine guns and daggers mop up the area and sweep it clear.

Suddenly I see a Russian whom we have left for dead start shooting again. A burst of fire knocks him down with a last distorted grin of agony upon his face.

A private shouts to me as he passes, "Kill the whole lot. No prisoners!"

He is foaming at the mouth with frenzy, like a madman. A grenade exploding a yard away stops him in his tracks and he falls.

He drags himself along the ground gasping, "The bastards! They've got me. . . ."

He tries to prop himself up on one elbow, but a final rush of blood into his mouth stifles his last shouts.

I am gripped suddenly by a terrible panic that makes my stomach heave. This time I'm going to stay where I am. There's no chance of getting out.

An inferno of dust, burning steel, stones flying in every direction —it's an impenetrable barrier.

I see a green shirt in front of me. I fire first. A yellow face, twisted with fear and hatred, slides slowly down at my feet.

Frantically I kick the twisted face, again and again.

And still there's the rattle of the heavy machine guns in my ears. Is there no way of stopping them?

Suddenly a dull rumble, which makes the ground shake, followed by the sharp, staccato barking of the 75's tells us that the tanks are here. And about time too. Half our assault force is out of action.

The walls crash down in several places as the monsters push through them at thirty miles an hour. They loom up among the clouds of dust on all sides, and the vibration is appalling, like an earthquake.

An hour later the factory is in our hands. There are no Russkies left to tell the tale of how the jam factory was lost.

August 1. Rostov has fallen.

After a serious clash at Bataisk, a few miles from Rostov, the road has been cleared.

We are pressing on southward, down roads lined with olive trees which rise gently toward the foothills of the Caucasus.

The swastika flag is flying from Voronezh to the Don, and our advance is general all along the front. Our summer offensive has succeeded.

The SS, stripped to the waist in their open trucks, roar out the song of the tanks:

> All the world over, worm-eaten bones
> Are shaking before our advance . . . !

The brilliant sun tans their skin, and the enthusiasm which fills the men's hearts and makes them sing is indescribable.

In every village we pass through, the peasants of the Yei valley wave to us, a little confused, it seems, by this sudden flood of Germans all heading toward the Kuban.

The Russian lines are broken, and we must rush into the breach to exploit our victory.

Faster, always faster.

In front of us lie the Caucasus, then Georgia and Turkey.

And behind the Euphrates are Syria and Egypt. Egypt, where the divisions of Rommel's Afrika Korps are fighting.

What a magnificent epic it would be if, after starting from the shores of the Black Sea, the panzer divisions were to end up within sight of Cairo and the Pyramids!

Actually GHQ must have had this in mind when they sent the greater part of Army Group South off in the direction of the Turkish frontier.

The black SS from the Russian front and the heroes of the desert war meeting somewhere in the land of the Pharaohs—what a foolish, but magnificent dream!

Unfortunately there are still some twelve hundred miles between the Vikings and the Suez Canal.

August 4. Violent clashes all along the pipeline.

Rear-guard units of a Volga Cossack division are entrenched in the surrounding hills. They keep the whole Kropotkin road steadily under fire from a small forest above the valley of the Krijtar river, a tributary of the Kuban. They have been shooting at us without a pause since dawn. Up to now we haven't been able to pinpoint their positions with any accuracy. They must have set up their 122 batteries very silently, during the night, for when daybreak came and we wanted to get on the road again so as to join up with the rest of the division, a violent barrage of shellfire descended on us.

The regimental CO immediately informed Division, who ordered a complete mopping up of the area by the regiment before moving on again.

The village we are occupying is beside the pipeline. At one time we thought the Russians were planning a counterattack in an attempt to destroy the pumping station, which is a few miles from here. On second thought, however, it seems to me that such a maneuver would be stupid and pointless. The pipeline, which has been wrecked for a length of hundreds of miles, is no longer of any strategic value.

This is the vast series of enormous pipes which carry the oil from the wells of the Ordzhonikidze and the Caspian area to the refineries of Rostov, on the Donets. The Russians will be obliged from now on to move their crude oil by tankers. And naturally they won't like this at all.

As we wait, the shelling goes on. The Cossacks are raining down a perfect deluge of shells on us, and these have already caused serious casualties among our men. At least ten have been killed.

In a little square, in the shelter of a brick building, I catch sight of Michael beside a gun battery, scrutinizing the wooded hills though field glasses. I walk up to him.

"Want to have a look?" he asks, making room for me.

I adjust the glasses, and in a few seconds I manage to pick out the little mushroom-shaped clouds that indicate gunfire.

There are at least two batteries of four guns, firing alternately. They must also have several heavy machine guns, to judge by the bullets which are continually sending smashed titles flying off the roofs.

It'll be a hell of a job routing them out of there. And they're blocking our way. All this is the fault of the Divisional Staff, who didn't think it necessary to send an advance unit to clean up any resistance, or even a Fieseler observation plane to see what was going on up in the mountains.

Major Stressling, temporarily attached to our regiment, walks across to us.

"Well, Neumann, see anything?"

He is smiling and looks as usual like a good natured baby. I think it superfluous to emulate Stinsmann, who has jumped to attention.

"That's all right, my boy. At ease!" the major says genially.

He has pure white hair and a red face. His bull neck is tightly encased in a stiff uniform collar and falls in folds at the back. He must be over fifty. It's surprising that he is only a major. Perhaps he's an old NCO of the SA who has come up through the ranks.

I turn to him again. "I was trying to count how many guns they've got, Major. I can make out eight or ten, and some heavy MG's too."

He makes a funny, evasive sort of gesture, says nothing, suddenly turns on his heel, and walks away.

A strange one. I wonder what his job is exactly in the regiment.

I wipe my forehead. It's as hot as a furnace here. My helmet becomes more and more intolerable as the sun gets higher.

I leave Michael with his binoculars and decide to go and hide in regimental HQ since I'm not on duty. Mortar bombs are bursting all around, and I have to edge along the walls very cautiously.

Suddenly I hear a distant noise, rapidly becoming louder. It seems to come from behind the tall concrete buildings, which are probably silos.

Then a strange procession appears around a corner of the street.

Amazing. They seem totally indifferent to the bullets and shells whizzing all about.

Suddenly, when I hear their lamentations, I understand.

It's a funeral.

A very strange thing it is, too, a funeral in the Kuban.

In front walks the priest, carrying a cross, with a sort of embroidered tiara on his head. Behind him come the women, their faces completely hidden by pieces of black rag. They wail incoherently, and shake and twitch as though they are suffering from some nervous disease. Other women follow them, not veiled, wailing even more loudly than their sisters at the head of the procession.

Then comes a sort of stretcher upon which has been placed the dead body of a woman, dressed in embroidered silks. Her face is already brownish in color, and clouds of flies swarm over it. A mass of flowers cover the corpse, and her hands have been joined together.

Men are carrying the dead woman, and one of them has tears on his cheeks. Obviously the husband.

A strangely melodious chant now begins, sung softly and piously by the mourners. It started up at a sign from one of the stretcher-bearers, and the sound floats, sinister above the macabre procession.

A sickly-sweet smell of death and flowers marks its passage. Slowly the people walk past, their arms swinging regularly as they intone the litany.

Rooted to the spot, I suddenly pull myself together with a jerk. The funeral cortege is passing only a few yards from me, without appearing to notice me at all. It is true that there are large numbers of SS in the district. Or perhaps it was a German bullet that killed the woman.

This frightful whistling of the shells falling continuously on the village, destroying house after house; the incessant din of explosions; the sound of regular, too regular, footsteps; the strident shouts which suddenly ring out; the cries of the weeping women; and all these people, as they follow the corpse to its burial place, where it will quietly rot away, still singing of their sorrow and chanting their last farewells, without even noticing the danger they are in . . . There is something profoundly inhuman about it all, something almost insane.

For a moment I try to visualize the burial ceremony in the village cemetery.

I envisage all the strange funeral symbols, made of metal, and often surmounted by a hammer and sickle—the rusty iron stars swinging and creaking above little metal turrets of wrought-iron and the twisted iron bars, bizarre and without any visible significance. Such is a field of the dead, in Soviet Russia. . . . The stars are rusting, the wind howls through the iron mausoleums. But it doesn't matter. There seems to be no link between the living and the dead after burial.

The dead are ignored. Perhaps this is one of the aspects of the Bolshevist philosophy.

I jumped as somebody tapped me on the shoulder. I was lost in my rather macabre thoughts, and I hadn't seen Karl come up.

"Hello, there! You look a bit gloomy. Must be that cheerful little ceremony that started you off."

"Hello, Karl. I was thinking."

"That's all right. But try and do your thinking five hundred yards farther away. You don't seem to have noticed that the stuff's still coming down. And if it gets under your skin it's damned dangerous."

It is true that tiny fragments of steel are whizzing all about us, lethal fragments. Ricochets or more or less spent shell fragments, they are nonetheless capable of inflicting quite a bit of damage.

"Let's get under cover at HQ," Karl suggests.

I suddenly remember that that's where I had been heading when I bumped into the melancholy funeral procession.

As we walk along, Karl informs me that the colonel is in a frightful rage. He is cursing Division for not having told him about the Cossacks infiltrating through the Yegorlyk valley. The result of this is that we will have to mount a pointless punitive raid without any strategic value.

When we enter HQ we find a few officers already grouped around the CO, listening respectfully and, perforce, signifying their approval of his angry outburst.

Leaning over a 1:100,000-scale map, he gives his orders.

"Battle Group Leichterner will advance straight to Hill 604, by way of the dried-up stream bed. Platoons Kolden and Niexen will cover Battle Group 2 to the south, west, north and east. The rest of Kolden's company will go around by way of the valley and will attack at"—he glances at his watch—"1630 hours from the northwest."

Karl, who is standing beside me, mutters; "This is the payoff. A whole day's mushroom picking in the forest!"

An hour later the trucks set off, and a little later we cross the pipeline, then the Rostov-Baku railway line. We've got at least twelve miles to go, around a small range of rocky hills, which will enable us to take the Cossacks by surprise from the left while the battle groups make a frontal attack.

A neat little operation, rather like the Battle of Cannae—provided that the Russians let themselves be taken by surprise. I have my doubts about this.

The half-tracked armored troop-carriers have now turned into a frightful stony track, barely recognizable as a road, but which Kolden says is marked in red on the map. This means "suitable for motor vehicles." Anyhow, it isn't the first time this has happened. During the advance on Kiev, the High Command distributed staff maps on which were marked the most wonderful road networks most of which existed only in the fertile imagination of the cartographer. Some people maintained that these maps were in fact the work of Red secret agents, who were no doubt well paid for their pains.

At any rate this damned map is getting us into a fine old muddle. It's becoming more and more difficult to move on, for the track is pitted with deep ruts, and huge hunks of rock have to be moved out of the way, since there is no room to pass on either side of them.

We have been going through deep forest for the last few minutes. Now the leading vehicle comes to a halt. The driver signals to the others following that he can't go on. We get out and are forced to admit that it is impossible to continue. The track suddenly becomes narrower, too narrow for our carriers.

So here we are in a fine mess, and it's impossible to go back. On the left is the rock face, on the right a deep ravine filled with pine trees and stunted bushes.

It is terribly hot in the undergrowth. The forest is swarming with thousands of birds and insects. It is almost possible to forget the war. High up in the sunlit pines the cicadas twitter endlessly of peace.

We are all dripping with sweat and half asleep.

"Oh, hell. We can't hang about here all day!" says Kolden suddenly, mopping his forehead.

In the distance the gunfire goes on, faint and muffled. The mountains between us and the Cossacks are an almost soundproof barrier. But if this marvelous map can be relied on, we ought to be nearer the Red positions now than when we started off.

One miserable little German detachment in the middle of the Kuban, horribly alone, lost in an unknown forest, without a sign or smell of any Russian for us to get our teeth into.

Perhaps we could try knocking on the door of some *isba,* if there is such a thing, and politely ask the way.

And as luck would have it, it's against us that these Cossack swine have decided to try out the trick of harassing our rear guard, as advocated by People's Commissar Krushchev.

God damn and blast him!

Meanwhile the rest of the division is moving on into the Caucasus. And here we are, looking extremely foolish.

Kolden is in touch with regimental HQ by radio and asks for

instructions. The reply has just come in. The colonel orders us to continue on foot.

Just our luck! SS units playing at war in an impenetrable forest and, what's more, on foot. Something to make the whole of Army Group South laugh its head off for weeks on end.

Grumbling, the men get out of the troop-carriers.

We plunge through the undergrowth, for after talking it over with Kolden and Lieutenant Masch, we have decided to cut straight through the forest.

About a dozen men are left to guard the vehicles. They don't seem too pleased about this. Presumably they have not forgotten the partisans' attack at Karasnaya.

Something occurs to me. I walk quickly over to Kolden.

"Look, Kold, they've been talking about Cossacks all morning. And they definitely said Volga Cossacks. How do they know?"

The Dutchman, panting as he scrambles over a piece of rock blocking the way, stops for a moment and turns to me.

"What's the matter, old boy? The heat gone to your head? What about the divisional intelligence officer? Anyhow, nobody but these mad Cossacks could get guns of that caliber into position at such inaccessible heights and in so short a time."

We are still climbing, and I can't be bothered to go on with the discussion.

We reach a sort of desolate plain, across which the wind is whistling.

But we can't hear the Russian artillery any more.

Kolden has also noticed the sudden silence on the part of the Reds, and we look questioningly at each other. The sun is sinking rapidly. It's nearly six o'clock. We have been marching for over two hours. What has been happening all this time to the battle groups and the support groups? The wind howls around the hills. There are valleys all around us, but we can't see a trace af smoke or any indication of a battle.

"Well, I've never seen anything like this before," grumbles Kolden.

Suddenly a private shouts out, "Over there! Looks like horses!" We follow his directions. Quickly I get out my field glasses.

Yes, by God. It can only be our Cossacks. They seem to be retreating or moving off. I shout, "Get down quick! We're right in the sun and they can spot us!"

What does it mean, this extraordinary withdrawal? Vainly I try to get my glasses into better focus, and look this way and that, but there is no sign of any SS.

"If only we had a radio transmitter," grumbles Kolden. But the RF107 has been left with the vehicles.

I try to count, even approximately, the number of horsemen. A hundred, a hundred and fifty perhaps. At any rate, they don't look as though they are particularly worried as they trot peacefully along a sort of gorge.

Near the end of this column, I can distinctly make out artillery pieces being pulled by horses.

It is all quite unbelievable! They look like troops on an exercise, returning peacefully to camp.

"They must be pulling out before the advance of the battle groups," I hear a voice saying, quite close.

I prop myself up on one elbow. The voice belongs to Lieutenant Masch. He is also lying flat on his belly, with his field glasses to his eyes.

A violet light is stealing over the hills. The wind that blows across the plain is getting cooler. It's time to make a decision.

"Pulling out?" says Kolden. "But where's Niexen's platoon? They ought to be right there behind the Cossacks."

"Perhaps they've lost contact, or taken the wrong road," hazards Masch.

The men are all lying on the ground, waiting for orders. We can't hang around here indefinitely speculating about the reasons for the Russians' solitary departure down the valley.

I turn to the Dutchman. "What do we do, Kold? We can't waste any more time. It'll be dark in an hour."

"There's only one thing to do," he growls. "Try and get in front of them. There are a hundred of us. We have eight MG's, and all the men have got machine pistols. With a bit of luck we ought to be able to deal with them. Tell your men to move off rapidly toward the edge of the forest. We'll go down and cut them off."

A few minutes later we are climbing down the other side of the hill, trying to make as little noise as possible. But despite our efforts, the rattle of pebbles rolling down and the crack of breaking branches seems to reverberate from valley to valley. We'll be lucky if they don't hear us coming.

It is getting steadily darker. It is already fifteen minutes since first we saw the Reds.

Finally, still advancing as silently as possible, we can hear the clatter of their horses' hooves against the stones; they are obviously quite near at hand.

"We've got 'em!" whispers Kolden. "Get your men deployed in a semicircle and get the MG's in position. Tracer to start with."

Suddenly the leading horsemen appear, about a hundred yards in front of us.

"Fire at will!"

All the automatics go into action at once, and the forest immediately resounds with a terrifying uproar.

The tracer makes a weird pattern, a thousand streaks of light in the dusk that give us a chance to check our aim.

The horses are whinnying frantically, rearing up on their hind legs, then hurtling dead to the ground. The Russians appear utterly confused. It is some time before they realize what has happened.

Shouts, cries of pain, howls of rage, then suddenly the sharp crack of a heavy Voroshilov and broken branches begin to rain down on us. They are recovering from their initial surprise.

It is almost completely dark now. This duel in the darkness, this fantastic battle of howling ghosts, is most impressive. Death is creeping through the trees, whistling in our ears, whining like a nest of disturbed hornets. We try to take cover as best we can behind rocks or pine trees.

On the left are vague running shadows. I let off a few long bursts in their direction. My submachine gun is getting red-hot, as I slip in magazine after magazine. Only the dry click which indicates that the last bullet has been fired tells me, in this total darkness, when it's time to put in a new one.

The Reds' resistance is getting weaker and weaker. We suddenly realize that they're in flight, making off into the forest. It would be sheer folly to pursue them in the dark.

Cautiously, machine pistols at the hip, we advance, our flashlights held up at arm's length in case some sniper should catch us unawares. But abandoned machine guns and the corpses of men and horses under the trees are all that remain of the Cossack detachment.

I bend down and turn over the body of an officer, easily recognizable by his two metal stars. There are broad straps of gold braid on the shoulders of his uniform against a royal blue background. The IO was quite right. They are definitely Cossacks. The man has a white stripe bordered with red on his left pocket. I believe this is the Order of the Suvarov, platinum star. In any case it's a splendid souvenir, and I tear it from the dead man's tunic.

I hear somebody groaning quite close to me. I flash my light in that direction. It is a wounded Russian, his wide-open eyes staring fixedly at me.

His lips move slightly.

"Finish me off, comrade. . . ."

Rather foolishly, I find myself deeply moved by this trembling voice, this hoarse croak. In spite of knowing almost no Russian, I understand at once. The Cossack is young, with fair hair. A thin trickle of blood comes out of the corner of his mouth.

I would like to do what I can to save him, but it's impossible. There are hardly enough of us as it is to carry the German dead and wounded down into the valley.

I take my pistol out of its holster.

When he sees the gun, he smiles in an almost friendly way. He is not afraid of death. It's difficult to kill a man in cold blood. But it would be less humane, surely, to leave him here, uncared for, to let him spend hours dying.

I press the muzzle of the gun against his temple.

"Good-by, Ivan. We're all brothers, after all."

I squeeze the trigger.

He suddenly twitches, then a horrible death grin distorts his upper lip, revealing the whiteness of his teeth.

I get up and turn my flashlight away, so that I shall no longer see that tragic grimace.

We have lifted our dead onto canvas stretchers, two SS at each end. The wounded are carried on the soldiers' backs.

A little later the slow-moving column starts off down the valley toward the troop-carriers, the men stumbling over the stones, inadequately picked out by our pocket lights.

It was dawn before we arrived back at base. There we learned that the battle groups had in fact failed to locate the retreating Cossacks. They had met the support platoons at about 1500 hours. They had all drawn a blank, and had therefore set off for the pipeline and returned to base.

August 27. Yesterday a detachment of mountain troops under the command of Lieutenant Spindler reached the summit of the Elborus. The swastika standard is flying there, dominating the whole Caucasus, more than eighteen thousand feet above the Black Sea.

We watched this fantastic exploit through field glasses, from the village of Shakhar, where we were encamped.

August 29. We have turned off northeastward onto the Pyatigorsk road, which crosses the desolate plains of the river Malka.

Since the beginning of the month our advance has been steady despite the frenzied resistance of the Reds.

Some tetrrible battles took place around Prokhladny. Lieutenant van Kolden was killed during one of these engagements. I took over from him as company commander. Two silver squares[3] now adorn the lapels of my black tunic.

[3] SS officers wore on their lapels small squares of silver thread. One square indicated the rank of Second Lieutenant, two the rank of Lieutenant.

September 8. All the oil wells of the Grozny district, through which we are now moving, have been destroyed.

The twisted frames of the metal derricks stand there like black skeletons among the vast clouds of smoke which hang above them, obscuring the sky.

The oil is burning.

The NKVD destruction commandos blew up all the installations and set fire to all the wells before the departure of the Soviet troops.

For days specialist engineers have been fighting the gigantic fires which ravage the whole area. The dull roar of burning petroleum can be heard from valley to valley, all along the Terek range.

Occasionally the air is rent by the explosions of enormous charges of dynamite intended to put out the fires in the wells.

At night they are colossal flares, lighting up the mountain peaks.

September 15. We have come nearly five hundred miles since Rostov.

The Caucasus offers a wide variety of remarkable contrasts.

In the subtropical region along the Black Sea, where we were at the beginning of the summer, there is a wonderful profusion of giant palm trees, of orange and lemon groves. Along the sides of the roads are olive trees and vast fields of tobacco and tea, and even banana trees. On the hillsides there are vineyards, the vines twisting and turning toward the eternally blue sky.

Nearing the Caspian Sea the mountains are wild, desolate and arid, their slopes covered with thick forests of oak, maple, beech and chestnut. Higher up are the pines, and then the fir trees.

What amazing scenery. What an incredible view there must be from the summits of the Kasbek or the Elborus.

From the snow-capped peaks it is possible, apparently, to see the mountain ranges of Armenia and Georgia, and the green valleys of Azerbaijan. In the valleys, too, the grass is as high as a man, and the multicolored flowers grow as tall as our bushes at home.

In the wide, dark clearings of the forests, hunting is still an adventure. Bears, wild boar, lynxes and wolves relentlessly pursue the wild goats and martens and the bezoar goats right up to the peaks of the mountains.

Above it all, huge eagles and vultures glide majestically, waiting to spot their prey, then swooping down.

A strange country, and a strange people too.

They are fierce, independent warriors, and I have the impression that they are equally indifferent to our occupation and to the dictatorship of the Bolsheviks. They seem to have an indomitable love of freedom. They are a proud people.

It is they who built those little stone and clay forts with watch towers which dot the hillsides above the mountain passes. For the last few days the rear guards, sacrificed by the Soviet High Command in order to cover the withdrawal of the main body of the Red armies, have been hiding out in these forts.

Entrenched in these old-fashioned blockhouses, the Russians fight to the bitter end, and we find nothing but dead bodies when we enter the forts.

September 25. The tanks carve a way straight through the Reds. We go on behind them, cleaning up any pockets of resistance in the area as we go. And so it continues; day after day.

In a series of short marches we are approaching Baku and the Caspian.

All along the great southern mountain ridge the German flag flies over conquered Russian territory.

On the other fronts the advance goes on with equal success.

Sebastopol has fallen. In the north, the great Moscow offensive is developing just as foreseen by the German High Command. Around Leningrad, the joint forces of Field Marshal von Leeb and the Finnish Marshal Mannerheim have encircled Russia's second city. In the east, the Volga is about to be crossed at Stalingrad, the siege of which has just begun.

In every sector our victorious advance continues.

It is only fair to say that nobody has any illusions about the difficulties still to be overcome. However, the magnitude of what we have already achieved is obviously the surest guarantee of our ultimate victory.

Every German hopes that the year 1943 will see, at long last, the final triumph of the German eagle.

Part III

TWILIGHT

12. I Once Had a Comrade . . .

December 2, 1942. We have been waiting here for several days.

Grouped around the little station at Proletarskaya, the men lie on the ground under their tents, or sit seven or eight together in the trucks or tanks. They are trying to protect themselves as best they can against the cold and the polar blizzard that howls angrily around our ears.

All along the river Manych, thousands of armored vehicles, tanks, gun carriages and heavy artillery are waiting for the trains to carry them off to the northeast.

Brought with all possible speed from the foothills of the Caucasus and the shores of the Caspian, dozens of divisions have been directed to the small railway stations situated around Lake Karitsen.

The Volga.

The men murmur the word anxiously. Apprehensively.

The Volga is our official destination, according to all the brass hats.

But the SS have no illusions.

The Volga means Stalingrad.

And Stalingrad, according to those who have been able to escape from that frightful inferno, means all too often death.

For some months General Paulus's forces have been surrounded in what used to be Tsaritsyn, by Zhukov's armies and Rokossovski's tanks. The Reds are dangerously close to Stalingrad at several points, thus threatening, by means of a pincer movement, to en-circle the German troops.

Von Manstein has been recalled urgently from the Balkans and instructed by the Führer to get the reinforcing divisions on the move.

Meanwhile, we wait.

The train, composed of cattle cars and a few passenger coaches, pulls in slowly at one of the platforms of the darkened station. We have just learned that the staff of Hoth's 4th Panzer Army, to which the Viking has been attached, has decided to send us northeast by rail, in order to avoid the damaged and snow-covered roads of the Yergeni Hills.

A loudspeaker intones nasally into the night.

"Company commanders and the platoon commanders will report at station HQ. Company commanders and . . ."

I give my gear to an SS standing beside me and walk toward the marshaling yard where our colonel has set up his HQ. The icy wind still whistles across the countryside, piling the snow in deep mounds beside the railway track.

About a dozen officers are already in the hut, gathered around a miserable oil stove which is making a vain attempt to raise the temperature a few degrees.

Standing at the far end, our colonel, looking preoccupied, is talking to a group of senior officers. Among them I notice General Gille, commander of the Viking since last November. He replaced Steiner, who has gone to Charlottenburg.

Noting that most of the company and platoon commanders have arrived, Gille takes a couple of steps forward and raises his hand for silence.

"SS! This is no time for a long speech," he raps out, his face hardening. "The enemy are hitting us hard, very hard. This is the final struggle of the wild beast before it dies. But it's a dangerous struggle! This time, SS, you will fight not only for the glory of our country, but for the liberation of your comrades who are surrounded and are counting on you to help them."

Silence falls, a tense silence. Then our general's grave voice goes on.

"You must exterminate that Russian beast," he shouts, emphasizing each word with a gesture of his clenched fist. "The time has passed to think of men, women and children. It is a ferocious brute that must now be destroyed . . . so that Germany may live!"

He stands to attention.

"Heil Hitler!"

He walks across to us now and moves about among us.

"It would be pointless to worry your men, gentlemen. But it would be equally useless to try and conceal from them the fact that we are going to Stalingrad."

He purses his lips and makes a vague gesture.

"Besides, there's nothing to worry about. The strength of the relief armies, which are hastening toward the Volga, will certainly pulverize the Yeremenko-Zhukov divisions!"

He glances around the silent room and ends:

"That's all, gentlemen! The army moves off at 2200 hours. See that your men are ready."

A few minutes later we leave. Almost immediately I run into Karl, who is chatting with another second lieutenant.

"This is no joke," I say. "What do you make of it all?"

Karl shakes his head vaguely before replying, "It looks bad for Paulus. All this shimozzle, setting off in such a rush, it doesn't seem very healthy."

I glance at my wrist watch. It is 2150. Ten minutes to go.

"Are you going up front with us?" asks Karl. "I believe they've hooked some fairly decent coaches on in front."

I nod. "I'll be better off there than in the straw. I've some orders to give, then I'll be along."

The engine is already coupled to the train. The engineer and fireman are busy, silhouetted blackly against the brilliant red light from the furnace. The pistons screech noisily and jets of steam shoot upward erratically from the cylinders.

The men of the 2nd Company, who since the Caucasus battles have been known as Battle Group Neumann, climb into their coach.

At last I catch sight of Warrant Officer Libesis, for whom I have been hunting.

"Libesis, I'll be up in front with Lieutenant von Reckner. If you want me, just come and get me when we stop."

He starts to salute but I stop him.

"Another thing, Libesis. Send a dozen men to the armored coach. It's an order from the colonel. With machine guns. That's all, Libesis!"

"Good night, sir!" he says, standing to attention.

The train moves off. I just have time to reach the front coach.

The compartments are dark and silent.

The Viking officers don't seem too enthusiastic at the prospects of this journey north.

Franz and Karl are together in one compartment at the front of the coach. They make room for me beside them.

The darkness is accentuated by the thick coating of frost and snow on the windows. As the train gains speed, the cold becomes more intense.

"We've got three hundred miles of this," groans Franz. "We'll have plenty of time to turn into icicles before we arrive, I expect."

"And we can't even play cards," says Karl. "You can't see more than a couple of inches in front of you. That's great. All the way to Stalingrad!"

"Never mind, there'll be plenty of distractions once we arrive," shouts an aggressive voice in the darkness.

"Shut up!" growls another. "Isn't it bad enough the way things are?"

Suddenly everybody is silent.

I try to huddle in a corner to keep out the bitter cold. But the seats are of wood and, however you sit, it's rapidly very uncomfortable.

Through the night the train thunders along at full speed, with a metallic jolting and shaking. Now and then there is a long whistle blast. Strangely like the cry of an animal in pain.

For a moment I listen to the regular rumbling of the wheels over the steel tracks.

A violent jolt wakes me up with a start.

Voices shouting in my car bring me back to reality.

"Get down, for God's sake! They're shooting at us!"

The partisans.

A metallic sound rends the air. I leap to my feet and adjust my helmet. I realize all at once that the train has stopped.

"Are we off the rails?"

Karl answers, "I don't think so. But they must have put something on the line. The train stopped before the firing began! Or perhaps they've cut the line."

"In any case they must have fired on the locomotive," an unknown voice cuts in.

With a violent push, someone flings me to the ground.

"You fool! They've got one of us already!"

And now I hear groans coming from one corner of the compartment.

I think rapidly. What should I do? The firing goes on, and I can hear sharp cracks, even inside the train. It would be folly to jump straight out. The swine must be waiting, and they'll be looking out for anyone who shows himself at a window.

A few seconds later the bark of heavy machine guns informs us that our train guards are going into action. And about time too!

With one hand Franz pulls down what is left of the compartment window; the frame is almost stuck fast with ice. I lift my head gingerly and look out toward a dark line of trees some fifty yards away.

The partisans have arranged their ambush at a point where the line passes through a deep forest. Vaguely I can distinguish the dark outline of the nearer coaches. Furthermore, we are on a curve. They think of everything!

A bullet slams into the coach just below the window and there's the sound of tearing metal. We can't stay here. It's extremely unhealthy. The swine are hiding in the wood, and are having fun taking pot shots at us.

Suddenly I make up my mind. I must rejoin my company.

I go out of the compartment, trampling over men stretched on the floor. After a long and difficult progress, bent almost double, down the corridor of the coach, at last I reach the exit door. Franz and Karl have followed me.

"If we get out, they'll shoot us," whispers Franz.

I glance around. The coach is of the old-fashioned type, and there is no connecting door to the next one.

"We must try the other side of the train," I say.

Our men have now opened fire from the rear coaches as well. But they must be shooting by guesswork. It is quite impossible to see anything whatsoever.

Gently I pull open the door which gives onto the other side of the track. No reaction. Are they only on one side, perhaps? But that would be extraordinary. Suddenly I notice the enameled plaque with the notice: "Danger. Do not open."

I have no time to worry about this and cannot afford to lose precious seconds. I jump down into the snow as quickly as possible. Two slight bumps indicate that Franz and Karl are behind me.

Without thinking, I start to run, bent almost double. A few moments later I arrive safe and sound at the far end of the train. Vague silhouettes loom up toward me.

I raise my head.

"Battle Group! Jump down here—quickly! Lie flat on the ground after you've jumped."

Then suddenly the Reds start shooting. The devils must have been waiting for the men to get off the train. That's why they let us go past. So that we shouldn't know exactly where they were.

The SS with their black uniforms against the white snow make perfect targets. A storm of bullets ricochets from the stones and pebbles of the track.

"The bastards!" a voice roars. "How many of them are there?"

Cries of pain re-echo in the night. Some of our men must have been hit.

Lying in the snow now, we spray the black line of pine trees with long bursts of fire. We aim at the red flashes which show up in the darkness and thus give away the Bolsheviks' positions.

From every window of the train men are now firing at the forest. The raucous bark of the MG's merges with the staccato rattle of the machine pistols, the sharp crack of the Soviet Dektyarovs and the deep roar of our Mauser rifles.

A sound of running footsteps, muffled by the snow. A private runs up to me.

"Lieutenant! Colonel's orders, sir. Battle Group Neumann—cleaning up operation, east side of railway track. With four MG's, and an antitank section in support."

A wave of the hand: understood. The man has already gone off again, swallowed up by the night.

A sudden feeling of anger gives me the courage to raise myself on one elbow.

"Libesis, Hättenschwiller's and Scheant's platoons! Follow me. The others—go around by the left!"

The idea is to try and surround them. If that is possible. . . . Because they're probably prepared for just that.

"Peter! Don't be such a crazy fool!" hisses Franz suddenly. "Get down, for God's sake!"

I flop down again on the edge of the track. Certainly this is no time to get shot through carelessness.

A minute later our advance begins. Crawling over the snow, about a hundred men are moving toward the Reds.

A storm of steel and lead is let fly all about us. The savages are well armed.

At thirty yards from the forest's edge our first hand grenades are lobbed in.

A moment's pause. The Reds don't seem to be too happy about the latest developments.

An idea suddenly occurs to me. I signal to an SS, who crawls up.

"Get me Sergeant Fällest! I want him here at once with one fully equipped section!"

Five minutes later the NCO commanding the flame-thrower platoon arrives. He moves bent almost double, for his equipment makes it impossible for him to crawl along on his belly. There are about a dozen men behind him, all carrying their special equipment. Asbestos gloves protect their hands, and their faces are hidden behind rubber and mica masks.

I raise my arm.

"It's all yours, Fällest!"

The Dane grunts an acknowledgment. He signals to his men to follow him.

A moment later the flame-throwers join in the fun.

Long jets of flaming gas shoot from the metal tubes with a roar like a furnace, lighting up the forest and at the same time picking out the Russians crouching behind the trees. On the left the delighted antitank gunners open up on them, shooting into their midst as though this were a gunnery practice on the range.

Like figures in hell outlined against the blood-red, fiery light, the men of the flame-thrower platoon move slowly forward, spraying the ground as they go.

A broad, white pencil of light suddenly pierces the darkness. The men in the armored coach, no longer afraid that their searchlight will be shot to bits, have at last decided to illuminate the forest.

The Russians now realize that the latest developments don't look too healthy for them. They are running away into the woods in disorder.

"Fire! Rapid fire! We can see them now!"

If we don't cut off their retreat at once, we'll never catch them later.

A dull explosion, a brutal sound.

A river of flame runs over the ground. Terrible screams and a frightful smell of burning flesh fill the air.

A shadowy form is writhing on the ground, half hidden by a sheet of flame.

A bullet must have hit his gas cylinder, or else the fuel has exploded for some unexplained reason.

A few SS rush forward. There is nothing they can do. The man is finished. Anyhow, they cannot possibly pull him out of that inferno. His face is rapidly turning brown. A few seconds later there is nothing left but a charred, blackened mass shriveling up among the dying flames.

There is no point in staying here any longer. The three platoons are now combing the undergrowth, the flame-throwers at their head.

The bark of the pine trees is beginning to catch fire all around us. Some of the trees are already well alight.

The antitank gunners seem to have caught up with the Russian rear guard. A few hundred yards ahead we glimpse, in the light of the leaping flames, thirty or so figures fighting a desperate hand-to-hand battle.

Red, distorted faces. Yells of rage. They are too close to fire their guns, and so they use rifle butts, fists and daggers.

Shriller cries are now audible. So there are some female partisans. . . .

"They've had it!" Franz cries out exultantly. Standing at my side, he is shooting like a man possessed.

A furious burst comes from a nearby copse.

Franz doubles up, and throws himself on the ground.

I empty my magazine into the copse from which the firing came. A silhouette beneath a fur hat leaps up like an uncoiled spring and runs a few uncertain steps.

A bullet quickly takes care of him.

I lean over Franz. He is lying on his side, clutching his stomach with both hands and groaning.

"Russian bastards . . ." he gasps. "They've got me."

Quickly I unfasten his greatcoat and loosen his belt. Blood is soaking through his underclothes.

Ruddy gleams from the burning trees cast a flickering light over the scene. I shine an electric torch on his wound.

Appalling. . . .

I am bathed in an icy sweat. Franz won't recover from this.

"It's bad, eh?" he articulates painfully.

Already he has difficulty in speaking. Suddenly and softly, he begins to sob.

I try to stem the flow of blood with the absorbent cotton in his field dressing, then with mine. But the wound is too deep. Immediate medical attention is essential. Only a Dektyarov bullet or an explosive one could have made such a deep hole.

The swine!

I force myself to joke with him.

"Good God, man! There's nothing wrong with you, and here you are, blubbering like a schoolgirl!"

Franz is not fooled.

"Don't bother about me, Peter. More important things to be done. . . ."

Suddenly he stops crying.

"Try to go and see my mother," he whispers. "Tell her . . ."

A long-drawn-out sigh, and bloodstained bubbles appear at the corner of his mouth.

"And then tell my father . . ."

I squeeze his arm, trying to smile.

". . . that it's possible to be an SS man without being a mad dog," he continues, looking up at me. "You see, he didn't want me . . . didn't want me to join."

His face is rapidly taking on a waxy tinge.

"Dear old Wittenberge. Think of me when you visit Schiller and see the chaps again."

"Don't worry, Franz. They're coming to get you."

"It doesn't matter any more. Perhaps it's better this way. Anyhow, I feel quite calm. Quite calm, now."

He chokes, and breathes noisily, gasping for air.

"You know, there's something I must tell you. I was always scared stiff. But it didn't show. Did it, Peter? Good old Peter. Say . . . good-by to Karl, and the others. . . . Good luck, Peter. . . ."

His features contract as though he were going through some intolerable agony. The whites of his eyes show suddenly. He is heavy in my arms. Horribly heavy. . . . Franz, dear old Franz on the beach at Hamburg and in the squares of Wittenberge. . . . Good-by, old pal!

A private comes up, running.

"They're finished, Lieutenant! About fifty prisoners. The others have all scrammed out of it. They won't get far. The forest's on fire."

Then he sees the body stretched out on the ground.

"It's the lieutenant of the 3rd! Wounded?"

"Dead. Help me to get him to the train."

"No, sir. I'll carry him on my back. Everything's on fire here. It'll be quicker that way."

Sparks are indeed raining down all about us. I hadn't noticed them. But we aren't far from the railway line.

I am incapable of any sensation. So it's all over for Franz. I think that now for the first time I really understand what death means, in spite of all the corpses I have seen. I have just enough strength to help the private hoist Franz's body over his shoulder.

The man starts running, and I follow him. Franz's eyes are wide open. His arms swing in the most horrible way.

Very soon we reach the train. Briefly I tell the private to put Franz's body on a piece of canvas and lay it quietly in one of the coaches.

For the moment I want to keep him away from the crematory car.

It's the last service I can do him.

Collected around the searchlight, outside the armored coach, are about a dozen Russians, dressed in long, greenish greatcoats and fur hats. They are guarded by the panzer infantrymen of the 4th Company, holding machine pistols.

Major Stressling is interrogating them, his face distorted with fury. Since the Caucasus, Stressling has been permanently attached to the regiment. But he has no specific command, and his position is somewhat anomalous. Some maintain that he is under direct orders from the SSFHA at Charlottenburg.

He suddenly walks up to one of the partisans and slaps his face violently, shouting at him in Russian. The man stares at him with evident terror, but doesn't answer.

I notice two women among the terrorists. Probably the ones I heard cry out not long ago in the forest. Their uniform is so like the men's that at first glance it's difficult to tell them apart. But they have the big, buxom figures of country girls, and those enormous breasts which could only belong to Russian women.

His jaw clenched, Stressling strides up and down in front of the Reds.

"Nothing to say, eh?" he growls, this time in German. "You don't know anything—nothing at all?"

He stops dead and plants himself squarely in front of one of them.

"I'll force it out of you!"

He turns to Lieutenant Leichterner.

"Tell your men to strip all these scum naked! That ought to refresh their memories."

A part of the regiment has now gathered in front of the armored coach. The SS watch the scene, lit up in the crude glare of our searchlight. Stressling sees them and turns to the colonel, who has come up in the meantime.

"It might be a wise move to post sentries all round the train, Colonel. We don't know that the partisans won't try and attack us again. And there may be other groups of them hidden around here."

The colonel looks at him coldly for a moment. It is obvious he doesn't like Stressling. Besides, he should have been the first to think of this somewhat elementary precaution.

"See to it, Ulkijaj!" he orders finally, turning to the Finn.

The latter salutes, arm outstretched, before he turns away.

I notice Karl elbowing his way toward me. From the stunned expression on his face, I see that he has heard.

"So he was the first to go," he murmurs dully. "Poor old Franz. He was quite sure he'd be killed. He told me so often he'd never see Wittenberge again. He never trusted his luck."

He grabs me roughly by the arm.

"They've *got* to be made to talk, Peter!"

I feel his nails digging into my arm through the serge of my uniform.

"Do you remember the oath we made at the Napola at Plön? Faithful to our friendship, no matter what happens. . . . We've *got* to avenge him, Peter."

"We'll avenge him, Karl," I say, gazing at him steadily.

We look up now as sharp orders are being snapped out. It is Stressling, still shouting.

"Two men to each of these scum! Take them by the feet!"

The Russians, half naked, are lying in the snow. Their emaciated bodies, already marked with dark stripes, are shaken by prolonged shudders. They know what to expect.

The two women have been placed a little farther back. The younger, lying on her stomach, seems to be unconscious. Her back is striped with broad, red weals, probably, a corporal tells me, the result of the punishment given her when she was captured; for they had quite some trouble catching her. The vixen had, in fact, practically torn out the eye of one NCO and had bitten several of the men savagely.

I turn back toward Stressling. He is talking to one of the Russians, or rather hissing through his teeth.

"Who are your leaders? Where are they hiding?"

"I don't know. . . ." the man stammers.

He is ashen pale and trembling violently.

Stressling bites his lower lip angrily. He seems to be thinking. He glances at the private who is guarding the partisan.

"Dagger!" he says simply.

The private understands at once. He draws out his dagger, bends down and aims the point at the throat of the Russian, who is wide-eyed now with terror.

"Do you understand that?" snarls the major, his eyes glinting with anger. "The knife at your throat?"

Mesmerized, the prisoner watches the point of the dagger slowly coming closer to his throat.

Stressling stands over him—a huge, sneering man, his legs wide apart, firmly planted there in his black leather boots.

"Will you talk now?"

The man makes no sign. He doesn't even open his lips.

"Kill him!" shouts Stressling, losing patience.

The private hesitates a moment and looks up for confirmation of the order. Then he drives the dagger home.

Karl and I glance at each other. A year ago this scene might have horrified us. Now it leaves us quite unmoved.

Personally, I am unable to feel the slightest pity for either the men or the women. Their sufferings are a matter of complete indifference to me. They even provide a sort of balm to ease my own grief. They relieve momentarily the insatiable thirst for vengeance which is devouring me. They have killed, like cowards, in the dark. For their country? Perhaps. But for our own country's sake, I fully accept Stressling's decision: death to them!

Through a sort of haze, I see men carry away the bleeding corpse. I ask myself then, Is it I who have changed? Such familiarity with death, its daily presence, must profoundly affect a man's outlook.

Stressling, in a furious temper now, continues his interrogation.

His anger at being unable to get anything out of the Reds seems to be increased tenfold by the fact that all the partisans, although clearly terrified, are obviously clenching their teeth in their determination not to talk.

Meanwhile the forest fire is beginning to assume dangerous proportions. Pieces of burning wood, carried by the wind, fall all around us, amidst great showers of sparks.

The colonel looks nervous. Making a sudden decision, he walks up to Stressling.

I ONCE HAD A COMRADE ...

"There's a risk of the railway line being cut by fire at any minute, Major! We can't wait much longer. We've been here for more than two hours already, you know. A troop train or an ammunition train may arrive at any time. There were several ready to go when we left Proletarskaya. Perhaps you could continue your . . . interrogation later."

Stressling turns to him abruptly, his face rigid. "I have very strict orders, Colonel. I think I have already told you what they are. Whenever possible the terrorists will be interrogated and . . . executed at the scene of their crimes!"

A heavy silence falls, and he concludes cuttingly, "I must ask you to have a little more . . . patience, Colonel."

Without a word, the regimental CO turns on his heel.

He has certainly made his point. Nobody can now be in any doubt that Stressling is under direct orders from the SSFHA at Charlottenburg. The genial, white-haired major is probably a member of Brandt's staff.[1]

The forest fire is gaining ground. Stressling peers anxiously toward the trees, then looks around as though searching for somebody.

"Sergeant Fällest!" he suddenly shouts.

The NCO leaves the ranks, steps forward, and salutes.

"Fällest, I saw you doing good work a while back," growls Stressling.

A gleam of irony crosses his face, but vanishes almost immediately.

"Bring your men here immediately," he orders sharply. "With their equipment. And hurry, Fällest!"

In a moment eight men of the flame-thrower platoon are there, looking rather surprised.

"Cylinders recharged?" On an affirmative nod from the NCO, he laughs, as he says, "Try one of them, Fällest. These damned

[1] Rudolf Brandt, ADC to Himmler, Commander in Chief of the SS, was also in command of the Einsatzgruppen. These were mobile units, attached to each Army Corps of the Wehrmacht. The officers of the Einsatzgruppen had, in theory, unlimited power and authority even over officers of a superior rank, whether SS or Wehrmacht.

moujiks must be cold, with their buttocks freezing in the snow like this."

Fällest stares at him and doesn't understand. Stressling doesn't bother to explain as he signals to a private standing opposite.

"Bring one of the swine over here. We must stop them wanting to shoot at us. This'll be a lot of fun. For them."

He suddenly notices the men who are watching this scene with curiosity. Their eyes are particularly attracted to the two half-naked women in the snow.

"You lecherous pigs!" he shouts. "This isn't a brothel. Get the hell out of here! All of you!"

The men scatter for a moment. But almost at once they stop and turn back. They are waiting, curiously, to see how the Russians will die.

A private drags one of the prisoners into the light. The man is half-unconscious. They seize hold of his feet and pull him into the beam of the searchlight.

"He certainly wants a warm-up," says Stressling. "Wake him up!"

An SS gets down on his knees and rubs the partisan's face with snow. The Russian's body is shaken by repeated tremors. He has been lying in the snow for over half an hour. It seems that he has nearly had it. And without the help of any SS officer.

The latter repeats his question.

"Who are your leaders?"

The man opens his eyes. He seems to be trying to speak. Then he falls back on the ground, completely exhausted. Only his eyes still show some semblance of life. But there is an expression of such determination in them that Stressling understands.

He signals to an SS of the flame-thrower platoon. "Let's get it over with. This has been going on long enough."

His lower lip twists into a parody of a smile.

"He's had it, never mind how. But he can still be an example to the others."

Fällest quickly turns to him. "But, Major . . . it's . . . it's impossible! I thought all this was just to frighten them."

"What do you mean, 'frighten them'?" bellows Stressling. "What the hell! Look around you! The train is about to catch fire, and us with it if we waste any more time. Either they talk, or they die. And since they've got to die anyhow, we'd better try everything to make them talk!"

He marches up to the NCO, his features twisted with fury.

"Enough of this, Sergeant! There are five, ten, thirty trains behind us. All heading north. If we don't use every means in our power, right now, to make these bastards talk—every means, do you understand me?—they'll go on ambushing our people. And either slowing down or even stopping our trains. Which is precisely what their damned leaders are after, Sergeant!"

Suddenly calming down, he adds, "The hours we spend here, are hardly wasted, since we're protecting the trains coming to the aid of our surrounded comrades."

Becoming sardonic and biting again, he concludes, "Get on with it, Fällest. And quickly!"

The platoon commander of the flame-throwers seems thunderstruck. But he manages to signal to one of his men, who steps forward, looking very pale.

"Wait a minute," Stressling snaps.

Once more he addresses the partisan. "Still nothing to say?"

The Russian's eyes are closed. Impossible to say whether he has understood the question or not.

The SS officer, with amazing *sang-froid*, now calmly orders, "Get on with it."

The man from the flame-thrower platoon takes a few steps back.

He signals to the two SS guarding the prisoner to get out of the way.

With clenched teeth and a strangely fixed stare, he hoists the metal cylinder onto his back. He glances at Stressling. He has made up his mind. The gas-pressure valve presumably controls a combustion device automatically.

A cascade of fire leaps out, accompanied by the roar of the flamethrower.

Appalling.

The scene can have lasted only a few seconds, but it approached almost the ultimate in horror.

This is the second time in two hours that I have seen a man grilled alive.

At first the Russian screamed atrociously, a sound that was hardly human, and twisted convulsively on the ground, tearing frantically at the earth with his fingernails.

As his body burned, it shriveled up horribly. The melting fat made wide, glistening patches, which burned in their turn with small, violet-colored flames.

Ashen-faced, the SS switched off the jet of flame at a signal from Stressling.

The victim went on twisting and turning for some moments on the black ground where the snow had melted, writhing in his last death agonies.

His last gesture was to raise his hand to his charred face from which the living flesh had been burned away. Then his body arched and fell back to the ground.

Dead.

The smell of burned flesh is so frightful that I am afraid I must vomit.

I turn my head away in an attempt to wipe out the memory of this monstrous spectacle.

A few yards away, lit by the beams of the searchlight, the partisans are now standing stupefied by the Dantesque scene which has just taken place before their eyes.

One of them has fallen on his knees in the snow. He is sobbing noisily as he raises his arms to heaven.

One of the women suddenly leaps up, screaming like a mad thing. Two men rush forward to silence her. Her companion is also overcome by hysteria and flings herself upon them using her nails like claws. She has to be pulled off one of the SS, whose face she has lacerated.

As for Stressling, he watches with a sardonic smile while the prisoners are kicked back into place.

"Enough!" he suddenly shouts. "We've already wasted too much time."

His hands behind his back, he walks over to the partisans and looks them up and down, one by one.

Then, turning back to the SS: "Machine guns! Let's be done with this filth!"

He turns on his heel at once and walks off in the direction of the engine.

The whole forest is now in flames. We are lucky that the wind is not blowing in our direction. Nevertheless it's time to go. Already trees are toppling, amid huge showers of sparks, only a few yards from the track.

A few long bursts. Half a dozen pistol shots ring out. Then silence.

The partisans have paid their debt. With interest.

An NCO runs the length of the train. We're off.

The murdered engineer and fireman have probably been replaced by two soldiers experienced with locomotives.

Karl had disappared when the partisan was killed by the flame-thrower. Perhaps he has gone back to the front coach.

I climb into the freight car where they put Franz's body. I grope around, looking for the corpse, and finally find it in a corner.

My hand touches an ice-cold face. Rigid.

I shiver.

Poor Franz. All that's left of him.

Horror and disgust.

Slowly, the train moves off.

December 4. Franz now lies in the little cemetery of a lost village, somewhere in the interminable forests of the Kuberle valley.

He sleeps in this Russian soil he hated so.

May his sleep be untroubled.

Taking advantage of half a day's halt, I asked the colonel's permission to bury him. The colonel was very surprised to learn that the body of the second lieutenant of the 3rd was still in the train. But he understood and finally gave his consent.

We did not want to bury him simply in the ground, and spent a lot of time hunting for a coffin. But there wasn't one to be found in the whole village.

We had to make do with two long mortar-shell cases nailed end to end.

Getting him into it was frightful.

Then we carried it to a deep pit dug beneath the pine trees.

Behind the box, draped with a swastika flag borrowed from one of the tanks, we walked very slowly—Karl, Michael and I.

His three comrades.

When we had filled up the hole with earth, we erected the "memorial roof" [2] on the little mound. Karl had carved it hastily that morning.

Our eyes filled with tears as we gave him the last salute:

> I once had a comrade,
> But a bullet flew toward us through the air. . . .
> Was it meant for him, or was it meant for me? . . .
> I once had a comrade, . . .
> Now he is dead.

[2] The SS rarely put up crosses over the graves of their dead. Their usual memorial was a wooden board painted white, about eighteen inches high, the summit of which formed a roof. A black Maltese cross adorned the center of the "memorial roof," below which came the inscription giving name, age and date on which the SS man had fallen.

13. The Road to Stalingrad

December 10. Since dawn von Manstein's armies have been on the move from Kotelnikovo. The great onslaught of troops to relieve Stalingrad is heading for the Volga.

At five o'clock this morning a tremendous artillery barrage opened the offensive by destroying the Red positions. Two hours later the range was lengthened. Nearly a thousand heavy tanks set off along the Gremiatskaya road.

The Viking is the spearhead of the attack. For the moment the resistance we have met from Malinovski's forces has been relatively weak.

Our orders state that we are to seize and hold a bridgehead across the Aksai, a tributary of the Don, until the arrival of our main forces.

December 14. Throughout these last few days our advance has been general all along the Don, despite the fanatical resistance of the Reds and the terrible pounding we have received from their mobile guns. There are now only just over thirty-five miles left between us and Stalingrad.

Tonight while waiting for the order to attack, I thought about the question raised by our sudden departure from the Caucasus.

After the tremendous effort that had carried us almost to the shores of the Caspian, the High Command in East Prussia suddenly decided to abandon almost all the Caucasus.

The bitter centers of Russian resistance at Grozny and the Ordzhonikidzes, and the consequent heavy commitment of our forces at these places, were not a sufficient justification for the sudden retreat.

It seems likely that Supreme Headquarters considered it more urgent that the southern divisions should hasten to the help of Paulus's armies, rather than capture the oil wells.

Certainly the acute developments in and about Stalingrad were the main reason for this sudden about-face of strategy at the "Wolf's Lair."

Zhutov, December 17. The new German quick-firing Oerlikon guns and the 88 and 105 mm antitanks have momentarily checked the Russian counteroffensive, which was spearheaded by their T-34 and KV52 tanks.

These steel and concrete monsters weigh fifty-two tons and have tracks four feet nine inches wide. They crush anything in their path.

Last night six of these juggernauts pushed their way through to a ruined windmill, in which were a party of the 1st Antitank Battalion and also the whole of my company. Sometimes we thought we should never leave it alive.

We had only three antitank guns and a few bazookas. The men suddenly lost their nerve, panicked and fled into the mill, thinking they would be safe there from the KV52's.

Then the Red monsters half-turned away, and we breathed again. But not for long.

The tanks had simply withdrawn a short distance in order to fire with greater accuracy. They began to pound the ruined mill with a devilish concentration of shells. Our situation was critical, to put it mildly.

A runner nevertheless managed to get out and telephone through to regimental HQ. Fifteen minutes later a battery of self-propelled 88's and six 20-mm Oerlikons succeeded in avoiding the Soviet fire and installed themselves in the cover provided by the ruined building and the heaps of rubble.

Then the battle began.

The enormous 155's of the Russian tanks were firing AP shells without a pause, and these brought down those parts of the wall that were still standing as though they were so much cardboard.

One well-aimed shell from an 88 knocked out a Russian tank. But as time went on, it became clear that we wouldn't win. The armor of the KV52's was proving formidably effective.

Division, warned again of our acute peril, finally decided to send us ten Mark IV's as reinforcement.

And about time too. Fifteen men had been killed, including Warrant Officer Libesis. Yet another veteran of the Galician frontier gone.

Until well into the night this battle of the steel giants went on uninterruptedly. As night fell, the tracer bullets and shells made a sort of fiery spider's web in the sky, with the red glare from Novo-Mogiesk, which had been alight since morning, as a background.

It was a most impressive spectacle, these thundering monsters hurtling flat out at one another, accompanied by the appalling rending noise of their metal tracks, and all lit up by the flickering ruddy flames of the fires, or suddenly thrown into relief by showers of sparks from a crashing house.

This titanic struggle, with its deafening accompaniment of cannons and heavy machine guns, was terrifying in a way. We had seldom before had an opportunity to see a battle between tanks at such close range, and at night.

One imagined that in dim, prehistoric ages there must have been fabulous struggles much like this between mastodons fighting to the death beneath a leaden sky and in just such a cataclysmic atmosphere.

Finally, at about midnight, the last KV52 was destroyed.

But there were only three German tanks left in action.

December 18. The main body of Malinovski's forces is blocking our way.

Repeated attempts to seize Abganerovo from the Reds have so

far proved unsuccessful. Nearly three hundred enormous self-propelled guns, located by the Russians in an arc on a front of less than
twenty miles, are shelling our positions. In addition, thousands of
heavy guns are dropping a continuous barrage over the whole
sector.

The Bolsheviks know what they're up to. They are trying, by
every means in their power, to hold us along the Don and the Sal
until their reinforcements, which also must be making for Stalingrad, have reached the Volga.

Some German companies, which managed to break through the
Soviet circle of steel in the Krasnoarmeisk area, have succeeded in
joining Hoth's 4th Panzer Corps.

What those men tell us about conditions inside the beleaguered
city is appalling.

December 19. All our attacks are stopped by a most formidable
barrier of Red tanks. Thousands of Russian guns are completely
blocking our advance.

German divisions are continually arriving in front of Abganerovo
to reinforce our attacks. The Army Corps from the central front,
sent with all speed to attack the Soviet defensive positions, have
linked up with units from Kerch and Sebastopol in the Nizhni-
Chirskaya area.

These are those same heavy artillery regiments which a few
months ago destroyed the "steel boilers"[1] of the fortress and silenced
the enormous Maxim Gorki guns, as long as a ship's mast and
firing two-ton shells to a range of ten miles.

December 25. A terrible Christmas Eve.

At two o'clock in the morning, after an unprecedented artillery
barrage and heavy bombing from the air, screaming hordes of the
Mongols, Cherkas and Tatars, who always go in front of Malinovski's tanks, attacked our positions.

[1] All around Sebastopol, the Russians had built steel fortresses, dug deep into the
rock, from which only the colossal muzzles of the Maxim Gorki guns emerged.

These creatures are not men. They are wild beasts whom nothing can stop, not even death.

In the crude glare of enormous searchlights, the German heavy machine guns, our 88's, huge 400 mm mortars and great shrapnel shells made hecatombs of this human river, but it was still impossible to check its flow.

The power of this flood, rolling on inexorably through the darkness, was beyond imagination.

When dawn came, the Red tanks, deployed along a line several miles long on both sides of Abganerovo, now moved off in their turn.

Hundreds of T-34's, KV52's, gigantic sixty-four-ton Joseph Stalins and American Shermans pushed straight ahead, destroying everything in their path as they went.

It was impossible for our antitank guns to fire as a battery. For each tank destroyed, fifty more were advancing with an infernal thundering, guns blazing, like the fierce dragons of Asian myth and legend.

Clinging to the armor like flies, there were about twenty Russians on each tank, waiting for the moment to jump down and hurl themselves on the German tanks.

Men against steel, they throw themselves at the Marks and Panthers, shouting like lunatics, heedless of their hundreds of dead comrades, over whose bodies they must trample in order to reach our tanks.

Ten might fall, twenty, a hundred. It made no difference. The survivors, catching hold of the moving vehicles, leaped onto the German tanks and attacked the gun turrets. Clinging to the smallest steel or concrete handhold, they set off antipersonnel grenades or set fire to cans of gasoline until such time as they either lost their balance or were hit by bullet or shell. Then they would drop from the vast machines and fall beneath the tracks, to be crushed into a horrible pudding of flesh, earth and blood.

The gunners and drivers of the German tanks were driven almost insane by this pack of angry wolves whom they couldn't even see, let alone shake off. They could not fire at them since the Russians were sitting astride their gun barrels and machine guns; so they opened their turrets and smashed in the skulls of the *moujiks* with iron pipes and wrenches.

"Hurrah, Stalin!"

And still the waves of yellow, grinning, screaming savages came rushing into the attack, drunk with anger and hatred.

We have fought to the limits of our strength.

But today there were just too many of them for us.

December 30. We were too late to save Stalingrad.

The town is doomed. The German relieving force has been defeated in a counterattack by two Soviet Army Groups.

Our job is to cover the retreat of the forces retiring southwestward and of the engineer units, whose task it is to blow up everything once the rear guard has passed—roads, bridges and any factories remaining intact.

The partisans harass us continually in their desperate efforts to hinder our work of destruction.

It is our turn now to be "scorched earth" commandos.

December 31. Dirty work.

In the area we are evacuating, there is a camp of Jewish terrorists who were arrested in and about Rostov and were about to be deported to the West.

The regiment of cavalry who were guarding them up to now has also retreated southwestward.

And so we have been detailed to carry out the "administrative dissolution" of the camp. This is the mild official phrase used by the SSFHA, and it means, quite simply, the liquidation of the prisoners. The order specifies that, because of insurmountable transport difficulties, it is impossible to transfer the inmates anywhere outside the zone of operations.

At the moment there are about a hundred prisoners, walking about in small groups behind the barbed wire. They are worried, that's obvious. And understandably so.

During the last few weeks they have watched endless columns move past, headed for Stalingrad. Later, they saw von Manstein's divisions, driven back by the Red counteroffensive, taking the Lake Manych road again, and once more the endless columns passed by the concentration camp.

Finally the 34th Cavalry, who were guarding them, also went away, leaving them to the mercy of the SS.

And God knows the SS have a terrible reputation.

Especially among the Jews—Jews who are also partisans.

They hear their own artillery, thundering more loudly every hour. It's coming nearer.

And they continue to walk up and down, hardly daring now to look or speak to one another. Sometimes their eyes rest briefly on the black helmets of the SS on the far side of the barbed wire, machine pistols at the ready.

And they are afraid.

At camp HQ there is intense activity. All useful documents are being burned. The cavalry must have forgotten a lot of them in their hasty departure.

The company telephone never stops ringing. It is the rear guard units reporting the progress of the Red advance, hour by hour.

Through the windows I can see the SS collecting the prisoners in one corner of the camp, probably telling them of their imminent departure.

But heavy machine guns have been set up in firing positions in an angle of the enclosure. The partisans are growing more and more anxious, and cower as far as possible away from those black, shining barrels which can and will spit death.

The roar of the Soviet artillery north of Zimovniki comes steadily nearer. It's a safe bet that the prisoners' most passionate desire at this moment is for their own troops to advance no farther, to be held by the Wehrmacht. This might give them a chance of survival.

Somehow or other I have managed to get a table to sit at and I take advantage of these last few moments before we move off to write to Hamburg. But the babble of voices all about me is too distracting. I decide to postpone my letter-writing until later.

It is a group of men, arguing heatedly, and in the middle of them I see Major Stressling.

Stressling suddenly gets up. He is smiling sardonically.

"I shall prove it to you!" he sneers.

Several officers standing about shake their heads. Among them I notice Karl, and walk across to him.

"What's up?"

"Oh, nothing much! They've been jawing away for nearly an hour and still can't agree. Stressling maintains that he has only to give the order and some of these Russians will themselves kill their comrades in the hope of saving their own lives. It's ridiculous to waste time like this! We should have left the camp hours ago. The Russkies are getting near, and the demolition units finished their job before noon."

"How did the argument start?"

"It was silly. An engineer lieutenant was explaining to Stressling that in the pocket of a Russian prisoner taken last night, they found those leaflets that the Reds drop in thousands over occupied territories. The leaflet listed all the alleged atrocities committed by the SS during the last few months. It urged the Red soldiers and partisans to shoot any SS captured in action, without trial."

"So what?"

"So Stressling said that if the SS troops are sometimes forced to be ruthless when carrying out their orders during repressive actions, it is all merely done in self-defense. We are compelled to safeguard the German Army by every means in our power."

Karl walks up and down for a minute or two, then sits down on the edge of a table and turns to me, looking thoughtful.

"Actually, there's something to what he says. If we can talk a group of Russian traitors into shooting the other Russians, it will prove that in certain specific circumstances—for example, when it's a question of saving one's own skin—all men become quite ruthless."

I walk up to him.

"And what magnificent propaganda it would make, too. Though fundamentally I suppose it simply proves that a man at the point of death will cling with all his might to the slenderest hope, the merest straw, and will commit the most base and sordid act, the most infamous treason, in order to go on living. To see the sun rise at least once more, just once more. Only men of the toughest moral fiber are able to accept the fact of dying in the full knowledge that they are about to be plunged into nothingness. And I think there are very few men like that."

"So according to you, men who sacrifice their lives do so without really knowing what it is they're doing exactly?"

"No, I didn't quite say that. But I maintain—and this is only my own opinion and not gospel truth—that in battle, under torture, during moments of great suffering, many men whom we regard as heroes are temporarily in a peculiar frame of mind. I think that if they really accepted the fact, in cold blood, that their heroism was going to make them into corpses, into rotting flesh, into carrion— then perhaps they would be a little less heroic. Or rather I should say that we would be a little less heroic, for we are all basically much the same. We love to play at being heroes, even, perhaps especially, to ourselves. And then one always thinks that it won't happen, or that it will happen to somebody else."

We stop talking. Through the windows we can see Stressling gesticulating inside the enclosure.

The other officers have gone out, and we now follow them.

Six Russians have been led up to the machine guns, probably on the orders of the major. Several SS are rapidly explaining how they work. The Reds are terribly pale. In spite of the cold, there are great beads of sweat on their foreheads. The other prisoners at the far end of the yard have understood. Some of them spit in the direction of the traitors, a gesture of contempt. A flood of insults comes from the huddled group of condemned men.

It is all quite fantastic. Fantastic that they could be persuaded, fantastic that the volunteer executioners should really believe their lives will be spared in exchange for assassinating their comrades.

Six SS stand behind them, Mausers at the ready. But there is really no danger of the Russians suddenly turning the machine guns in the opposite direction. Still it's better to take no chances. A final revolt of conscience, perhaps, or a desperate rush upon the enemy. . . . In such an event they would have to turn the guns about. But the SS are watching, and very closely.

The men condemned to die are calm, most of them sitting stoically on the ground. Some are on their knees and seem to be praying.

Gradually they are all collected in a corner of the yard in front of a high wall, half in ruins. They look around, desperately, like animals caught in a trap. But there's nothing they can do, nothing even worth attempting.

Suddenly I understood why Stressling had waited so long before giving the order to open fire.

The population of the little village has been herded up to the camp gates. The soldiers are now organizing the people around the barbed wire so that they shall miss nothing of the spectacle about to be produced for them. Their eyes wide with terror, the villagers look alternately from the machine guns to the prisoners and back again.

The thunder of the Soviet heavy artillery to the northeast of the Kuberle is getting louder. Tanks dash along the road at full speed, overtaking heavy convoys of our naval artillery, also in full retreat. It is most unwise, to say the least, wasting precious time on this sinister and quite pointless drama, with the head of the Russian vanguard perhaps only a few hours away.

A shrill whistle blast rends the icy air.

The SS push the muzzles of their Mausers against the Russians' necks, and all six machine guns begin to *rat-tat-tat* at once.

The massacre is amazingly brief.

The rattle of the machine guns muffles the screams of terror and pain from the partisans as they fall one on top of another, cut down by the bullets.

When it's done, our men take over from the traitor-executioners. About ten SS walk across and complete the operation. Pushing the corpses aside with their boots, they finish off the dying with a bullet through the head; in ten minutes their macabre work is completed.

Stressling steps forward and gives a brief order.

"Now get this filthy gang out of here, all six of 'em!"

I can hardly believe my ears. It is fantastic that the Major should have really decided to let them go.

But I misjudged him.

The gates of the camp are open, and suddenly I understand.

The villagers, watching the drama, have just seen six traitors kill their own comrades. The major has had his reasons for bringing them all up to the camp.

Immediately the liberated partisans are outside the gates, the people rush upon them; shouting, hurling insults, tearing at their faces, drunk with fury, they begin raining blows on the ex-prisoners with anything they can get their hands on—stones, branches, pieces of iron.

After a moment or two the "free men" are nothing but broken, mutilated, bleeding bodies, corpses which the villagers are still beating in their hideous rage.

They have paid their debt.

Stressling, smiling strangely, looks very pleased with himself.

February 10, 1943. We are now holding the same positions as last summer, on the Kalmius, from Bestsinskaya to Nikolaevka, near the estuary that runs into the Gulf of Taganrog.

There is no purpose in describing in detail the circumstances which compelled the High Command to order a retreat to the south-west.

Four hundred thousand German dead have fallen in the struggle to hold the Don line.

And it has not been held.

The communiqués from Ortelsburg and the reports from No. 7

Wilhelmplatz[2] announce that strategic reasons are responsible for the fact that we are now entrenched on the far side of the Don. Solely, they say, so that we may be in a better position to beat off the Russian attacks.

But perhaps the High Command in East Prussia also considers it advisable that we should end the winter in positions fortified since last year and easily defended.

However, it is disquieting, to say the least, that the word "defense" appears more and more frequently in the communiqués.

February 12. Today we heard that Stalingrad has fallen.

On February 2, Paulus, appointed Marshal of the Reich by radio only forty-eight hours before, signed the capitulation of the German forces in the presence of Zhukov and Marshal of Artillery, Nikolai Voronov.

About twenty generals, including Paulus's staff—von Daniels, Schlömer, Rinoldi and von Drebber—surrendered to the Soviet troops.

Many people say that the Führer promoted Paulus to the rank of Marshal as a desperate measure, because he believed that the Supreme Commander of the 6th Army would then blow his brains out—as he had announced his intention of doing—rather than fall into Russian hands.

I remembered the conversation I had with Karl in December. Certainly there are plenty of examples to prove his point. Heroism is one thing—death is quite another.

There was a radio broadcast this morning of the ceremonies which took place in Berlin in commemoration of the hundreds of thousands who fell at Stalingrad. The bells of all the churches were tolling in Berlin; the flags were at half-mast. All activity in the capital had stopped. There was weeping in the streets.

The people are beginning to realize what war is like.

February 16. Kharkov has fallen to the combined forces of the

[2] The address of the Propaganda Ministry in Berlin.

Soviet generals Vatutin and Golikov. It was evacuated just before being caught in a pincer movement from the north and the south-east.

The Red offensive is developing along ominously mechanical lines. In the course of a single month the Bolsheviks have pushed our front back almost two hundred miles.

February 20. Once again we are advancing.

A lightning offensive, which recalls the glorious days of last July, has been launched from Stalino toward the north, in the direction of Kharkov.

General Popov's forces, who face us, being exhausted by their rapid advance, had spread out on too wide a front. This enabled our panzer divisions to break through their lines at several points.

March 15. Kharkov has been recaptured.

By the troops of the Vlasov Army, who were sent in ahead of the German forces. These men fight like tigers, just as fiercely against Russia as for her. Extraordinary! Only in this case one cannot ascribe it to that "love of the Russian soil" which is said to give them such courage and make them so very warlike.

It's a different approach that's needed here. So their officers repeat to them morning, noon and night that they must get rid of the Bolsheviks if they are later to win for themselves a Russia freed from oppression. Thus they still have the satisfaction of fighting for their country!

A sight worth its weight in roubles is to see the Yergeni Cossacks galloping in formation, dressed in German uniforms, brandishing their rifles and shouting like—Cossacks. And they say that you can't manufacture ideals like macaroni or cakes of soap.

14. On Leave

April 28. For hours now my pass has been carefully stowed away in my wallet. But I daren't think about it.

"Eighteen days' leave."

Including the long journey both ways, that means almost three weeks far away from the Donets plains.

I could almost shout for joy.

It is my first leave since the beginning of the war. But I hadn't hoped to get it this spring. I know of officers in armored divisions who came to the Eastern Front straight from Greece in 1941, and haven't been back in Germany since.

Karl went quite pale when I told him the news. He would have loved so much to go too. And I'd have been glad of his company on the journey.

He gave me an interminable list of things to bring back from Hamburg, and asked me to go and see his parents if I had the time.

April 29. "Be seeing you, Neumann!"

Slowly the truck which is taking us to Mariupol moves off.

One can already see, through the lacy branches of the pine trees beside the road, the blue waters of the Kalmius Bay, then the vast Gulf of Taganrog.

Opposite us, on the far shore, are the port installations of Yeisk, faintly visible through the slight heat haze. The Todt organization rebuilt the port in 1942. But now the Russians are there again.

234

Two hours later we arrive at Mariupol.

The sun is shining, and the town is a blaze of brilliant color—red roofs, white walls, multicolored shutters.

Mariupol has suffered terribly from bombing, and from the ceaseless attacks and counterattacks. But the inhabitants have succeeded in hiding the scars and making their town look quite gay.

Street traders are all over the place, shouting and gesticulating as they offer their shining silks, fruits and pitchers of Crimean wine.

One would never believe that the war is only fifty miles away.

April 30. The train rolls rather slowly along the railway lines through the Dnieper valley; they have been relaid a hundred times, and then destroyed again. A little way beyond Zaporozhe we cross the river.

Zaporozhe. That was the place where we had arrived too late to stop the destruction of the giant dam. How many of our comrades now lie beneath the fir trees in those little graveyards that line the banks of the Dnieper!

The train is filled with men going on leave, and they shout out of the open windows.

I spent some time chatting with an artillery lieutenant, who has told me about the siege of Leningrad last winter.

The town has been surrounded since September 1941, and the Russians have not yet surrendered. To the north, Mannerheim's Finnish troops are blocking the Karelian Isthmus. For months Leeb's armies and the SS police divisions have been vainly attacking the Red defenses.

Last winter, to solve their munitions supply problems, the Russians built a railway in a mere two months. This railway skirted the northern approaches to the German fortress of Schlüsselberg.

It had one peculiarity, which surely made it unique.

It was built on the ice of Lake Ladoga. . . .

To the despair of our artillery, the ice held throughout the winter despite almost daily shelling. It was only when the ice melted in the spring that the line was broken and the Russians were compelled to carry out a general retreat.

The lieutenant told me that from the German advance positions in the Pulkovo outskirts it was possible to see quite distinctly, through field glasses, traffic moving about the streets of Leningrad, and even the barricades built around overturned streetcars.

May 2. Zhitomir, Lublin, Warsaw, Berlin, and at last the banks of the Havel.

I breathe great gulps of good German air into my lungs, the scent of the forests of my childhood and the peculiar smell of those tiny blue lakes, which look almost emerald among our dark fir trees.

Everything must surely be the same, everything *is* the same, but somehow it all seems strangely different. It is as though all these roads, all these little paths which I have bicycled along so many times, are now in some way unreal, are part of a dream.

Unless it is my eyes that have changed.

I wanted to stop at Wittenberge before going to Hamburg since I had to see Franz's parents.

As I got out of the bus, I saw several faces which were familiar to me. But I couldn't put a name to them. People were turning around, looking curiously at me.

I could hear them saying, "That's young Neumann, you know! He's an officer in the SS now. Yes, I told you so. . . ."

Wittenberge has been bombed by the Americans. The front of the Town Hall has been completely destroyed. The glass roof of the shopping arcade has no panes left.

I soon reach Franz's house.

All of a sudden my heart seems to miss a beat. In my imagination I can see his window opening the way it always used to when I whistled from the street, and hear his cheerful voice shouting, "O.K. I'll be right down!"

He won't look out of that window, ever again.

I ring the bell. It is his mother who opens the door. She is very startled to see me.

"Herr Neumann! Peter. Come in, come in, dear boy!"

She has changed terribly. The dark bags and wrinkles under her eyes make her look like an old woman already.

I try to smile.

"Hello, Frau Hättenschwiller. I thought I'd just look in and see you on my way home. I wanted to tell you—"

A strangled sob. She takes my hand and makes me sit down.

"How did it happen? I mean, how did he die?"

"Bravely. Like a good German. With great courage. He asked me to kiss you and his father for him."

This was not quite true, but I thought it would please the poor woman. She is weeping very quietly, her shoulders shaken by sobs.

She looks at me tearfully.

"Where is he buried? They haven't burned my poor boy, have they?"

"No. I was able to save him from the crematorium. He is somewhere in the Manych plain. Karl and I saw to his . . . burial. Perhaps, after the war, you could have him brought back here."

I couldn't bring myself to say, "You could have his body brought back here."

She says in a trembling voice, "And the district where he is? It's occupied by them now? My Franz, is he being trampled underfoot by those savages?"

She throws herself across the table, sobbing uncontrollably.

I haven't the strength to stay there any longer, nor to wait for Franz's father to come in. I get up. If I stay, she'll make me start crying too. That would be the last straw. An SS with tears pouring down his cheeks.

"I must go now, Frau Hättenschwiller. My train leaves in half an hour."

This is another lie. But I can't sit here and watch this woman crying. Suddenly I wonder whether she knows it was I who persuaded Franz to join up.

In a sort of daze I walk down the road to the station. I have nothing more to do here anyhow. Karl's parents have been gone since the beginning of the war, and I don't want to see Michael's father.

May 3. I have found Hamburg terribly bombed by the RAF Mosquitoes.

In the streets around the docks, half the buildings are nothing but ruins. In the industrial district of Wilhelmsburg most of the factories have been destroyed. The old quarter of Sankt Pauli and the districts along the Elbe have also been bombed repeatedly by British aircraft.

Almost everywhere I have seen interminable lines of refugees. The poor wretches line up for hours at a time outside the soup kitchens, which apparently stay open night and day.

A strange reception at home.

Father embraced me almost absent-mindedly when I arrived, although it is more than two years since I have been home. Then he shook his head and started filling his old pipe.

"You've changed, my boy! An officer, eh? I suppose I ought to be proud of you. I hardly managed to make corporal myself. But that was at Verdun. That was a different sort of war. It was a war of soldiers, that one. There was no Gestapo in those days. And no planes coming to murder civilians!"

He sat down. "No SS either."

He settled himself more comfortably in his armchair and looked at me.

"Well, what's going on over there? They say the Russkies are driving you back across the frontier."

He looked at the floor.

"Of course they don't tell us that in the news broadcasts. Luckily there's always the English radio."

"You listen to the English radio?"

"Yes, I do, my boy. And why not? Must we be satisfied with all the nonsense we get from your Himmler and that little Goebbels man?"

He seemed to me suddenly a most contemptible person. But I asked him, quite calmly, "Do many people . . . listen in to London?"

"Why on earth should I know or care? Anyhow you don't discuss that sort of thing with the neighbors. They've got sharp ears, these State Police boys, and they're all over the place!"

He seems terribly embittered. He has really never gotten over his imprisonment. Obviously he hates the régime. The SS, too, he dislikes. I remember that when I was leaving for Bad Tölz he produced every argument in an attempt to make me change my mind. He will never forget the bad turn his son-in-law did him and the SS interrogations at Wittenberge in 1938.

Mutti tells me that she often sees Lena and her husband, but secretly. They have a lovely youngster whom Father has refused to see. He doesn't even want to hear their names mentioned.

May 9. As a result of walking about the city and keeping my ears open to people's grievances, I realize that things on the home front are not too good.

The restrictions are becoming more and more intolerable. The meat ration is minute. Bread is issued by the ounce. Potatoes are unobtainable. Last winter there were things to be had but at prohibitive prices. The Gestapo got hold of all the war profiteers who were cashing in on the black market and locked the lot up in the camp at Oranienburg.

Luckily I've brought whole sheets of unused service food coupons with me. A sergeant gave me about twenty of them before I left for Mariupol. This is somewhat irregular, but at least it means that we can all eat as much as we want. For as long as I'm on leave, at any rate.

May 16. Klauss insisted upon introducing me to his Hitler Youth leader. We spent the day at the camp at Lintzellt, on Lüneburger Heath.

All the boys clustered about me, hanging on my words. I really felt I must be the very incarnation of German heroism.

I had to tell them a hundred times about life at the front, and explain the strategy of attacks and counterattacks, and describe the battle of the Caucasus and the dash to capture the oil wells.

May 19. Rummaging around in a cupboard looking for one or two things I want to take back with me, I came across a tin box, which I opened without thinking.

It contained seven letters, all from Brigitta. All written between July and December, 1941.

"Peter darling, I implore you, please answer my letter. Why this silence?"

"My own Peter, what's happened to you? How can you be so mean as not to write to me?"

"My love, even if we never see each other again, ever, you *must* write. To explain."

The last one said: "My poor darling, I understand, and I shan't bother you any more. I hope you will be happy."

I went to find Mutti in the kitchen, where she was washing dishes. Without a word I handed her the letters.

She turned pale and murmured, "Peter! Those letters came while you were away, and I didn't want to send them on to you at the front. I'm sorry, dear."

"And why haven't you told me about them since I've been here?"

She looked up. Her lips were trembling.

"It was difficult, Peter! You see, she came to Wittenberge to see you. I explained to her you had joined the SS. Then she made me promise not to tell you about her visit. And she went away, in tears."

"But why? Why?"

"She was wearing a yellow star, Peter!"

"A yellow star? A Jewess, you mean?"
"Yes, Peter."

May 20. I had to see Brigitta again.

All night I wondered how I could find her. Her last letters had
been posted in Munich. Perhaps I would be lucky enough to find her
still living with her aunt at Pasing.

By nine o'clock my mind was made up.

I gave Mutti the first excuse that came into my head, that I was
going to see Karl's parents in the Heinnich, and I went off. I don't
know whether she believed me.

At ten fifteen I took the express to Munich from the Kirchallee
station.

I arrived a little before midnight.

According to the regular travelers on the train we were very lucky
to reach Bavaria without any delay. Usually the air-raid warnings
and British bombers force the trains to stop. Sometimes the locomotives are hit, and then the passengers have to wait for hours for a
new engine to be brought along.

I went out into the square in front of the station, wondering how
I would spend the rest of the night. It was obviously out of the
question to turn up at Pasing at this hour.

The town was in darkness, and one couldn't see more than three
steps ahead. Civil defense regulations, presumably.

I suddenly remembered a beer hall on the Karlsplatz which used
to stay open late. That one, or another one. . . .

I began to walk down the Prielmayerstrasse.

Crossing the Karlsplatz, I entered the Neuhauserstrasse. The Café
Schwarzensohn was on this street. And I could already hear the
heavy, rhythmic beat of a Bavarian or Tyrolean orchestra.

I pushed open the door and entered the café.

There was a thick curtain of smoke through which I could
vaguely discern waiters hurrying to and fro, jostling past with
laden trays. It was incredible how they could run, carrying dishes
from one end of the room to the other with never a spill.

The tables were almost all taken by servicemen from the Wehrmacht and the Luftwaffe, and there were few vacant places.

I sat down at a table by the cashier's desk and ordered a dark Pilsen from the waiter, who was back with it immediately.

As I had guessed before coming in, it was a Tyrolean orchestra that was endeavoring to drown out the customers' conversation.

After a quarter of an hour, I began to be very bored. The noise and smoke were getting on my nerves.

"May we join you, Lieutenant?"

Two men in black uniform were standing before me, men of the Totenkopf Verbänd.[1] I had not seen them arrive.

"Please do. I am alone."

They wore NCO's stripes. They were obviously stationed in Munich. But I asked them. It was a way of passing the time.

"No, we are at a concentration camp not far from here. A place called Dachau, about twelve miles from Munich."

I had heard of this camp and knew its sinister reputation. I didn't envy the men guarding the prisoners. I knew that it was usually SS who had been wounded at the front who were attached to Himmler's camps. Or else the sadistic military types, former educators of the SA who had transferred to the Totenkopf.

"Are there a lot of people in your camp?" I asked.

The younger of the two smiled.

"We keep the numbers as low as we can. But prisoners are turning up from all over Europe. Especially from Poland, the Sudetenland and France. A lot of Jews. If we had to house them all, Munich itself wouldn't be big enough. So, we make room."

"I see. You . . . eliminate—?"

His smile suddenly became rather fixed.

"That's right, Lieutenant. We eliminate. . . ." He sneered rather strangely.

"How?"

[1] Special Death's-Head units, extermination units also used for guard duties in the concentration camps.

The elder of the two answered sullenly, "Better not discuss it—especially not here!"

Stupid of me. These boys hadn't come to the Schwarzensohn to talk about their work.

Funny sort of work, all the same. Spending your life killing people.

He must have felt a certain confidence when he saw my double Iron Cross, my battle honors and the silver SS Decoration, for he went on, "We're only concerned with the—well—the technical part of it, you know. The crematorium. It's nothing to do with us how they're liquidated!"

The other sergeant now chipped in, "At first they used exhaust gas. Several trucks were driven up close to the gas chambers. They ran the engines for a few minutes, and it was done. The gas was piped into the rooms. Now I think they've something quicker and more effective. A poison gas."

"Were you ever there, at any of the mass executions?"

The NCO suddenly looked uncomfortable.

"Only once. I didn't want to see another. You've got to be very tough. They've got specialists to do it. It's awful to watch. All the people come in naked, carrying their soap and washing things, thinking they're going to the showers. Then they seal the concrete doors on them hermetically and let in the gas. There are spy holes through which you can watch what's happening inside. When the prisoners see the jets of white vapor instead of the hot water they expected, they understand at once. They begin screaming and flinging themselves against the doors like lunatics. But it doesn't take long. At least so the doctors and the Stubendienst[2] fellows say. Actually these Stubendienst prisoners are usually responsible for cleaning up afterward. The corpses and—well—the rest of the mess."

"Then you have to do the rest?"

He settled himself back more comfortably in his seat and lit a cigarette. After blowing out a long cloud of smoke toward the

[2] Prisoners responsible for "blocks" in the concentration camps.

ceiling, he said, "Not exactly. It's the prisoners themselves, or rather some of them, who do the most repulsive part."

He straightened up.

"And it's more hygienic than burying them, you know."

He glanced toward the orchestra which was still playing, and added as though talking to himself, "There are words written over the doors of the incinerators: 'Disgusting worms must not be permitted to fatten on our dead bodies. Flame is pure. It is by flame that we must be destroyed. I have always loved heat and light so. . . . That is why we must be burned. We must never be buried!' "

"Don't you think we could talk about something else?" asked the younger man. "Tell us what it's like in Russia," he added, turning to me.

The first bus next morning took me to the little square where I had gone with Brigitta on several occasions before the war.

It was a damp, misty morning that made the working-class suburb of Pasing appear even more melancholy than usual.

I tried to find my way, but the buildings had been bombed here too, and everything looked different.

I entered a bakery smelling of newly baked bread fresh from the ovens.

"Excuse me. Can you tell me where Frau Halsted lives?"

The woman looked me up and down in silence for a moment. Then she answered dryly, "Third street on the right, before the road fork. Number thirty or thirty-two."

I thanked her, and a few moments later was standing outside a humble house. There was a brass plate on the door which said: "Frau Halsted, *Dressmaker.*" I rang the bell, and almost at once a window opened. An old woman's head appeared.

"What do you want? Oh, it's you again, is it? Well, what is it this time?"

Thoroughly confused by this, I asked, "May I see Fräulein Halsted? Brigitta."

The woman was leaning out.

"Brigitta? Just a minute, I'll be right down."

A few moments passed, and then she appeared at the front door.

"Why, it's Peter Neumann! I should have recognized you. I thought you were one of those police. They're here the whole time, badgering us!"

She smiled sadly at me.

"We're Jewish, you know. They've already locked up my poor brother and my sister-in-law. Now they're trying to get my niece. . . . Germany has sunk very low, I'm afraid. But here I am, talking away, and not even asking you in. Brigitta's still asleep, but she'll be so pleased, I'm sure she will! She's talked about you a lot. Come in, come in!"

It was then that I understood the rather peculiar attitude of the woman in the bakery. She too must have mistaken me for a policeman.

"Would you like a cup of coffee? It isn't very good, but it's warming. But what a silly old woman I'm getting to be! You're in a hurry to see Brigitta, aren't you? Go on upstairs, sir."

She pointed toward a door on the first floor. "That's her room up there."

Seeing that I hesitated, she added, shaking her head, "She's told me all about it, you know. Poor little thing, she does love you so."

The door suddenly opened and there was Brigitta, dressed in pajamas. She was no longer a young girl. She had become a woman. She was very pale.

"Peter! It's not possible!" she gasped.

I ran up the stairs.

"Brigitta. I never knew. I only read your letters two days ago."

"It doesn't matter. Come in, Peter."

She took me by the hand and closed the door behind us.

"We had a long talk, your mother and I. She said you were in the SS. Did she tell you about me?"

"But what difference does that make, Brigitta?"

"But still, suppose *they* knew you had come here?"

"I'm on leave from Russia, Brigitta! Twenty-two months at the front. I think I've seen enough out there to know how to deal with *them.*"

She suddenly threw herself into my arms.

Her breathing became uneven, and she broke away from me.

"Come, Peter! Come. I have waited so long," she whispered hoarsely.

I took her gently in my arms and laid her on the bed.

"Peter, my darling . . ."

"Do you live alone with your aunt? What's happened to your parents?"

We had been talking for some time, but now her face suddenly hardened.

"My parents? That's a long story. One day in July of 1941 they came to interrogate my father. They were police from the Gestapo B Section.[3] They said he had falsified his identity card. Which was true, as it happened. Our real name is Halstedysch. My grandfather was Polish. My aunt, my father's sister, was able to change her name legally before the war. But my father thought it would be easier to change his on his own. So they took him to the local Gestapo office and then sent him to prison. Two months later, he was sentenced to five years' detention. Then, nobody quite knew why, he was sent to Oranienburg. At first we were allowed to visit him. But without any warning, and for no apparent reason, the Kripo[4] stopped our visits."

She pressed her head against my shoulder.

"He told us that his life there was not unbearable. But there were SS in black uniforms supervising all our conversations. Perhaps that's why he spoke the way he did, and didn't dare say anything."

She raised her eyes to mine.

[3] In charge of the apprehension of Jews, Freemasons and members of religious orders.

[4] Kriminalpolizei (Criminal Police), among other matters, responsible for the sending of prisoners to concentration camps.

"I don't think they're the same sort of SS as you. At least you're a fighting soldier. Those others are plain murderers!"

I laid my hand over her lips.

"Hush, Brigitta. Go on."

"From then on we were ordered to wear the awful yellow star. Nobody at the office had known before that I was Jewish. I didn't want to go back. It was so awful, so humiliating. To be branded like an animal. In the street people turned away in disgust. Another torture was going into a shop and having your purchase handed to you at arm's length, as though you were a leper. In the end, we really began to believe ourselves that we were some sort of lepers. We felt suffocated, trapped, unable to breathe. We could hardly bear to go on living. It was too much for Mama. She died last year, cursing the Nazis with her dying breath."

She jerked back her head fiercely.

"I curse them, too. Because they killed Mama. But perhaps not as much as I curse my ancestors. Those people who gave us this appalling heritage to lug along with us forever, like a ball and chain. I hate them! I hate them! If you only knew, Peter, how much I loathe them. I am Jewish myself, but I bear them nothing but ill will. By what right, for what reason, have they handed us down this curse, this terrible blemish?

"You know, I don't think I'm unique in feeling this way. When they're together or linked up by some common interest, the Jews appear to help one another, to love one another, but I think a Jew's worst enemy is another Jew."

She cuddled up to me.

"Or maybe I'm crazy. My aunt is always telling me I am. She says I'll make myself ill with all these ideas. But you see, I have suffered so much from it all. Even as a child, there was only one thought in my mind: that people shouldn't find out. If you only knew what I went through at school! You remember Streicher's paper, the *Stürmer,* which had to be pinned up on the bulletin boards in all schools and colleges? I can see the kids now, running after us and throwing stones at us. It was frightful. And the teachers did nothing to stop them. It was partly because of that that we moved and my father tried to adjust his identity papers."

She managed to smile bravely.

"Peter darling, I've talked enough about all that. Tell me what your life is like at the front."

There was a moment's silence; then before I had time to reply, she went on.

"It's funny, though. To think I've slept with an SS officer. And poor Mama hated them so. But those others are not like my Peter. They were monsters!"

She shrugged her shoulders and pouted.

"Monsters? It's silly to say that, really. They were policemen, or guards. They did their jobs as policemen and guards, and that was all. You can't condemn a man for being the sort of man he is, a coward maybe or just spineless, any more than you can condemn a tiger for being cruel or a donkey for being stupid! Those others were made the way they are, like the tigers and the donkeys."

I interrupted. "Please, Brigitta, you mustn't be so bitter. As you said yourself, let's talk about something else."

"You're quite right!"

She stretched out, folded her hands behind her head and raised one knee.

"All the same, it's very strange!" she murmured dreamily, her eyes on the ceiling.

I leaned over her.

"My darling Brigitta!"

She smiled at me tenderly.

"Peter, I love you, you know that. Now tell me, when must you go back to Russia? I'm so afraid you're going to leave me all alone again, for a long, long time."

"I have to go back to Hamburg tonight. And my leave is up in two days. But the war will be over soon, Brigitta!"

She pressed her body to mine again.

"And what about when the war *is* over? Do you think I have any illusions left? You came here because you wanted me, I suppose.

But after the war. . . . You know, there's not much chance of happiness and peace for us Jews."

For us Jews.

Suddenly I realized. I loved her, and I was afraid for her. But the others, all those others. In Russia and elsewhere. Those people for whom I had had no pity.

It was very strange.

Part IV

NIGHT

15.   The Clash

After a hundred days' of quiet, all hell broke loose again on the Eastern Front.

That was on July 5, 1943.

And it was Kursk, the greatest battle of all time.

Nearly a million men hurled themselves upon each other. Three hundred divisions were in action.

The clash was appalling.

Von Kluge's armies opened the battle, attacking on a front of barely thirty miles with a concentration of guns and men never before committed into action on so narrow a front.

A hundred divisions, of which thirty-one were armored and ten motorized, hurled themselves upon the Red positions.

But five hundred guns per mile, four thousand heavy or medium tanks, an aerial armada of two thousand planes and the seven hundred thousand men commanded by Koniev, Rokossovsky and Popov formed a wall of steel which the Wehrmacht proved incapable of breaking through.

The Soviet Marshal Koniev, at the head of his armored forces, was in the very forefront of the battle, directing operations and issuing orders to his eighteen subordinate generals by radio.

This time the Reds knew their own strength.

During two years of battle, their war machine had had time to be made perfect. Two years of terror, of liquidations, of unceasing

253

work, had conjured thousands of factories, steel plants, blast furnaces and munitions plants out of the ground.

The German armored spearhead could not advance more than ten miles. And those ten miles had cost one hundred thousand dead and nearly three thousand tanks destroyed.[1]

And then on July 15, the Red Army launched its counterattack.

Ten thousand new Soviet tanks, commanded by Rokossovsky, were launched against Orel and Kharkov.

Orel fell on August 5, Kharkov on the 23rd.

On the 30th, Tolbukhin's screaming horde of 30,000 Cossacks seized Taganrog.

On September 8, Stalino was lost. On the 24th, Dnepropetrovsk was evacuated, after a terrible battle.

The northern Dnieper was reached on October 5, and the leading Bolshevik units crossed the river at Kremenchug and Pereyaslav.

The bridgeheads, garrisoned at once by fresh divisions from the Far East, were rapidly turned into strongpoints. By November 2, almost the entire left bank of the Dnieper was in the hands of the Red Army.

On the Moscow front, the situation was at least as serious. The Soviet spearhead had broken through to the key position of Smolensk.

The whole front was disintegrating.

For a brief moment the Wehrmacht succeeded in holding back the giant Russian war machine outside Dymer, Krivoi Rog and Cherkassy. But Koniev's armies had only stopped to reform and draw breath. They were soon advancing once again toward the frontiers, and the gigantic Red steam roller now crushed the desperate German resistance.

On Christmas Day, 1943, Zhukov's Army Group started to march westward again.

---

[1] The figure is enormous when one considers that on the French front, in 1944, the Germans could never muster more than 2,900 tanks against the Allies.

Korsun, Shevschekovski, Shanderowska . . . hellish caldrons in which the best of our comrades died.

Four thousand two hundred men killed in three weeks; such was the terrible toll exacted in our defense of the Cherkassy pocket.

The Viking, attached now to the 8th Army, was encircled just west of the Dnieper, in December, and with it were the Motorized Brigade Wallonia and the remnants of the 72nd and 112th Infantry Divisions.

Early in January the steel jaws began to close. From our entrenched positions along the tributaries of the river, we could see through field glasses the Soviet propeller-driven sledges moving up, skimming rapidly over the snow, bringing up the cannons and mortars which were immediately made ready for action.

Our positions soon became untenable, being continually bombarded by enormous 400 mm mortars, the terrifying mobile gun called the "Molotov" and, worst of all, the diabolical Katiusha.[2]

Six, nine, twelve, twenty-four barrels firing at once.

By the end, we didn't even dare lift our heads. The ever-present certainty of imminent death completely destroyed all our powers of reaction.

Taking advantage of a foggy night and a desperate counterattack, three companies of the Viking, of which mine was one, succeeded miraculously in breaking through the encirclement.

Behind us, the Russian jaws continued to close inexorably.

A few days later we learned from the Swedish newspapers and from Moscow Radio the story of the last days of the Viking and of the Wallonia. They had put up a heroic resistance.

On February 8 they rejected an ultimatum.

On the 18th, the Reds gave the signal for the final mopping-up operation.

Fifteen fresh divisions were hurled against the German position, now held by men weakened by hunger, privation and cold.

[2] Literal translation: "Little Catharine."

Few survived.

But they did not surrender.

March 3, 1944. The survivors of the Viking division have been sent on orders from on high to Krasnystaw, a little town to the south of Lublin.

We are beside the Wieprz, only about twenty-five miles from Rawa Ruska. Rawa Ruska, which we left one day in June 1941, heading east . . . and the Russians are now sixty miles from the place.

The division is reorganized rapidly. Several thousand volunteers have arrived from Germany and the occupied countries. Among them are many Belgians, Dutchmen and Norwegians.

General Gille, our divisional commander, has had a lot of trouble, it seems, getting these reinforcements and also the new equipment and weapons from the SSFHA. The brass hats at Charlottenburg didn't actually tell him to build his own trucks and guns, but it seems they almost did.

Comfortably installed in their underground bunkers, these fine fellows have no very clear picture of what the Ukrainian campaign is like.

March 8. We are alerted in the middle of the night and sent in the direction of Kowel, which Zhukov's armies are threatening.

A long column of trucks, all lights extinguished, takes the regiment toward the front.

March 19. Kowel has disappeared in a storm of steel.

The Soviet Stormovik planes scream across the town, almost scraping the rooftops. We can clearly see the helmeted pilots in their plexiglass cockpits.

The Russian airmen fire their four-barreled machine guns at us. With each fresh burst, some of our comrades fall mortally wounded. The Luftwaffe is still nowhere to be seen.

We are dug in on the outskirts of the town, beside the Turja, a wretched stream which flows God knows where. The German tanks are dug deep into the ground to form hedgehogs, and each one is a miniature fortress in itself. They blaze away at the Bolshevik positions.

Heavy shells are exploding overhead, to become thousands of small and deadly bits of white-hot steel that whistle down and bury themselves in the ground.

The ground shakes as though this were the cataclysm to mark the end of the world.

After several hours of this frightful din, constant explosions and shellfire, one's mental processes are paralyzed.

It is sometimes not hard to see how people can welcome death as a deliverance. Indeed, it's very easy. Death, which means silence, peace and quiet.

And this inferno goes on for two days. But during these two days, the constant Red attacks have been repelled everywhere. Our orders were to hold fast.

March 20. The lieutenant who is in charge of operations at division HQ reports Red infiltrations all along the embankment. We are to go and meet them, and cover the railway line.

A radio message gives me my orders from advanced HQ, which is somewhere near what was Kowel station.

Following behind three Tigers sent by Division, my company advances slowly toward the Russians.

Dull rumbles, followed by great sighing sounds like the blast of a furnace.

"They're firing Big Charlie," [3] somebody near me shouts.

Since the heavy artillery is joining in, it would seem likely that Division has observed new Soviet armored formations moving up from the east. The Russkies must capture Kowel at all costs. The town is actually the key junction of the roads leading farther into Poland and to Slovakia.

Nearly all the men in my battle group are new recruits. It's

_____
[3] A heavy 600 mm railway gun.

difficult to make them camouflage themselves properly. The platoon commanders have to shout orders and give warnings almost all the time. Even despite this the men are steadily being shot down. They roll over on the ground, as though astonished by what has happened to them; then they begin to moan quietly. Some call for their mothers. Funny sort of SS men, this crowd! It's true, though, that the poor kids have been sent straight to the front after only a couple of months' training.

Poor kids. . . . I talk of them as though I were very old and experienced. And I'm just twenty-four. But these thirty-two months of almost uninterrupted active service have greatly aged me.

Following behind the Tigers, we move along the axis of what was once a street but is now a desolate track flanked by smoldering ruins. The name of the street is on a plaque which hangs from a small piece of iron on one wall: "Bronplac." Where are all the people who used to live on Bronplac? It is hard to believe that these ruins were once homes, that human beings could have ever lived their lives in peace between these crumbling walls.

A company of the antitank battalion is in position on our left, firing toward the level crossing.

The Russkies can't be far away.

All of a sudden, we hear music, quite close at hand. We gaze questioningly at each other. What can be going on?

Then I see a propaganda truck a dozen or so yards away, and I realize what's happened. The road must have been blocked at the start of battle by Russian gunfire, and the truck can't get back. So the men of the Propaganda Unit are playing their phonograph to keep themselves amused. Now I've seen everything! Strauss waltzes, in the middle of a battle.

It would certainly be original, if nothing else, to be killed in action to the strains of *Tales from the Vienna Woods.*

But suddenly we hear a different sort of music.

The Bolsheviks are attacking. Led by some twenty Maxims on wheels, they emerge in close formation from behind a ruined block of buildings. It's quite rare nowadays to see these old-fashioned Maxims. Still, I've no time to think about that now!

The 122's mounted in the Tigers and the MG's all begin to fire at once. The Reds are brought down in great heaps, one on top of the other. But slowly, yard by yard, they advance upon us. Their compact sections re-form as they come on, apparently none the thinner for the loss of so many men. As though on parade, they march almost rigidly, their rifles held before them.

The way they do things is confusing to us since it does not correspond to any strategic concept. Only the troops in front are able to fire. Their commanders obviously reckon on losing a hundred, maybe a thousand men, but presumably believe that they will inevitably force a way through our positions in the end.

A great roar suddenly comes from all these thousands of men marching steadily to their death.

They are singing.

They must have thought that the music from the propaganda truck was meant to give us courage, and out of bravado they have begun to sing at the top of their voices.

It is a Ukrainian song which they often sing when going into the attacks. But today this thunder of thousands of heavy boots, this horde of men indifferent to their fate, this artillery duel and the discord produced by our music and the singing of the Russians, all combine to make one feel that it is the appalling collision of two worlds.

The man from the Propaganda Unit, over there in his truck, is broadcasting a record of the SS march through his amplifier.

And the Russians are still marching relentlessly toward us, though cut down in their masses by our heavy machine-gun fire. The living trample over the bodies of the dead.

And the loudspeaker blares.

Hot steel and lead finally win this battle against the obstinacy, determination and courage of the Reds.

The three Tigers, which have been joined by about ten Mark

II's, see that the Russian attack is wavering and with a thunderous rumbling they now go into action. Engines at full speed, they race into the leading Bolshevik ranks.

Terrible cries, shrieks of agony, the appalling cracks of broken bones, a horrible mess of blood and entrails sticking to the tank tracks, and then the machine guns to finish the job. It's all over.

The Lvov-Bialystok railway line is still clear for the passage of our troop trains.

Mission completed. . . .

March 30. Karl was wounded during the disengagement battles on the outskirts of Kowel.

I found time to visit him at the advanced aid station before the ambulance took him to the hospital train. This train would carry him to the hospital at Kracow, which is where all the seriously wounded from our sector go.

He was very pale, lying on a stretcher. The aid station had been set up in an old cotton mill, or so I guessed from the rows of smashed machines which must have once been looms.

"Hello, Karl. You've done all right, my lad! Now you're sure to finish the war quietly."

I looked at the blood- and pus-stained bandages which swathed the lower half of the body.

"Is it your leg?"

He tried to smile.

"Both my legs. I'm the second of us to go. . . . After Cherkassy, though, I thought I'd escaped."

"Escaped? You're crazy! Come on, Karl, you're not going to let a miserable little leg wound get you. You're always complaining! If I were in your place I wouldn't."

"Don't try to be funny, Peter. My left leg is completely torn off. They haven't even bothered to take the splinters out of the other one."

He was talking in a hoarse voice which I hardly recognized. His face was wan, and he was breathing with great difficulty. I was suddenly overcome by an appalling fear. I was certain that Karl was going to die; and if that happened, then I knew I wouldn't, couldn't escape.

An Army doctor walked up to us, not wearing SS insignia.

"Leave him now, Lieutenant. He needs rest."

In the Wehrmacht they take no notice of our SS ranks. They pretend not to know what they are. Actually, I believe they almost despise us.

I salute.

"Yes sir."

He walks away, and I follow him.

"Excuse me, sir, are you looking after the lieutenant?"

He replies that he is.

"Then can you tell me if his wounds are really serious?"

"Amputation of the left leg. We hope to save the other, but it will be difficult. Anyhow, we're giving him priority. He won't have to wait for the hospital train, he'll go by 'corrugated.' " [4]

I thank him, and walk back to Karl.

"What did he say?" he asked.

"That everything is all right, and that you'll be at Zakopane[5] within two months."

I shake hands with him.

"Good-by, Karl. Remember me to all the fellows when you're back in Wittenberge."

He looks at me gravely.

"Good-by, Neumann, and good luck!"

I don't have the courage to turn around again before I leave, though I can feel his eyes fixed on my back.

It should cheer him up no end, to see a man who can still walk.

---

[4] The Germans used this name for the Junker 52's and Junker 88's, the fuselages of which were made of thick, corrugated steel.

[5] SS convalescent hospital, situated south of Kracow, near the Slovakian frontier.

16. Holding Fast

May 29. Major Stressling has sent for me to come to his office at advanced HQ.

"Sit down, Neumann. GHQ at Charlottenburg has entrusted us with a very important assignment. I shall need men of courage, who have proved their worth. So I have detailed your men to come with me to White Russia. I asked you to come and see me here so that you'll have your men ready by tomorrow morning. Any questions?"

I get up, filled with curiosity, and a little taken aback by his extraordinary announcement which has been made without any preamble.

"Where are we going, and what exactly is our assignment, Major?"

"That, my boy, you will learn later!"

May 31. It was only yesterday evening that we set off in half a dozen trucks.

At Brest Litovsk, we officers were able to move into more comfortable, lighter vehicles.

This morning we reached Minsk.

Everywhere there are long rows of ruined modern buildings.

The White Russian capital seems to have been very badly bombed.

June 2. Vitebsk. The town is in a state of siege. The Russians are only a few miles away. The city is an outpost stronghold of the *Vaterlandslinie.*

The Fatherland line. That is quite explicit.

And if the *Vaterlandslinie* is broken, there will be nothing for it but to withdraw as quickly as possible into Poland and our old lines outside Brest. But this time we won't be on the offensive.

June 8. Clean-up commandos, that's what we have become.

They told us as much this morning at 4th Army GHQ. We are to share the honor of carrying out this operation—an honor which we could well have done without—with detachments of the 10th SS Division (Reichsführer SS) and of the 9th Division (Hohenstaufen).

June 11. We only learned today that Anglo-American troops have tried to land in northern France. The High Command of the Armed Forces communiqués announce that the Allies are about to be driven back into the sea.

June 20. Since early this morning thousands of Russian guns have been hammering away at our advanced blockhouses around Nevel and Vitebsk.

Endless formations of Soviet planes are flying over Litvinova, which is where we are. Every now and then the Bolsheviks spray us with phosphorus.

This is the first time I have seen with my own eyes the terrible effects of phosphorus. The men's bodies seem to shrink as they burn, as though they are being dissolved by some frightful corrosive acid. We have seen men completely charred and blackened and reduced to the size of ghastly, grotesque dolls.

Can't we find some weapon that will be effective and cruel enough to bring these barbarians to their knees? Our people keep talking about secret weapons. If they exist, the time to use them is now.

June 22, 1944. A date we shan't forget in a hurry.

The Russian monster is roaring for blood on every front, from the Baltic to Gomel.

The attack began at dawn, and within a few hours the infernal thunder of the tanks over the roads and across the fields was audible in Litvinova.

June 27. Vitebsk has fallen. The 4th Army is being driven back. The 9th Army has been broken through at several points by Cherniakhovski's armored divisions.

June 28. We have orders to arrest all deserters and shoot them immediately, in case of resistance.

That's clear enough! The SSFHA has foreseen everything, even the retreat. It's a horrible job we have to do, but this is no time for sentimentality. The Russians are breathing down our necks and they're not sentimental.

June 29. "SS Control! Halt!"

All military trucks and cars heading west are checked on the Mogilev-Minsk road.

Those officers and men who cannot produce written orders to prove that they are on duty are ruthlessly shot.

Stressling, who is in charge of operations, has apparently received a formal order to this effect during the last hour.

A Mercedes, camouflaged with branches, stops at our roadblock.

A captain and two other officers are in the car. Judging by their white faces, they must have realized what this is all about.

About forty SS, in black helmets, are lined up on both sides of the road, machine guns at the ready. The army officers look at them as though they don't understand. Or perhaps they understand only too well.

I walk up to them and salute.

"SS Control. Your movement order, please."

The captain takes a piece of paper from his tunic pocket and hands it to me. I look at it and hand it back to him.

"I'm sorry, Captain. This is your front-line identification permit. I said your movement order. Is this all you can show me?"

Abject fear is written all over the faces of the three men. They are obviously staff officers who, having no effective command, must have decided to head for Minsk on their own. But at a time when all our resources should be mustered to try and hold the Bolsheviks, it is neither more nor less than treason to run away without fighting.

Stressling now walks up.

"Get out of that car—and in double-quick time!"

The three men get out. An SS climbs in immediately and parks the car on the far side of the road.

"Your papers, gentlemen!" says Stressling, his face hard.

He reads them carefully, then looks up.

"Ninth Army Staff? What are you doing here, on this road?"

"We were going to Minsk, Major. . . ."

"Oh, so you were going to Minsk, were you?" roars Stressling. "Well, I don't believe you'll get there!"

"But you have no right to—"

"Oh, so I've no right?"

He signals to me.

"Neumann! Liquidate this bunch of traitors!"

A few moments later the three staff officers are led into a field, off the road. I don't know if all this is in order, but I am covered by Stressling's orders. Still, this is the first time I've ever commanded a firing squad. And it's Germans who are to be killed. I try to analyze my feelings, but I discover, almost with terror, that the whole thing leaves me quite cold. As though it were somebody else to whom it was happening.

"You're not going to kill us?" gasps one of the men.

"It's no good, Gurault," says another one. "They're SS. A lot of filthy, damned murderers!"

I line up four of my men, their backs to the road. Three others are facing the officers.

I turn to the SS, who are holding their machine pistols at the hip.

"Ready . . . !"

"*Heil Hitler!*" shouts the captain.

"Filthy swine!" replies an SS.

"Machine pistols! Fire!"

The four submachine guns simultaneously bark out their single, deadly burst, and the staff officers fall to the ground without a sound. I walk over to them. They need no bullet to finish them off.

June 30. Minsk is in danger of becoming a frightful caldron if Rokossovsky's armored units and Cossacks do succeed in surrounding the place. Already since yesterday there is only one road still open toward the west, the Rakow road.

July 1. All the neighboring villages have risen. Partisans now appear in broad daylight everywhere; and as soon as night falls they shoot up our outposts and ammunition transports.

A mopping-up operation has been ordered for a small village near Minsk.

A captain I have seen before is in command of this. He has a square jaw, a hard face, a scar on his left cheek, and the insignia and flashes of the 1st Leibstandarte A.H.

Two half-tracks take us there.

Perched on the running boards and hood, about a dozen SS with machine pistols cover the road ahead. Terrorists are everywhere, and what is worse, a large proportion of the local inhabitants have now thrown in their lot with them.

But only a proportion. The others are running away from the Bolshevik advance as fast as they can. An extraordinary situation!

After a few moments we reach our destination, which seems to be a proper enemy strongpoint. A company of riflemen is already in position, shooting at the Russians.

"Battle Group! Prepare to attack!" shouts the captain.

He jumps down from his half-track and starts running, by leaps and bounds, toward the nearest houses.

We follow him as best we can.

The Reds have slow-firing machine guns. Maxims, presumably. But they are quite enough to inflict considerable casualties among the SS and the men of the infantry unit who are following up behind us.

Hand grenades begin raining down on the roofs and hurtling through the windows, raising clouds of dust.

It is as hot as the inside of a furnace and the men take off their tunics and sling them through their belts.

In shirt sleeves, or stripped to the waist, they advance yard by yard toward the partisans' positions.

The corpses of women are scattered about.

A group of females with naked breasts are clustered about one of the Maxims.

The gun must have jammed; in a few seconds we are among them, without any casualties to ourselves.

One of them levels a Dektyarov at us. She has no time to fire. An SS rushes at her and snatches the rifle from her hands. With a scream of fury the woman throws herself upon him, clawing at him with her fingernails. The man pushes her away with one hand, drops his machine pistol and finally overcomes her.

But there is too much firing going on, and too many bullets whistling all around us, for us to bother with women.

The SS pushes the prisoner with his rifle butt.

I don't think we have anything more to fear from her now, so I intervene.

"Take her back to the truck! And see that she's well guarded!"

The man, obviously delighted, grabs his captive by the shoulder and pushes her roughly forward. I watch for a moment. With one hand he grips hold of his partisan, while with the other he is taking certain liberties which make the Russian girl scream with fury.

Oh, well, she'll calm down. A soldier deserves an occasional reward.

The cleaning up of the town is carried out methodically. The houses are cleared of their rebellious occupants one by one.

Grenades and 9 mm bullets are the surest guarantee of their future loyalty.

Suddenly dull rumblings can be heard from the road. A column of tanks passes at full speed, heading west.

Heading west! I don't like the look of that.

If the tanks are clearing out, I can't understand why we are still here. Or perhaps the reason is all too plain!

There is the sound of running footsteps behind us. One of the SS who were on guard by the half-tracks comes rushing up.

"Lieutenant! The tank crews say that the leading Russian tanks are only five miles away!"

His breathing is jerky, and he is very pale.

"Well, are you scared?"

But there is no point in putting on this act of bravery, for my own heart is thumping hard. The Russians won't give the SS any quarter. It's time to pull out. This place is beginning to smell very unhealthy.

I stop a platoon commander who is headed toward the fields, where a few Russians are still holding out.

"Call your men in at once. We're withdrawing."

"But, Lieutenant—"

"No but's! Good God, do as you're told, man! And fast!"

I try to control myself, to calm my nerves, but a shameful fear grips my entrails. For the first time a voice inside my head is telling me to run away, to clear out, not to wait for the others. To think that only yesterday I was in command of a firing squad that shot other men for much less than that.

I do my best to tell myself that it isn't the same thing. That this whole setup is crazy. . . . That I can't be expected to fight 50- or 70-ton tanks with 9 mm bullets. . . .

Ten minutes later most of the men are back in the half-tracks. The *moujiks* seem quite bewildered by this sudden change of plan. We will be gone before they realize that it isn't just a trick, that we really are pulling out of their village.

The captain of the LAH now comes up.

"Did you order the retreat, Lieutenant? And if so, what are your reasons?"

"The Russians have crossed the Baranovichi road. They'll be here any minute! What are you going to do? Kick them back?"

"OK, OK!"

At this particular moment I couldn't care less about rank. The only thing that matters is to pull out. And as quickly as possible.

"Who's this women?" the captain suddenly shouts.

True enough, I'd forgotten all about her.

"Get her out of here immediately," he roars.

Without ceremony the Russian woman is thrown onto the ground, helped on her way by a few kicks.

A pity. But she'll get over it. The sun is shining, and her compatriots will soon be here.

With a squeak of tires and a rattle of tracks that kick up clouds of dust, our half-tracks move off, rapidly gaining speed.

Almost at once we are caught up in an armored column which is also going at full speed.

All along the road we pass interminable files of Ukrainians pushing handcarts and dragging wheelbarrows in which are the wretched remains of the homes they have had to leave behind.

Collaborators? The families of Russian officials who have been working in German offices? Who knows?

Whatever they are, they are escaping to the west.

They are afraid, too.

August 16. Karl is dead.

I have rejoined the Vikings somewhere along the middle Vistula, and it was here that I learned from Michael that he didn't survive the flight to Kracow. It was his dead body which was carried out of the JU52.

Stinsmann was like a man demented when he told me the news. His eyes were blood-red.

"They'll get us all, to the last man," he cried.

He also escaped alive from the hell that was Cherkassy.

We see very little of each other, and I have the impression that for some obscure reason he avoids me. Our relations are on a strictly official basis. There has never been the same friendship between us at the front as there was at Wittenberge.

17. Fear

The great wave of Soviet armies on the northern front drove across the Polish plain, forced its way through the Carpathians, invaded Slovakia by the gorges of the Upper San Valley, passed through the endless forests of the Tisza, and in the autumn debouched into the Hungarian *puzta*.

At the same time, sweeping southward between Moldavia and the Black Sea, Malinovski's tanks and Tolbukhin's Cossacks engulfed Rumania and seized Bucharest. After a six-day blitzkrieg Bulgaria also capitulated. Stopping only long enough to arm their new Rumanian allies, the Russian southern armies, now using Bucharest as their main assembly point, began to advance again. By the beginning of October they had reached the Tisza, in the middle of the Magyar country.

Now the Soviet High Command had only to concentrate Zhukov's, Malinovski's and Tolbukhin's Army Groups for the assault on Budapest, the final bastion covering Austria.

Our resistance, desperate though it was, proved everywhere quite incapable of checking this mighty tide of men and guns surging inexorably westward. The dozens of divisions sent urgently to the Western Front in late summer had greatly weakened our steel barricade built against the Bolsheviks, and their absence had certainly contributed to the collapse of the Eastern Front.

On December 14, the Soviet artillery began to give the German positions in Budapest and on both sides of the Danube a terrible pounding.

That night twelve thousand guns, angled at 45 degrees and massed all around the Hungarian capital, were fired simultaneously and the darkness dissolved in apocalyptic flashes. Twelve thousand guns began to pulverize the city beneath a deluge of steel.

At dawn on December 22, cavalry, Cossacks, three thousand heavy tanks and fifteen infantry divisions assaulted the Magyar capital.

The battle raged for forty-eight hours, and it equaled, if it did not actually surpass, in brutality and horror the final, terrible hours of the siege of Stalingrad.

In this hellish caldron, as at Stalingrad, each district, each street, each building was fought for beneath a shower of high explosives and incendiary shells, and the cruelty and carnage surpassed the very limits of inhumanity.

At the beginning, the SS of the 6th Panzer Corps and those Hungarian divisions which had refused to obey the orders of the traitor Horthy were supplied by the Luftwaffe. But soon, because of the crushing numerical superiority of the Russian planes, the German Air Force vanished from the skies above Budapest.

In certain sectors, General Bach-Zelewski's SS troops and the German-Hungarian forces under General von Friessner, entrenched in ruined houses, held on for days against attacks by Bolshevik troops enjoying a numerical superiority of fifteen to one. Wave after wave of Stormovik assault planes, almost scraping the rooftops, roared over, firing explosive bullets and pouring phosphorus on the heroic defenders, who still refused to give up. When the Reds at last succeeded in penetrating the positions, there were only dead bodies left.

Finally, on February 12, 1945, the guns ceased firing in Budapest.

An oppressive silence suddenly hung over the city like a curtain of lead, a silence even more tragic than the deafening roar of bombs and street fighting.

Budapest had not surrendered.

But there were no men left alive to stop the screaming hordes who now poured into the city, from the Debrezcen Gate to the Castle Hills. Drunk with fury and vodka they murdered, raped, pillaged, and set fire to what remained of the ruined buildings.

March 24, 1945. The hanging figures sway gently back and forth from the girders of the metal bridge over the Rába.[1]

An occasional near-by shellburst causes the bodies suddenly to twitch, and their field-gray uniforms to bellow out, giving them, for a few brief seconds, an almost lifelike appearance.

But the brownish faces, already half eaten away by putrefaction, and the frightful smell that comes from them soon destroy that momentary and appalling impression of life.

Plain wooden boards hang upon their chests, indicating why these men are now corpses. There is only one word written to each board: "Coward."

They died because they were afraid, afraid to die.

Fantastic irony. . . .

Here at Györ they simply hanged all the deserters from the arches of the bridge, without any form of trial.

Like all their predecessors, like the three officers shot outside Minsk, they have paid with their lives for a moment of lost faith, of folly, or of gloom.

Yet these are the same men who took part in the glorious breakthrough at Sedan, who entered Paris. They were in the campaigns of Crete and Yugoslavia. They marched on Alexandria across the burning sands of Cyrenaica. These are the men who suffered bestially in the icy steppes of the Moskva, men who, boulder by boulder, captured the fortress of Sebastopol, men who somehow survived the hell that was Stalingrad.

And now there they are, some thirty of them, their flesh rotting, their poor eyes pecked at by the crows. Perhaps there is a Valhalla for the heroes who have failed, and they are there, with the hundreds of other "field Grays" who have also been hanged, from the Beresina to the Danube, simply because they too had their doubts.

How one changes, in a few months. Last summer I would have ruthlessly shot any man who deliberately ran away from the front. In those days I didn't know what fear meant.

[1] A tributary of the Danube, in extreme western Hungary.

I wonder now what my reaction would be if they once again ordered me to shoot a fleeing man.

Thinking it over, I believe I should obey. It is vital at this moment to check panic. Maybe we've been lied to about a lot of things. It's possible. . . .

But one thing is certain, it's too late to do anything about that now. Germany must muster all her resources if she is to survive. We must fight on, to the end.

March 25. Six NSKK motorcyclists roar past our convoy at full speed, clearing a way with furious blasts of their horns.

An Auto Union, much camouflaged with foliage, follows close behind them, jolting over the uneven road.

A black and silver pennant flies from the mudguard.

Colonel General Sepp Dietrich, recently appointed Supreme Commander of all the SS Panzer Corps, is headed straight for Wiener Neustadt.

The roads westward are cluttered with interminable streams of refugees, and these have to be cleared onto the shoulders every few minutes.

The Hungarians are fleeing in their thousands toward the Austrian frontier. As though a frontier could save them now!

March 26. There are no longer any passenger coaches or freight cars available for the refugees. All rail transport is reserved for the movement of troops and munitions, by order of GHQ.

The last trains which left Magyaróvár consisted of nothing but a series of platforms, bare boards, upon which the people were crowded, huddled together.

There was not a murmur of protest, not a single objection from this mass of humanity. Fear had turned their faces into waxen masks, almost indistinguishable the one from the other.

Terrible scenes take place each time these refugee trains are attacked by Stormoviks, YAK's or TU70's. The planes fly very low, and with a tremendous roar they pitilessly machine-gun the mass of people, who scream and scream. Instead of lying down, they remain stupidly on their feet. When they are hit, the men's faces assume a sort of surprised look. As for the women, they nearly always fall with their arms raised, screaming horribly.

When the planes with the deadly stars on their wings have flown away, the dead bodies are tossed over the side, to provide room for the thousands of men, women and children who have been tramping along for hours on both sides of the railway track, waiting for others to die so that they may have a chance to live.

March 27. A sudden change of orders has brought us back to Györ. The leading Russian troops had already entered the town yesterday. They were immediately thrown out again.

The town is quite dead.

Most of the inhabitants have fled. The shutters on the windows, half torn off by explosions, rattle in a most sinister way. A stench hangs over the town—the stench of wet, charred wood, of smoke or of something less easily defined, something redolent of disaster, of abandonment, of unrelenting fate.

Our orders are to hold up the Soviet advance guard, which is re-forming just outside the town gates, for as long as possible.

As we move toward the eastern gate to occupy our defensive positions, the bombardment by the Red artillery becomes increasingly more violent. It seems as though every minute a new Russian battery is joining in.

I have about two hundred men under me. Four days ago I was promoted to captain. This is nothing to be proud of. The regiment has lost three-quarters of its officers. In the course of this last month, several sergeants have become second lieutenants.

This hodgepodge of a company that I command is made up of SS from the 2nd Division (*Das Reich*) just back from the Western Front, and some forty men of the 3rd Panzergrenadiere Totenkopf.

And they'll all doubtless make one pretty pile of corpses before long.

Suddenly I glance up. There are warning shouts to be heard on all sides.

"Look out! Mines! Stay where you are!"

A terrific explosion. Another. . . .

"The swine! They didn't even warn us!" a voice screams.

When the smoke has cleared, I see some fifteen bodies lying on the ground, horribly mutilated. An arm high in a tree, torn off with the sleeve still on it, a watch strapped about the wrist, and possibly still ticking. Nameless remains spattered against the walls.

Close beside me an SS is wiping his bloodstained face and shaking his head stupidly.

"Well, I never . . ." he repeats over and over again.

He can hardly believe in his own luck.

A reflex had made me throw myself to the ground at the first explosion. It was this which saved my life. The second mine went off only ten yards from where I lay.

Once again German explosives have killed German soldiers.

Once again Division forgot to warn us that some of the streets leading to the town's eastern exit were mined.

Such mistakes are really criminal. Abominable.

A wounded man crawls along the ground.

"The bastards! The filthy swine! The filthy—" he groans, painfully.

Two SS take him, one by each arm, and half-carry him off toward the aid station behind the lines.

He leaves a long trail of blood behind him.

One hour later we are dug in, facing the Babolna road.

According to a lieutenant of the Totenkopf, the leading Russian troops appeared a moment or two ago. They are probably waiting for reinforcements. They are not, it seems, led by tanks. So this must be an isolated motorized detachment taking its chances. It's true that since the early afternoon there has been practically no resistance between Györ and the bulk of the Russian armies.

Our orders are very firm. We are to hold on to our defensive positions regardless. A pity, really. If it weren't for these orders it might not be too difficult to knock the Russkies off balance before their armored support turns up.

At the moment the Katiushas are spraying death at us the way a hose sprays water. They fire a dozen rocket shells at once, and when these all explode together at ground level, they scatter thousands of small steel fragments with edges sharp as razor blades.

Their heavy artillery has just joined in the fun as well, and is firing over our heads. This probably means that the attack will not now be long delayed.

And here we are, impatiently waiting for them.

With orders to hold them back!

But how? There aren't more than five or six hundred of us, all told.

It is a ghastly feeling, like being caught in a rat trap.

And how ludicrous it all is.

Here we are, too weak these days to hurl ourselves at the throats of these Asiatic tribes.

Yet a sort of cold anger makes us grind our teeth. Our fingers close around the triggers of our guns. Our hands grip our grenades more tightly. Our eyes are fixed more intently on the road. We have one dream left, and in order to make it come true, I believe we would willingly lay down our lives. It is to kill Russians, to destroy thousands and thousands of Russians like so many poisonous insects. To see Russian blood spurting in all directions. To drown in a lake of Russian blood.

So that Germany may live.

For the moment we crouch in our one-man foxholes, dug with great speed, trying to protect the back of our necks as best we can with our arms. A wound in the chest is very dangerous. But one in the neck is usually fatal.

About ten aircraft fly over, with a diabolical whine.

Black crosses! They must be the new Messerschmitt 262's, the jets. I fear that they too have arrived too late.

My nose is in the mud, and suddenly I have a tremendous desire to laugh.

I remember the instructors at Vogelsang who trained me to dig foxholes so fast.

First you do this, then you do that.

What's the routine for digging deep enough so that your foxhole can become a regulation grave, and your body won't rot as fast as it would in the open, and the tracks of the giant tanks won't crush it into pulp?

I also think that I should have accepted the offer which was made to me in October to go to Friedenthal, a place near Oranienburg, not far from Berlin, where they were recruiting those who could speak English for some special mission. At least I wouldn't be swallowing great mouthfuls of the disgusting soil of Hungary.

March 28. Since dusk fell, the Russian artillery has almost completely stopped firing on Györ.

Only an occasional machine-gun burst rends the night air. This is when our SS patrols run up against the Soviet reconnaissance troops.

Our eyes ache as we try to make out in the darkness the nature of the vague menace which we can feel lowering over the dark plain.

Suddenly, toward midnight, a luminous pinpoint, followed by ten, a hundred, a thousand others, appears far to the east. And almost at once a blinding white line of lights is advancing toward us.

The Russians are attacking again, the headlights of their vehicles full on and their searchlights trained on us.

They are advancing at full speed.

The metal girders and overturned trucks which have been placed so as to hold up the enemy advance are caught in the lights of the leading armored vehicles.

Our 105 and 88 antitank guns have started to bark. But the gunners have told me that each gun has only ten shells. This is the maximum it has been possible to allot them. And they have also shared out in each battery the cases of ammunition marked: "Attention! These shells must only be used for instructional purposes or for training!"

And this is the sort of stuff with which we have been ordered to hold back the onslaught of sixty-four-ton monsters!

The Red tanks are now forming up in a great semicircle. They fire at the few walls still standing, which crash with a tremendous roar, raising clouds of dust.

There is no time to be lost.

I run to the field telephone, which is connected directly to regimental HQ.

"Viking Eagle here! Viking Eagle speaking! Cannot hold for more than ten minutes. Some of the guns are already out of ammunition."

I have to shout at the top of my voice to make myself heard. The thunder of the guns and the Red shells bursting all around me are deafening.

Suddenly the line goes dead. A shellburst must have cut the wire.

Too bad. I won't risk having my company massacred for no purpose. The attacking forces are too strong for us, and there is really nothing we can do here.

I order a general retreat. And high time too. The Red tanks are already moving through our first defenses.

The gunners abandon their useless pieces and also withdraw westward, toward the center of Györ.

The sinister dark, deserted streets of the town re-echo to the tramp of German boots and to the rumblings of the leading tanks, which are already forcing their way through the roadblocks and ruins.

A sudden thought flashes through my brain.

The bridge!

The engineers are waiting on the west bank for the moment when they will press down the plunger that will explode the bundles of cordite tied to the piers of the bridge.

Running now, the grenadiers, gunners and SS cross the Rába.

On the far side, shouts and loud orders show that the engineers are getting very excited.

They have every reason to be. The infernal rumbling of tanks draws closer every second.

Finally the last of my men has run across. I throw myself after him, slithering and stumbling over the debris strewn across the narrow iron footpath.

A terrific explosion.

The last bridge this side of the Austrian frontier has been blown.

On the far bank the Soviet machine gunners are already taking up position, frantically firing long bursts at us.

But they're too late.

March 29. At dawn today we entered Austria.

The eyes of the people, fleeing in all haste, are filled with a great reproach. How come that we, the warriors who were going to chase the Red Army beyond the Urals, have not even succeeded in stopping the Bolsheviks' advance, or at least in holding them beyond the frontiers of the Fatherland?

Well, we have failed. And we are still retreating. It seems to be really serious now. But the communiqués of the German Radio tell us of the vast number of new launching platforms for our V-1's and V-2's. They state that the first radio-controlled flying bombs are about to come into action on the Eastern and Western Fronts.

Are about to. . . . How ludicrous!

The radio has also broadcast a speech by Goebbels urging Germany to hold on just a little longer, so that the technicians will have time to complete the construction of the secret weapons, weapons that will make it possible for us to defeat both Russia and America and win the war.

Meanwhile, the Bolsheviks are on German soil, at Nickelsdorf. They are getting dangerously near to Vienna.

March 30. A dark railway station on the banks of the Leitha. Hundreds of refugees are waiting for a problematical train to take them to Vienna, leaning against each other, huddled together. The cold is intense. All who have managed to find room inside the station buildings are lying on wooden benches or on the bare floor.

The heavy artillery and the almost uninterrupted waves of Russian bombers, headed for or returning from Vienna, make the windows rattle—or such of them as are still intact. Terror stalks among this crowd of people, whose only remaining hope is to somehow fling themselves onto a train hastening through the night toward the west, and life.

We, too, are awaiting a train to take us to Swechat. We are crowded together on the platforms, which are swept by icy gusts that make the smashed iron girders of the ruined roof above our heads creak and rattle in the wind.

A moment or two ago, a violent argument started among a group of men standing beside the stairs that lead to the underground tunnel.

I walk across to them.

They are officers of the 1st Division, the Leibstandarte. They are gathered around a sort of brazier and are discussing the Führer's latest order, which has just been issued to them. This instructs them to remove the divisional stripe from their sleeve, the stripe on which is embroidered "Adolf Hitler" in silver letters. Hitler's decision was taken after the failure of the last counteroffensive in March. The Reich Chancellor has said that he regards their retreat as treason and desertion. He wishes to demonstrate his disapproval by this official and public gesture of reprimand.

The insult was violently resented by the whole of the LAH. They were thunderstuck at first by this totally undeserved reproach. Then astonishment gave way to indignation. Some of them tore off their decorations as well as their stripes and sent the lot addressed to the Chancellery in Berlin, in a latrine bucket. In it, too, they put an arm taken from a corpse.

All this is worrying, and terribly indicative of the attitude which prevails in the SS at this time.

It is essential that we hold on, however, if we are to avoid annihilation.

Mechanically I make my way toward the center of the station.

"Excuse me, Captain! Are they still quite far away from us?"

It is a woman's voice, and I cannot quite see, in the darkness,
where she is.

I walk up to her. She is young, wrapped in a black shawl, sitting
on the floor.

"Don't worry. Their leading troops are still a long way off. Anyhow, if there's any danger, you'll be evacuated."

My eyes are getting accustomed to the darkness and I can see her
face now. She is very pale, young, with curly hair falling all about
her shoulders.

I sit down beside her on the low counter which must at one time
have been used for checking in luggage.

I notice that she is sitting in an icy-cold draft which presumably
explains why she is all alone in this remote corner of the station.

"Aren't you cold?"

"What differences does it make? Besides, I couldn't find anywhere
to sit in the heated waiting room."

She speaks calmly, without rancor. She has realized that in times
of tragedy, when men are risking their very lives, pity becomes
irrelevant.

"You're in the SS? But, of course, how stupid of me; there's
nothing but SS in the station!"

I can see that she would like to say, "But what are you doing
here? Why aren't you fighting?" It's a question I have been asking
myself. But transport has been so disorganized, and what with the
refugees cluttering up the roads, 6th SS Panzer can hardly organize
the troop movements as rapidly as the staff doubtless desires.

We start talking. I can see through the broken windows that the
battle groups have fallen in. But there is no indication that the
arrival of our train is imminent.

She tells me that her husband was killed in France last September.

She is from Eisenstadt and is trying to make for the west. She has been told that the Red soldiers are raping all the women as they advance.

The hours go by. The cold becomes more and more intense.

"Oh, I'm so cold," she says.

I move closer to her and put my arm around her shoulders.

"Is that better?"

"Thank you. You are very kind."

I take off my greatcoat and make the woman lie down on it.

"Try and rest a bit. You'll probably have hours to wait."

I stretch out beside her. I can feel her breath against my face. An almost intoxicating smell comes from her hair.

This ruined railway station, the dull boom of artillery, the icy darkness and the unknown woman in my arms. How strange it all is.

"What's your name?"

"Hanna. And yours?"

My lips are a few inches from her face. It is she who puts her mouth to mine and presses her body against me.

18.   The End

April 3. All along the German-Hungarian frontier, the front is one gigantic, blazing inferno. The battles now taking place are desperately fierce.

Wiener Neustadt is about to be captured by the Russians, who have launched this last offensive with a fighting strength beyond our imagination. On a front of sixty miles, between Bratislava and the Semmering Pass, a million men are marching on Vienna.

April 4. The Soviet tanks are at Mödling and Wiener-Neudorff, and less than ten miles from the capital. It seems now that nobody and nothing can check the Bolshevik onslaught.

The men are completely bushed. An uninterrupted week's fighting has brought them to the limit of human endurance. Morale could not be lower. Discipline has suffered as a result. A sergeant of the 3rd Antitank Battalion yesterday refused to obey an order to go out on patrol. He was immediately shot.

How long ago are those glorious days when the Viking, with standards fluttering in the winds of victory, was marching toward the east!

April 5. A haggard and disheveled woman who managed to cross the lines told us about the Bolshevik entry into Baden.

The shelling went on for several hours after the last German troops had evacuated the town. It was as though the Russians wanted to make really sure that they had dealt with all resistance. With some ten other women, she had taken refuge in a cellar.

At about six in the evening the leading Russian tanks lumbered into Baden, all guns firing at the roadblocks which had been built in the streets.

Behind them came the cavalry at a gentle trot, and then the infantry regiments.

The greater part of Tolbukhin's troops were Mongols and Asiatics. Prominent cheekbones, flat noses, brutal faces. Through the manholes of their cellar, the terrified Austrian women could hear the Reds shouting in savage, guttural voices.

A few hours after they entered the town, they were hunting women.

Shooting out locks, kicking open doors or battering them in with their rifle butts, the Bolshevik hordes methodically set about their woman hunt.

Hour after hour new Russian regiments poured into the old spa, now transformed into one gigantic brothel. The women were shut up in specific buildings, there to satisfy the mad lust of hundreds of men, who lined up even in the street, awaiting their turn.

The Austrian woman who told us all this added that some Soviet officers had tried, with revolvers in their hands, to stop this bestiality. But the Red soldiers, drunk with raw spirits, rage and hate, wouldn't listen to them. They didn't care any more.

April 6. The Russian guns are thundering at Meidling, in the southern outskirts of Vienna.

Trenches have been very hastily dug by the people in front of the Simmering gate, along the Gürtel,[1] and between the Aspang station and Schönbrunn.

The older men have been mobilized into whole regiments and have been armed with rifles and a hundred bullets each. They wear gray armbands, but no uniforms. That is the Volkssturm. Boys of

[1] Peripheral road around Vienna, which encircles the city like a girdle and leads to the Danube Canal.

fifteen have also been armed. All this oddly assorted collection has been moved up to the lines in an endless procession of trucks.

Useless massacre. Very few of them will ever return, that is quite certain.

The Viennese, for the moment, are carrying on with their jobs in an incredibly cool fashion. The public services are all functioning. There are still a few streetcars running.

But in the queues outside the grocery stores, it's easy to see that people are tensed up, suspicious and surly. The troops who march past, singing on their way to the front, evoke no spontaneous gestures from the crowd, as they would have done even a few months ago. The soldiers march through an almost eerie silence.

No cheers, no shouts of encouragement come from all these people, who seem suddenly and strangely lifeless.

Certain municipal authorities have apparently voiced a desire to have Vienna declared an open city.

Sepp Dietrich, who is Commander in Chief in Vienna, immediately dealt with them. They will never cause us any trouble again.

The Austrians are scared.

The days of celebration at the time of the *Anschluss,* when the Wehrmacht was greeted with an enthusiasm bordering on frenzy, seem very far away.

April 7. Brushing aside the two Volkssturm divisions and the armored regiments defending south Vienna, the Red tanks broke through our lines this morning, between Maria Lauzend and Interstadt, two suburbs of the city.

This is the news which splutters like a trail of gunpowder all along the Gürtel, where we hold the final defenses and strongpoints destined to slow down the diabolical Red onslaught as much as possible.

The official radio has been silent for several hours.

On our portable radios, however, we have been intercepting strange appeals to the people, urging them to rise. These have been repeated frequently and come from some secret transmitter. Some group presumably in the pay, or under the orders, of the Soviets.

The broadcasts always begin with the following proclamation: "This is Free Austria calling. The Austrian Provisional National Committee is speaking to you!"

The National Committee and the Communist Party are beginning to show themselves openly in the city. Placards have been stuck up on walls at night, urging the citizens to help the Allies drive out the German troops!

I think if I were to surprise one of these traitors in the act of pasting up his shameful posters, I should kill him then and there, with my bare hands.

In the meantime, we are fortunately still masters of the situation. The Viennese must obey us whether they like it or not.

Roadblocks have been built in all the avenues and streets which lead into the Gürtel.

The purpose is to protect the center of the capital, the ministries and government buildings in case of a Russian breakthrough.

The trees have been cut down so as to block the streets. Old trucks, piles of scrap iron, overturned streetcars and antitank ditches will make it difficult for the Reds to break through.

The streets in the center of the city are all deserted.

From time to time a squadron of Stormoviks drones overhead, skimming the rooftops, firing one or two bursts, jettisoning its bombs haphazardly and then disappearing eastward.

The shells of the Red artillery, which is firing now from the north and the south, are dropping everywhere, digging huge craters. It looks as though the gunners are shelling the city without any strategic target. Their sole purpose is to destroy.

According to the latest news we have received, they are fighting in the Favoriten and Simmering districts, and also at Meidling.

The Russians have also succeeded in breaking through in the northwest and are advancing toward Dornbach.

For over an hour we have been awaiting orders.

The smoke from the fires hangs like a tragic pall over Vienna, hiding the sun, yellowing the walls, accentuating the painful feeling of an indefinable agony that tears at one's guts and sets the blood pounding dully in one's veins.

The faces of the men, mostly new recruits, are hard. They are beginning to wonder what they're doing on this side of the Gürtel when there's already fighting in the suburbs.

April 8. The battle is raging all along the Ottakring.

About sixty T-34's and a few sixty-ton monsters are hidden behind the railway line that circles the city. So far none of our antitank guns has been able to get at them.

The vicious fire of the Red automatic weapons makes it impossible to place our guns with a sufficiently accurate angle of fire so that they can penetrate the armor of the enemy tanks.

Since last night we have been out of touch with the rest of the regiment. I have taken over command of the few hundred men here, a fair number of whom are not SS.

This is no time to ask questions or to go off in search of one's own units. We must try at all costs to hang on and stop the Bolshevik advance toward the great canal.

I am waiting for Sergeant Stinsmann, who has gone off to try and find Division. At present I am using him as a runner to the units that are trying to hold the Russian tanks three streets away, in the Hauptstrasse.

The men, crouching behind any sort of cover—sandbags, ruined walls, trees, piles of plaster from the destroyed buildings—are defending these streets yard by yard.

Our situation is extremely critical. In spite of repeated requests, Division refuses to send us tank support. Their excuse is that the available armor hasn't enough fuel and therefore must not be sent into action until the last possible moment.

What last possible moment? Does this mean the moment when our positions have been overrun?

A sound of running footsteps. Michael throws himself down beside me. He is breathless.

"The Reds have taken the Observatory. They are advancing on the Lazarist Church! If we don't pull out, we're in danger of being surrounded!"

I move closer to him and say, "I got through to the HQ of the 3rd not ten minutes ago! They're still holding out! There's no danger for the moment!"

I have to shout at the top of my voice. The noise of the explosions and heavy tank guns firing is deafening.

"Ten minutes ago maybe that was true! But the Russkies are pouring in from every side," he says. "They're everywhere. They must have broken our lines from the north and west."

We are lying flat on our bellies in the middle of a chaos of plaster, scrap iron and broken glass. Showers of stone and metal are hurtling over in all directions.

A screech, a sharp explosion, and a machine gunner is hit, rolling over on the ground and clutching at his stomach.

I run up and take his place. The number two is still at his post, shaking with nerves. The MG is red hot, despite the water the private keeps pouring over the barrel to cool it.

In front of me, at the corner of the Wattgasse, I can see nothing but green shapes, far away and indistinct. I press the trigger in a sudden access of cold rage which makes me grit my teeth.

But there are far too many of them. We must pull out before it's too late. Their leading tanks are advancing slowly, crunching toward the barricades.

I raise my hand.

"Attention! Immediate retreat!"

A second's hesitation. Then, keeping as near as possible to the walls, stumbling every minute over the dead bodies and the piles of rubble strewn across the smashed pavement, the survivors from the Ottakring run back toward the shelter of the Gürtel defenses.

April 9. All night a fierce and desperate battle has gone on between us and Tolbukhin's engineers advancing through the tunnels of the Vienna Underground Railway. Fighting blind, we never know exactly where the enemy is. Dull explosions with frightening blast effects echo and boom down the tunnels. There is fierce hand-to-hand fighting, with daggers. Bestial screams, and for us flight, always flight.

And in every sector the Russians are advancing steadily toward the canal.

Since dawn we have been entrenched in the Military General Hospital buildings, against which the Russkies are launching their tanks in groups of twenty or thirty. They have not so far succeeded in breaking through our barricades.

In the hospital corridors, hundreds of wounded lying on the bare floor wait for someone to come and attend to them. Some have horrible wounds, with blackish, puffy edges, wrapped any old how in paper bandages. Gauze and absorbent cotton have been unobtainable for a long time.

In the operating rooms they are cutting, suturing, amputating. It is all without anesthetics, for the last bottles of chloroform and ether have been used up.

A terrible smell of blood, gangrene and ethyl chloride hangs over everything and clings to the walls.

From every window soldiers are firing into the Wänringerstrasse or toward the barbed-wire entanglements of the Spitalgasse, behind which the Russians are concealed.

The sky is amazingly blue. The trees in the hospital garden are beginning to blossom. Or rather they *were* beginning, for the bombs, shell grenades and shrapnel are methodically stripping them of their branches and reducing them to bare trunks.

A tragic spring. Nature has awakened only to die.

For four days now we haven't had a moment's rest. I don't know whether my nerves have been strained beyond the limit, but I find that the appalling noise of explosions and the thunder of the guns

are becoming insupportable. I feel as though this din which seems
to fill my whole head has destroyed my will, and may drive me over
the borderline of sanity if it goes on much longer.

April 10. A special court-martial was convened within two hours,
and in a few minutes has condemned to death those members of
the Volkssturm found guilty of desertion in the face of the enemy.

There they are, about ten of them, guarded by SS with their
machine pistols in their hands. Those men know that they have only
a few minutes to live.

None of these old men, who were enlisted voluntarily or otherwise in their quasi-military units, has ever possessed the morale to
give him even a minimum of confidence in the orders he received.

They are almost all Austrians. It is quite obvious that if the
truth were told every Viennese is really waiting and hoping for just
one thing—the arrival of the Reds. They believe that this will bring
them, if not liberty, at least peace and the assurance that their lives
are saved.

I can't now help feeling that the Viennese would sell us to the
enemy with pleasure and betray us remorselessly if we gave them
the chance. The extraordinary thing is that the people here seem to
be quite beaten and utterly demoralized by the Red advance, in
complete contrast to what happened in Budapest, which is not even
German territory. The *Anschluss* was indeed a bad bargain, from
our point of view. The Austrians are a race without character or
will, superficial, pleasure-loving and frivolous, a nation that whines
and trembles like a beaten girl.

A brief word of command makes me look up.

"Squad! Ready!"

An NCO is in charge of the execution. The Volkssturm men are
lined up against a half-ruined wall. Some of them are in tears. They
all still wear their armbands.

"Aim!" shouts the sergeant suddenly, lifting his arm.

An interminable second passes.

"Fire!"

It is not an execution, but a veritable massacre.

The Russians, who have been serenading us without a break since morning with the Dantesque music of their "Stalin organs" would doubtless be delighted to learn that we too are liquidating our local warriors.

Street by street, alley by alley, tree by tree, they are advancing inexorably toward the hospital.

People who have managed to pass through their lines tell us that in certain places, notably near Schönbrunn, they have already organized victory balls. A bit premature. They say also that in the suburbs occupied by the Bolsheviks, the white flags of surrender hang, like badges of shame, from every window. On the tiniest balconies and in all the shops the red-and-white Austrian flag is also to be seen.

April 11. This is the fifth night of the siege of Vienna, which is still being defended or, to be more exact, which *we* are still defending.

The dirty, gray waters of the Danube Canal reflect the sinister glow of the fires raging almost everywhere in the city. To the south, the blood-red sky is often blotted out by enormous clouds of black smoke from the gasoline dumps at Hetzendorf, which have now been burning for hours. During the day the smoke hides the sun and makes it almost impossible to breathe.

The beams of the Russian ack-ack searchlights weave a brilliant spider's web, but we never see the puffs of smoke which mark the explosion of ack-ack shells in the sky.

And for a very good reason. It is a long time now since the Luftwaffe left the skies above Vienna, never to return. The Stormoviks, the Tupulevs and the gigantic four-engined Lavotchkin bombers, the MIG's and the YAK's are now the lords of the air.

An occasional short machine-gun burst tells us that on the opposite side of the canal, along the ancient Elisabeth Promenade, the Red gunners are awake.

For the moment our sector is quiet. I don't like this because as a rule this phony calm bodes ill for the future.

Yesterday, on the other hand, the Russian artillery never ceased pounding our positions all through the night. What mysterious order can have stopped them from shelling us this evening?

The population is hiding in the cellars and does not raise a finger to help us. If we have no water, we can go to hell for all they care. If our rations have not come through, nobody will give the SS so much as a bowl of soup or a slice of black bread.

The people believe that the situation is hopeless and that our stubbornness will achieve nothing except to make their city suffer the same fate as Budapest, and "antagonize" the Red Army.

Antagonize the Red Army! A truly astonishing phrase to hear on the lips of German citizens!

With the coming of a pale dawn that accentuates the sadness of the half-ruined houses and gaping windows, the shelling begins again.

During the night a wall has been built by a company of engineers. It protects us, more or less, from the fire of the Russian automatics. Holes have been cut in the masonry, through which we can fire at the Russkies.

For the moment, a parachutist regiment is still holding the Rudolf Barracks sector, and so we can carry on happily in our own defensive positions without undue fear of being outflanked.

But from every building machine guns and rifles crackle steadily. Expert snipers, hidden on the roofs behind the chimney pots, shoot away at each other in a real hail of bullets. Sometimes they hit their target. Then a body falls, rolling over as it drops through the air to crash on the ground.

With every part of every building that is lost, our danger increases. The Russians have apparently nothing better to do than climb up to each floor of each house, four steps at a time, massacring all the inhabitants they meet. When they reach the top floor, they settle down at once behind the sandbags provided for civil defense, which they have brought up from the various landings, and begin to shoot at us like madmen.

April 12. Vienna is in her death throes.

Nobody has any doubts now. The battle is lost. But history will prove one fact quite clearly. The German troops who defended the Danube capital may have given in before the colossal, monstrous power of the Russians—but this was due mainly to the fact that the Viennese themselves sold their city to the enemy. The Viennese were afraid, and this fear lost us the battle.

All they talk about in Vienna is the resistance movement of the National Liberation Party and the heroic Austrian partisans.

It is all quite incredible.

Particularly coming from a people 95 percent of whom, at the *Anschluss,* voted in favor of becoming a part of Germany. A people who danced in the streets, drunk with joy, at the time of the victory over France. Who, when the war against Russia started, shouted even louder than the Berliners, "On to Moscow!"

Unfortunately our efforts to save this miserable refuse of humanity has cost us the lives of hundreds of thousands of our soldiers, men who died bravely on the field of battle.

They are still fighting outside the Urania Theatre and in the customs and excise offices. A few pockets of resistance are also holding out along the canal and in the pillboxes in the Prater.

If there were only some way of getting out of this town. . . .

But for days on end all contact with Division has been virtually cut. And a serious decision must be taken.

We know that the Reds are shooting without trial all men captured wearing SS uniform. I have about a hundred survivors with me—most of whom are not Vikings. There is no question of surrendering. But still less of letting ourselves be massacred by the Russkies.

Each man wants to fight to the death. But everything is lost now, totally, irrevocably lost. And one wonders whether death itself is of any use. The Russians are everywhere, like flies buzzing about a carcass. A hundred, five hundred, a thousand may be exterminated. They are immediately replaced by ten or a hundred times that number. And to make matters worse, the survivors are totally indifferent to their comrades' death. Death means nothing to them. So what's the use of it all?

"Captain, the Reds have brought up three more tanks. If we don't try and get out now, in an hour's time it'll be too late."

It's Michael who's talking to me, and I turn to him.

"So it's 'Captain' now, is it? That must be a sign that things are really bad!"

I try to smile, but something closes around my heart like a vice. Can this really be the end?

He sits down heavily beside me. We can't hear the rattle of the machine guns any longer. There is something very sinister about this sudden silence. The dull boom of the heavy artillery, somewhere in the west, shows that they're still fighting over there.

"Do you remember the forest of Teclino, on the Olchanka?" Michael murmurs.

"Cherkassy! That was ghastly, too, but we got out, somehow."

We are crouching in the shelter of some sheds beside the canal. We doubtless owe this brief respite that the Russians have allowed us to the fact that they are probably busy clearing the old War Ministry building near by. Unless they are hunting for women or getting drunk. My fingers itch to do something, yet I am powerless.

"What are we to do?" Stinsmann goes on dully.

"I haven't any idea! All I know is that in a few hours it'll be every man for himself."

The men, lying behind sandbags and protected by a triple row of barbed wire, have their fingers clenched about the triggers of their guns. But nothing is moving in the neighborhood of the group of Russian tanks a few hundred yards away. It would be quite pointless to waste bullets against a couple of inches of steel.

The hours drag slowly on in a strange silence broken occasionally by a short burst of MG fire or the loud crack of a rifle. Somebody blazing away. From fear, or loss of nerve. The Reds are quite content to watch us. It looks as though the Urania sector doesn't interest them any more. But away to the southwest, the shooting has started again, probably in the Ring or about the pillboxes in the Hofburg gardens.

Night falls.

There is a dull rumbling. It comes from the Prater and the Untere Donaustrasse, where a battery of Red self-propelled machine guns is now installed on the far side of the canal. We're caught like rats in a trap now.

There is just time to make a decision.

Cautiously I creep up to the lieutenant who is in command of the two platoons covering the Stubenring, which we can look along as far as the turn by the College of Commercial Art. There are Red tanks and armored troop-carriers everywhere. The Russians must have received special orders, for they aren't showing themselves. Or else they think that the Aspern Bridge and Urania sectors are held by bigger forces than are actually here.

The glares from the fires impart a permanent red glow to the sky. The ack-ack searchlights, however, no longer pierce the clouds. Suddenly there is the distant, urgent sound of church bells ringing. The Bolsheviks are celebrating their victory, or maybe it's some parish priest who can't wait. The guns still roar, but the firing is spaced out, and it sounds farther and farther away.

I lean toward the officer.

"How long will your men's ammunition last?"

The lieutenant, his face streaked with blood and black with dirt and a three days' growth of beard, seems to be at the end of his tether. His eyes are horribly sunken in his head. But he manages a smile of sorts.

"At the rate we're firing, there's enough to last us for weeks!"

I glance at my watch.

"It's now 2040 hours. At 2200 hours, what's left of the company will try to swim down the canal in the direction of the Aspern Bridge ruins. Those who can't swim must follow along the edge. Two platoons will stay here to . . . draw the Russkies' fire. I shall command one of these platoons. You will ask for a volunteer for the second."

"I'll do it myself if you like, Captain!"

"Good. One other thing. Tell the men to blacken their faces. With anything they can find. Burnt cork or something. Only one magazine to be taken. The rest of their ammunition will be left for those who remain behind!"

"Yes, sir! *Heil Hitler!*"

It is now completely dark.

The Russian tanks are still in position. They have not yet attacked. I think I understand why. According to the latest news, picked up during our retreat along the canal yesterday, surrender talks are going on between the notorious Austrian Provisional National Committee and Tolbukhin's staff. Perhaps the Russians have decided to wait until the capitulation of Vienna is an established fact, realizing, as they must, that the capital is at their mercy.

The three platoons which are going to slip past the Russians have assembled in silence at the water's edge. The canal is sluggish and filthy, full of refuse and corpses, both Russian and German.

Also floating down with the current toward the Danube are the silver eagles and the insignia of the SS torn from the men's uniforms.

Without a sound, the men strip off their badges of rank, destroying without trace all those symbols which were once their greatest pride, and those decorations which are the proof of their past valor. All military papers are also torn to shreds and dropped into the water.

It is ten minutes to ten.

In the distance an accordion is playing, and the wind blows the music across to us.

We hear the motors of invisible trucks going by, loaded with troops singing and shouting into the night.

The Reds have observed the attempted flight of the SS.

Suddenly the machine guns in the tanks grouped at the far end of Wiesingerstrasse, facing across the canal, all start firing at once at the vague shapes swimming or running in the direction of the Aspern Bridge ruins.

We reply as best we can. But the Russkies, protected by their armor, aren't in much danger from us.

From the far side of the Unters Donaustrasse, the self-propelled machine guns now join in. Tracer bullets are soon making a fantastic, lacy pattern against the night sky. Every fiery line is the track of a murderous cone of flying steel.

We've had it this time. The most we can hope for is that in the chaos maybe as many as sixty men will somehow escape. And even that is problematical. The Reds are scattered along both banks of the canal.

Men are falling all the time, dead. I escaped, heaven knows how, at Dnepropetrovsk, at Kharkov, from the burning oil wells of the Caucasus, from the Cherkassy caldron, from the blazing inferno that was Budapest—but I shan't escape from the slaughter in the little square by the Urania Theatre.

Searchlights are suddenly turned on us. Prolonged bursts manage to put out two of these blinding beams of light which pierce the darkness, hunting for us, reaching into the smallest and most shadowy corners.

Men caught in the white brilliance of the lights are torn to pieces immediately by the Reds' bullets and fall back into the water like broken dolls. Their bodies are swept away by the current, to float down the Danube now red with German blood, beside the corpses of the many thousands more who fell in their struggle to defend it.

The sounds of motors revving up furiously.

The Russians have probably radioed to their tanks and armored cars to advance on us. Yes, there are the T-34's moving toward us from the Stubenring and the Radetzkystrasse. Simultaneously, on the far side of the bridge, other tanks suddenly appear around the corner of the Praterstrasse.

At this moment the machine pistol I have been firing jams. Angrily I throw the useless piece of metal into the greenish water, where are reflected the brilliant searchlight beams. I snatch another one from the clenched fingers of a private who is moaning quietly. He gives me a last glance of reproach as he tries vainly to keep hold of his gun. But that poor fellow won't ever need a gun again.

The leading Reds have reached the ruins of the bridge.

Nothing more to be done. Except pull out.

In the darkness I hear Michael's excited voice.

"Peter! Don't leave me. If we've got to finish here, let's be together."

"Come on! We'll see if we can't reach the bank and get underneath the wharf. It'll give us some protection, at least for a while, if we can get there!"

The crackle of the automatics and orders shouted in Russian re-echo all about us, above the stone parapet.

I go toward him.

"Michael! Your papers?"

"I destroyed them just now."

"Come on, then, and let's see how far we can get!"

"Good luck, Neumann!"

Groping in the darkness, he catches hold of my hand.

Keeping close to the wall directly beneath the parapet, we run a few yards. Then we find that the canal bank is blocked by piles of rubble and plaster which we have to climb over. On top of this rubble is barbed wire, which we crawl through. Our hands are torn, our knees bleeding, but we don't feel pain any longer.

Suddenly a searchlight glares.

I flatten myself against the barbed wire. In his anxiety, Michael has tripped and rolled down several yards.

I am still in darkness. The Reds must have spotted something, maybe it's Stinsmann. A Maxim opens up, firing slowly and jerkily.

Then there is a series of sharp cracks and yells. A great crowd of the swine are now shooting, the savages.

The bullets whistle over my head. It's Michael they're aiming at. For a moment I regret I didn't try to make it alone. I always knew that would be the only way.

Inch by inch I creep forward into the shadows. Stones clatter down.

Suddenly the searchlight goes out.

They must think they've got us. Or else they don't care, and were simply amusing themselves.

I wait a minute or two. The footsteps recede.

"Michael?"

I hear his answering whisper quite clearly.

"I'm here, under the arch."

I crawl toward him. He is groaning softly.

"A bullet in my foot. But I think I can walk!"

His breath comes in gasps. I help him to his feet. Bending double, we make for the steps which lead down to the canal.

We reach the bottom step and slip into the cold, black water. The bottom is slimy and is a gentle slope.

The water comes up to our knees, our chests, our necks. But I can breathe. We are in our depth. It would have been impossible to swim without attracting the Russkies' attention. I can see their vague outlines thirty feet above us and can hear them running. They must be hunting for the fugitives. Shots ring out all the time. I decide that it was really a very good idea of mine to make for the wharf. The best one I've had, so far. At any rate, they haven't seen us again yet.

Michael is breathing noisily. I'm sure that if I don't hold his arm firmly, he'll go under.

"I can't go on, Peter! My foot feels red-hot."

"Try and tape it, Michael! Just a few more yards and we'll be under the wharf."

"To hell with your damned wharf! I'm in agony. What good is all this to me now?"

"Don't be a fool. We've got to try and get out of here!"

A few more yards and we reach the supporting pillars under the wharf.

Above us, we can hear hurrying footsteps. A guttural, shouting voice, echoed by hoarse grunts.

Very cautiously we lie down full length in the shallow water. Fortunately the gaps between the planks above are narrow and the damned *moujiks* don't think to look down. They're too busy watching out for possible swimmers going down the canal. A few yards from us, two dark shadows are clearly silhouetted. A perfect target. What a pity!

Our eyes are getting accustomed to the dark. We can vaguely make out the long greatcoats of coarse wool, belted about the waist. The faint lights of the torches with which they are searching the canal suddenly catch on their helmets. For a second I glimpse a young man's face surmounted by a sheepskin hat with earlaps.

The water is icy. In order not to be seen, we are lying almost entirely submerged beneath it. Only our mouths are above the surface. The ripples push foul refuse of every sort against our lips. With a feeling of repulsion I think of all the carrion which must be floating with the current down to join the Danube.

A sudden whistle rends the night air.

At last they are going away.

Painfully I get to my feet. Somehow I manage to help Michael into a sitting position on a huge stone in the water.

"You don't still think we can pull it off, do you?" he mutters painfully.

"Take it easy, Stinsmann! Our only sensible course is to wait. It's impossible to get back up on the quay just now. In an hour or two, we'll see."

"I can't go on, Peter. It hurts too much. Too bad, but I'm going."

He tries to get to his feet, but falls back again immediately with a cry of pain.

Seconds pass. I can hear his teeth chattering.

I am also terribly cold, and the frozen clothes that cling to my body make me shiver the whole time.

The night is incredibly dark. The pillars supporting the wharf look like strange ghosts, eternally on guard.

Up there on the Unters Donaustrasse the wind rattles among scrap metal in the ruins and whistles through the loose wires that hang down, cut by gunfire. The shutters bang and clatter ominously and with a haunting regularity.

The thousand and one noises of Vienna, now in the process of being raped and enslaved, reach us through the darkness, muffled noises, blending with the gentle ripple of the water against the piles and with the sound of the flotsam carried by the current bumping together as it sweeps past.

Sudden, sharp rifle cracks, which echo back and forth among the ruined buildings. Short, distant bursts of fire. A machine gun opens up. The shrill whine of an antitank gun, located heaven knows where. The heavy thud of boots on the pavement. A mopping-up patrol hunting for victims. Trucks tearing by at full speed, jolting and rattling over the smashed roadway. The dull roar of field guns, like the distant rumblings of summer thunder. A tank with a racing engine. The squeak of tracks turning on asphalt, the shouts of drunken soldiery. The high-pitched screams of the women they are chasing.

Somewhere a harmonica sobs out its sickly-sweet music. German or Russian? Who knows?

The hours go by. We wait.

Exactly what it is we are waiting for we really couldn't say ourselves. We are simply waiting. A man must at least pretend to hope. Though we are certain this time that there is no hope.

Michael beside me groans dully. I can do nothing for him. I can't do anything for anyone any more. Captain Peter Neumann! Tracked down, hunted, dying of fear and cold in a sea of filth.

Suddenly I pull myself together. I take Michael by the shoulders.

"Good God, we must try, all the same. Pull yourself together, man, I can't hear anything at the moment. Maybe the bastards have pulled out!"

He doesn't answer and makes no attempt to get up, I have to drag him through the water. He is terribly heavy.

At last we reach the concrete canal bank. As best I can, I climb up onto the parapet, dragging Michael after me. They're bound to spot us sooner or later if he goes on moaning and groaning like this.

There is no suspicious sound from the quay. I am suddenly filled with hope. Under cover of the darkness, we might even manage to reach the viaduct, and from there the little alleyways around Radetzkystrasse.

"Michael. Michael, answer me."

I lean over him. I can hear his jerky, staccato breathing. All of a sudden I feel a blazing anger. If it weren't for this fool, it would be so much easier for me to get away. And then I regret my reaction. Poor devil. It might so easily have been me who stopped that bullet.

"Michael! Say something! You're not dead, are you, for God's sake?"

"Let me alone. I can't go on. Let me die here, but just let me alone!" he gasps.

I grope around for his foot in the dark. If only I had a flashlight. Or some matches. I run my hand down his leg. Suddenly I feel a wet, warm mass and jagged fragments of splintered bone. I shudder. His ankle is smashed. Below it hangs his foot, but turned the wrong way. The bullet must have completely destroyed the bone.

We can't stay here.

I catch hold of him around the waist and drag him slowly toward the arch, beneath the parapet. I prop him against the wall. I take off my tunic and put it gently beneath his ankle.

Suddenly I am aware of vague, reddish reflections lighting up the ruins a dozen or so yards away.

Cautiously I crawl over the stones, trying to reach the top. Stopping to listen at each step, I slowly climb up to the street.

Then my heart stops beating.

A hundred yards away some fifty armored cars and trucks are formed up in a semicircle between the Aspern Bridge and the Urania. The Russians are seated near them, warming themselves at their camp fires, which are burning in the middle of the street.

The swine! They're waiting for daylight before cleaning up the district. They must suspect that there are still a few SS hiding hereabouts.

The extraordinary thing is that they seem to feel so safe. Grouped together like that, one well placed machine gun could cause a massacre.

On the far side of the bridge other moving shapes can be vaguely seen. They must be watching the canal. It's too late for that, now.

I look at my watch. It is nearly eleven o'clock. Only eleven o'clock? But we were an eternity in the water. I can't hear my watch ticking. It has stopped. So it must be one or two o'clock in the morning. In a few hours it'll all begin again. And between now and then, we've got to find a way out.

A way out? They are everywhere, swarming like maggots between the Franzens Bridge and the Praterstrasse.

After an interminable effort, crawling a yard at a time, I succeed in carrying Michael on my back as far as a ruined building which looms up out of the darkness on the far side of the wharf. The metal framework, or what remains of it, is swinging in the air, and it rattles. I think this must have been an old customs shed, or perhaps the offices of some steamship company.

Several platoons of one of the *Das Reich* regiments were fighting in this sector all day. From the barricades in the Urania, we watched the Russian SP guns and their heavy T-34 tanks firing uninterruptedly into their positions all afternoon. The survivors must have managed to pull out in the early evening.

Among enormous blocks of stone and piles of scrap iron, I make out dozens of dead bodies in the darkness, heaped one on top of the other.

I search for some time, groping until I find a little space where I can lay Michael down. He is still moaning softly. In spite of the cold, there are rivers of sweat pouring down my face.

Worn out, without hope and at the end of my tether, I sink to the ground. The darkness is total. But it suddenly occurs to me that if I could only see I could at least try to dress Michael's wound.

An idea comes to me, and I get up again.

Crawling on all fours, I run my hands over the crumpled uniforms, crusted with dried blood, over the dead men's frozen, rigid faces. My fingers touch terrible, oozing wounds. Overcoming my revulsion, I rummage in the corpses' pockets. Finally, after searching for a very long time among all this carrion, I find what I have been looking for.

Matches.

With trembling hands, I take one out of the box and strike it.

I am momentarily dazzled by the bright light and hold the match above my head so as to see better in the sepulchral gloom all around me.

I stand transfixed with horror.

About thirty SS are lying there, hacked to pieces by bullets, torn by shellbursts. Their agonized, distorted, grinning faces loom up out of the blackness. Their wide-open, staring eyes all seem to be staring fixedly at the light.

With a sizzling sound, the match flickers and goes out. Once more I am engulfed in the night, which is even darker and more terrifying now. More threatening.

Stinsmann's wound is ghastly, and there can be no hope for him.

My medical knowledge is extremely sketchy, but I am sure that only immediate amputation could save the knee joint and the rest of the leg.

His calf is already going black. That prolonged immersion in the water, full of decaying flesh and refuse, must have infected the wound.

I strike another match and look at his face. His eyes are deeply sunken. His skin has gone yellow and waxy.

His eyes follow all my movements. Suddenly I see his lips move. "Bad, is it? It's . . . gone rotten, I suppose. Doesn't matter now."

I slide down to the ground beside him. Slowly he gropes around for my hand.

"Peter. Don't leave me . . . to them. Promise."

I shrug my shoulders as though he could see me. We haven't even got a gun.

I hear his voice in the darkness, and it is like a prayer.

"I'm talking nonsense. You'd never desert me, Peter!"

The hours drag past, desperately slowly, and yet at the same time with tragic speed.

The last night.

All the years of desperate struggle, of ceaseless fighting, of inhuman suffering, to end like this.

To die like rats in a trap, like hunted beasts, in the sinister murk of the ruins, surrounded by putrefying corpses. Or else to be taken prisoner, a fate worse than death. Anyhow the SS never are taken prisoner. And it's better that way.

The last night.

I think of all the dead who line the road I, or rather we, have taken. All those who have made the supreme sacrifice in this cruel, ruthless, pitiless struggle. All those who must go to eternity cursing us, shaking their gaunt heads, trying to throw off the dead weight of the tomb which crushes them, in one final orgy of hatred and impotent, bitter anger.

Some were guilty, some innocent. They didn't know, they didn't want to understand. Or we couldn't explain to them.

It doesn't matter now. It's too late, much too late.

Despite all this, perhaps because of it, I cannot, I must not, have any regrets.

A day will come when others will be sorry, perhaps. And among them may be numbered those who helped defeat us.

I think of my friends. . . .

I think of you, Franz, sleeping curled inside the rough wood of the ammunition cases, under the tall, black fir trees of the Yergeni Hills. Poor Franz. May the soil of Russia not lie too heavily upon you.

And you, dear old Karl, so full of laughter and the zest for life. Your grave, one among a million other unmarked graves, can be nothing now but an almost invisible mound, covered with grass and scatterings of wild flowers.

All my comrades, who fell at Rawa Ruska, on the Dnieper, in the snows of the Caucasus or on the icy steppes beside the Volga— in spite of all things and all men, may you rest in peace.

I get up. An irresistible urge compels me to examine once again the faces of the men lying all around me in the mysterious gloom of the warehouse.

Striking match after match, I walk among them.

My last company inspection.

The flickering matches faintly light up the young faces, some calm and in repose, others tormented, with deep lines of suffering upon them and mouths twisted in the final grimace of death.

I once read somewhere that at the moment of death, of the plunge into nothingness, a man lives through his whole life in one sudden, vivid flash of memory.

I am reliving my life again as I walk among these dead.

That poor kid, the down still on his cheeks, his fists clenched over his ghastly wound; he is so like what I once was a long time ago, so full of youth and enthusiasm, as I was when I proclaimed my faith beside the banks of the Havel.

A tragic mask of wax is this unhappy, unlucky soldier; written on his face with its clenched jaw is that fixity of purpose, that dauntless will which enabled the keen young officer to lead his men into the attack, heedless of the bullets whistling past his ears and the deadly hail of flying steel.

The matches are finished. And I know that I shall not have the courage to look for more.

I notice two silver squares in the darkness. It is a lieutenant of *Das Reich*. He might have fallen in the forests around Moscow or in the inferno of Stalingrad or in the mountains of Alsace. But Fate has decreed that he shall rot away, a wreck among ruins, beside this wretched canal.

The yellowish light of the last match revealed a khaki greatcoat and a red star. A Russian. I wonder what he was doing here. Probably a prisoner, executed before the retreat. He too must have found peace in a distant Valhalla, the paradise of all us poor wretches, where he will have found millions of his sort, united at last in the blessed world of the hereafter.

A world which perhaps looks indulgently upon the monstrous follies of human vanity.

April 13. Slowly the night draws to a close. Dawn breaks. Dimly at first, gray and sickly, as though it must struggle to penetrate the ruined buildings, then a day like any other, a day made for living.

With each passing moment, the shadowy phantoms of ruined houses loom up more clearly in the grayness.

A light mist hangs over the canal, in which I see swollen uniforms turning and twisting eternally around the wharf, among the refuse.

As the sky lightens, the enormous shell craters in the bank appear more distinctly through the gaps in the stone sides of the shed. Mountains of rubble, of coal, of clinkers and rusty iron line the canal bank. Among it all are rails, glistening with dew, grotesquely twisted by the explosions and rearing up toward the sky as though in prayer.

Farther away I can see the Russian trucks, armored cars and tanks beginning to move off. Hundreds of helmeted men are moving around them. Others have already organized some sort of ferry between the two banks, up by the Aspern Bridge.

I turn back toward Michael. His face now has a gray tinge. His nostrils are pinched. His chest rises and falls. His breathing is rapid and irregular.

I think of the promise he extracted from me.

As soon as daylight came, I searched among the dead men in the warehouse, rummaging about everywhere, turning over the bodies, in the hope of finding a gun. But the survivors of the company must have disarmed those who fell before they retreated, as was our usual custom. All I could find was a Mauser with a broken butt and half a dozen bullets.

For more than an hour they have been clearing the ruins.

Every now and then there is a sharp detonation.

Lying flat on my stomach in the cover of a heap of plaster, I see the six men arrive.

I wedge the broken butt of my Mauser against the corner of a large, cleft stone and wait.

It hurts me to keep my eyes wide open. I stare fixedly at the advancing shapes, which show up distinctly in the light of the rising sun.

When the first of the Russians is about a hundred yards away, I take aim.

He is a young man, with a round pudding face. He walks a little ahead of the patrol, and frequently turns back. Probably to exchange a joke with his comrades.

When I fire, he looks very surprised. I see a black hole appear beneath his helmet, in the middle of his forehead. He slides to the ground.

The others begin to shout. They run toward the warehouse, ducking behind the ruins every few steps.

A second bullet. A third.

Another Russian is hit, and drops his gun.

When they reach the entrance to the building I suddenly stand up. I have worked out all my movements in advance.

I know that I only have to swing my gun around to have Michael's head in my sights.

"Faithful unto death."

As through a fog, the Hitler Jugend oath floats dimly across my memory.

I press the trigger. I hit him in the temple. He doesn't even move. To make quite sure of killing him, I slide another bullet into the breech.

Once again I fire.

This time it hits him in the back of the head. Just the head. His face is intact.

The Russians are still advancing. Ducking behind the heaps of metal and stones.

The idiots. They probably think there's a whole company of us here.

They are firing short bursts, and tossing grenade after grenade.

Why couldn't they have killed me?

A bullet. Badly placed. Or perhaps only too well.

Weeks of half living in a state of semiconsciousness, being moved from field aid-station to ruined hospital.

One evening the loudspeakers in the camp gave out two shattering announcements:

The "tyrant" is dead. Germany has surrendered.

Those nights, those interminable nights, spent in working out the different ways of ending it all. It is so impossible to die. . . .

In the ruins of Warsaw the burying of rotting flesh, the methodical clearing of the streets.

The sneering brutality of the Soviet guards. Sometimes a sharp report. And again. For fun, this time.

I have been out of luck. In spite of the rumors that the SS were to be ruthlessly exterminated. But they need men. Millions and millions of slaves.

I look at my hands, my body, my clothes.

Why couldn't they have killed me?

APPENDIX

Nazi Youth Organization and SS Ranks

The Nazi Youth Organization, over which the Reichsjugendführer, or Minister for Youth, Baldur von Schirach, presided, contained four suborganizations. These were:

The Hitler Jugend, or HJ, boys of 14 to 18 years.
The Deutches Jungvolk, or DJV, boys of 10 to 14.
The Bund Deutscher Mädel, or BDM, girls of 14 to 18.
The Jungmädel, or JM, girls of 10 to 14.

The hierarchy among the boys was as follows:

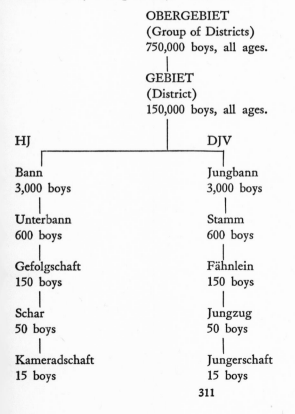

OBERGEBIET
(Group of Districts)
750,000 boys, all ages.

GEBIET
(District)
150,000 boys, all ages.

HJ	DJV
Bann	Jungbann
3,000 boys	3,000 boys
Unterbann	Stamm
600 boys	600 boys
Gefolgschaft	Fähnlein
150 boys	150 boys
Schar	Jungzug
50 boys	50 boys
Kameradschaft	Jungerschaft
15 boys	15 boys

311

The female organization was identical, though the units had different names. The SS, both the military, or Waffen, SS and the ordinary SS, was similarly organized on military hierarchical lines. The units, with their military equivalents, were as follows:

Gruppe	Army Corps
Brigade	Division
Standarte	Regiment
Sturmbann	Battalion
Sturm	Company
Truppe	Platoon
Schar	Section

SS Ranks:

Reichsführer	Commander in Chief of the SS (Himmler)
Oberstgruppenführer	Colonel General
Obergruppenführer	General
Gruppenführer	Lieutenant General
Brigadeführer	Major General
Standartenführer	Colonel
Obersturmbannführer	Lieutenant Colonel
Sturmbannführer	Major
Hauptsturmführer	Captain
Obersturmführer	Lieutenant
Untersturmführer	2nd Lieutenant
Fähnrich	Ensign
Hauptscharführer	Warrant Officer 1st Class
Oberscharführer	Warrant Officer 2nd Class
Scharführer	Sergeant
Unterscharführer	Lance sergeant
Rottenführer	Corporal
SS Sturmmann	Private first class
SS Mann	Private